Field Key to Winter Twi
and planted deciduou
woody climbers (xylopnyτes, ιναιιε
British Isles

A companion volume to *The Vegetative Key to the British Flora*
(including taxa from Europe, North America, South-east Asia and
beyond)

John Poland

Illustrations by
Robin Walls

Photographs by
Philip Tomkinson
Kevin Widdowson

2018

© John Poland

ISBN 13: 978-0-9560144-1-2

Published by John Poland, Southampton
in association with the Botanical Society of Britain & Ireland

Front cover design by Paul Westley, Norwich

Typeset and Index by Gwynn Ellis, Cardiff

Printed by Hobbs the Printers Ltd, Brunel Road, Totton,
Hampshire SO40 3WX

Front cover (top left to bottom right): *Acer platanoides, Populus alba, Rhamnus cathartica, Hydrangea petiolaris, Myrica gale, Betula lenta, Viburnum lantana, Salix lanata*

Thanks are due to the following organisations
for financial support

Botanical Society of Britain & Ireland

Hampshire Ecological Services Ltd

The Botanical Research Fund

The Wild Flower Society

CONTENTS

PREFACE

This field guide hopes to make winter botany fun and unlock a whole new world of identification. It aims to further extend the recording season of botanists to a year-round pursuit, as well as pique the interest of the inquisitive rambler. Identifying trees and shrubs once the leaves have dropped might seem impossible but naked twigs are just as distinctive as their leaves, in fact, often more so in many cases.

Sadly, many botanists in Britain and Ireland currently ignore trees in winter, or recognise only the commonest species. Contrast this with North America where it seems virtually every state has its own winter tree guide - they clearly love trees regardless of the season. Despite the fact that trees and shrubs are immobile, they are well-travelled across the globe, and we have a significant number of species in our islands thanks to our Victorian plant-collectors who brought back numerous new and exotic species from the four corners of the world.

As naturalists we tend to look down more than up when in the field so perhaps we can't see the trees for the wood, so to speak. Woody plants are everywhere. Just a quick walk around your local streets, cemeteries and parks should yield 50+ species so this is really something that can be done on those otherwise dull winter days. For those feeling a little more adventurous, there are many botanical gardens and arboreta accessible by road or rail (some suggestions are given in the Acknowledgements). You can even identify them by silhouette on the way!

Twigs have a wide variety of distinctive characters once you know what to look for; from leaf scars resembling monkey faces to buds wearing hula skirts - the variation is remarkable. Characters are not just visual and you will need to use all your senses to hear the audible snapping of crack willow, feel the roughness of sweet chestnut, experience the odours from mice to stewed cherries and perfume and the taste from aspirin to rosewater. Occasionally a little imagination is required when likening ID characters to more familiar objects, such as the 'elephant's trunk' of horse-chestnut limbs.

It has taken over six exciting years to write this key and I have learnt many new characters in the process so I hope you will find the result equally as enjoyable to use. As I write this, buds are already developing so I look forward to another fascinating winter adding more species. It should be remembered that twigs are useful aids to identification at all times of year. Even during late spring when buds are bursting into leaf, a few dormant or moribund buds can usually be found - one of the few instances where dead twigs may be more helpful than living ones.

I welcome any suggestions, corrections or additions for a future edition. In the meantime, go out and enjoy the wintery world that awaits.

J.P. Poland
Southampton, Hampshire

July 2018

ACKNOWLEDGEMENTS

I have made much use of several Botanic Gardens (and National Collections) and thank particularly the Keepers and Trustees of Kew, Cambridge, Edinburgh and the National Botanic Garden of Wales. Both the Sir Harold Hillier Gardens and Royal Horticultural Society (RHS) Garden Wisley were exceedingly helpful in permitting the study of specimens from their vast collections. Many other arboreta, parks and gardens with a novel selection of trees were visited, some of the most memorable ones included: Brockhole on Windermere, Calderstones Park, Cannizaro Park, Chelsea Physic Gardens, Fletcher Moss Gardens, Holehird Gardens (Lakeland Horticultural Society), Isabella Plantation (Richmond Park), Lovell Quinta Arboretum, Savill Garden, Syon Park, The National Arboretum at Westonbirt (Forestry Commission), Winkworth Arboretum (National Trust) and Worden Park. These are all fascinating places worth visiting during open seasons throughout the year.

Gwynn Ellis typeset the entire volume and also compiled the index. Carl Glanville-Ellis skilfully assisted with graphic design. Eric Clement cast his critical editorial eye over the manuscript and made many invaluable comments, spotting many errors (often subtle) which would have otherwise been missed. Arthur Chater imparted much knowledge on tree-focused trips around Wales, London and sometimes much further afield. Mike Wilcox kindly proof-read the text at very short notice.

I would like to thank our artist, Robin Walls, for his excellent line drawings which are invaluable in assisting the user. Philip Tomkinson took the high-quality photographs in his studio, with many additional photos taken by Kevin Widdowson (who also commented on the test keys). Colin Smith acted as a photographic editor, removing imperfections and selecting the best photos from a fresh perspective. Replacement photos of some missing species were provided by Bruce Patterson, Pat Breen (Oregon State University), James Bunyan (Tracks Ecology), Don Drife (The Michigan Nature Guy), John Peterson & John Seiler (Virginia Tech Dendrology) and Karren Wcisel (Trees and Technology).

Many others have helped in various ways; I must mention: Carol Armstrong, Linda Barker, Jan Blizzard, Wolfgang Bopp, Peter Bourne, Phil Budd, Mark Carine, Catherine Chatters, Deborah Chubb, Anne Comer, Penny Condry, Calum Cooper, Andy Cross, Tara Dempsey, Sue Denness, Martyn Drabik-Hamshare, Mark Duffell, Dave Earl, Julie Etherington, Carmen Green, Alan Hale, Alan Harrington, Janet Higgins, George Hounsome, Liz Howe, David Jewell, Andy Jones, David Leadbetter, Brian Laney, John Kiernan, Louise Marsh, Heather McHaffie, Bettina Metcalfe, Jonathan Mitchley, John Norton, Jill Oakley, Philip Oswald, David Pearman, Matt Parratt, Alistair Penstone-Smith, Andrea Place, Matthew Pottage, Chris Preston, Richard and Kath Pryce, Martin Rand, Richard Reeves, Jeremy Roberts, Victoria Russell, Jonathan Shanklin, Stuart Skeates, Mary Smith, Polly Spencer-Vellacott, John Swindells, Ian Thirlwell, Willemien Troelstra, Tim Upson, Kevin Walker, Debs Wallace, Joanna Walmisley, Graham Walters, Tatiana White, Richard Wilford, Delyth Williams and Rhoddy Wood.

Several societies have also added support and unwittingly aided the key-writing process by inviting me to run winter workshops and exhibits for their memberships, so thanks to the following: Botanical Society of Britain and Ireland, Chartered Institute of Ecology and Environmental Management, Field Studies Council, Friends of Holland Park, Hampshire Flora Group, Lancashire Botany Group, London Natural History Society and the Wild Flower Society. The Tree Register is also an understated charity, of which membership is highly recommended for access to all manner of dendrological resources including the remarkable 'Tree Register' itself.

Finally, my sincere apologies go to anyone who has been inadvertently left off this list - please do contact me for a complimentary copy!

3

BIBLIOGRAPHY

The following publications (amongst many others) were consulted. These would be a useful addition to any winter tree enthusiast's library, particularly those marked with an asterisk (*).

BLAKESLEE, A.F. & JARVIS, C.D. 1926. *Trees in Winter: their study, planting, care and identification.* The Macmillan Company, New York.

CAMPBELL, C.S. & HYLAND, F. 1975. *Winter Keys to Woody Plants of Maine.* University of Maine Press, Maine.

CLARK, G.T. 1981. *Winter Twigs of Arkansas: A Field Guide to Deciduous Woody Plants.* Rose Publishing Company, Arkansas.

CLIBURN, J. & WALLACE, G. 1990. *A Key to Missouri Trees in Winter: an identification guide*, revised edn. Conservation Commission of the State of Missouri.

*CODER, K.D. 2014. 'Advanced twig anatomy: Starting Little to Get Big. (Part I)'. *Arborist News* **23(1)**: 12-18.

*CODER, K.D. 2014. 'Advanced twig anatomy: Everyone needs buds. (Part II)'. *Arborist News* **23(2)**: 12-19.

*COPE, E.A. 2001. *Muenscher's Keys to Woody Plants: an expanded guide to native and cultivated species.* Cornell University Press, New York.

*CORE, E.L. & AMMONS, N.P. 1958. *Woody plants in Winter; a manual of common trees and shrubs in winter in the Northeastern United States and southeastern Canada.* West Virginia University Press, Morgantown.

EDLIN, H.L. 1973. *Forestry Commission Booklet No. 20: Know Your Broadleaves.* HMSO, London.

ELWES, H.J. & HENRY, A. 1906-13; reprinted 1994. *The Trees of Great Britain and Ireland.* Cambridge University Press, Cambridge.

FOUNTAIN, M.S. & JONES, L.C. 2008. *Winter Key to Deciduous Woody Plants of East Texas.* Missouri Botanical Garden Press. St. Louis.

FRALISH, J.S. & FRANKLIN, S.B. 2002. *Taxonomy and Ecology of Woody Plants in North American Forests (excluding Mexico and subtropical Florida).* John Wiley & Sons, New York.

FULLER, G.D., MATTOON, W.R. & MILLER, R.B. 1955. *Forest Trees of Illinois: how to know them*, revised edn. Reprinted by Forgotten Books.

*GILKEY, H.M. & PACKARD, P.L. 2001. *Winter Twigs: a wintertime key to deciduous trees and shrubs of northwestern Oregon and western Washington*, revised edn. Oregon State University Press, Corvallis.

GODET, J-D. 2011. *Guide des écorces des arbres d'Europe: Reconnaître et comparer.* Delachaux et Niestlé, Paris [good photos of bark at different life stages].

GRAVES, A.H. 1952; reprinted 1992. *Illustrated Guide to Trees and Shrubs: a handbook of the woody plants of the northeastern United States and adjacent Canada*, revised edn. Dover Publications, Inc, New York.

GRIMM, W.C., revised by Kartesz, J. 2002. *The Illustrated Book of Trees: the comprehensive field guide to more than 250 trees of eastern North America.* Stackpole Books, Pennsylvania.

HARLOW, W.M. 1959. *Fruit Key and Twig Key to Trees and Shrubs.* Dover Publications.

HOSIE, R.C. 1990. *Native Trees of Canada*, 8th edn. Fitzhenry & Whiteside in co-operation with the Canadian Forest Service, Ontario.

*JOHNSON, O. 2004. *Tree Guide.* HarperCollins Publishers Ltd, London [indispensable for ID generally and even has a handy twig ID chart at the front].

JONES, R.L. & EUGENE WOFFORD, B.E. 2013. *Woody Plants of Kentucky and Tennessee: the complete winter guide to their identification and use.* The University Press of Kentucky, Kentucky.

LAIDLAW, W.B.R. 1960. *Guide to British Hardwoods.* Leonard Hill [Books] Limited, London.

*LANCE, R. 2004. *Woody Plants of the Southeastern United States: a winter guide.* University of Georgia Press, Athens, Georgia.

LUBBOCK, J. [LORD AVEBURY]. 1908. *On Buds and Stipules.* Kegan Paul, Trench, Trubner & Co. Ltd, London.

MAKINS, F.K. 1946. *British Trees in Winter.* J M Dent & Sons, London.

MAY, A. & PANTER, J. 2000; reprinted 2012. *A Guide to the Identification of Deciduous Broad-leaved Trees and Shrubs in Winter.* Field Studies Council, Preston Montford.

MITCHELL, A. 1992. *Field Guide to the Trees of Britain and Northern Europe*, revised edn. Collins, London.

PANCHEN, Z.A., PRIMACK, R.B., NORDT, B., ELLWOOD, E.R., STEVENS, A.D., RENNER, S.S., WILLIS, C.G., FAHEY, R., WHITTEMORE, A., DU, Y. & DAVIS, C.C. 2014. 'Leaf out times of temperate woody plants are related to phylogeny, deciduousness, growth habit and wood anatomy'. *New Phytologist* **203(4)**: 1208-19.

PARNELL, J. & CURTIS, T. 2012. *Webb's An Irish Flora*. Cork University Press, Cork.

PETRIDES, G.A. 1990. *A Field Guide to Eastern Trees: Eastern United States and Canada* [Peterson Field Guide Series]. Houghton Mifflin Company, Boston.

POLAND, J. 2008. 'Nipping ID in the bud'. *BSBI News* **107**: 24-26.

POLAND, J. 2018. 'Identifying woody plants (xylophytes) in winter'. *BSBI News* **137**: 46-48.

POLAND, J. 2018. 'Bud burst phenology of trees and shrubs: a brief introduction'. *BSBI News* **138**: 43-45.

POLAND, J. & CLEMENT, E.J. 2009. *The Vegetative Key to the British Flora*. John Poland in association with the Botanical Society of the British Isles, Southampton.

PRESTON, R.J. 1976. *North American Trees (exclusive of Mexico and Tropical United States)*. The MIT Press, Massachusetts.

PRICE, D. & BERSWEDEN, L. 2013. *Winter Trees: a photographic guide to common trees and shrubs*. AIDGAP, Shrewsbury.

PRIME, C.T. & DEACOCK, R.J. 1970. *Trees and Shrubs: Their Identification in Summer or Winter*, 6th edn, revised and enlarged. W. Heffer & Sons Ltd, Cambridge.

SCHNEIDER, C.K. 1903. *Dendrologische Winterstudien: Grundlegende Vorarbeiten für eine eingehende Beschreibung der Unterscheidungsmerkmale der in Mitteleuropa heimischen und angepflanzten sommergrünen Gehölze im blattlosen Zustande*. Verlag von Gustav Fischer, Jena.

SCHULZ, B. 1999. *Geholzbestimmung im Winter*. Verlag Eugen Ulmer GmbH & Co., Stuttgart.

*SCHULZ, B. 2018. *Identification of Trees and Shrubs in Winter Using Buds and Twigs*. Kew Publishing.

SCHWANKL, A. 1956. *Bark* [Open Air Guides]. Thames and Hudson, London [a handy guide to the bark of commoner trees, very descriptive with b/w photos].

SLAGTER, D. 2014. *Winterflora bomen en struiken: herken bomen en struiken in de winter*. NatuurMedia, Amsterdam.

STACE, C.A. 2010. *New Flora of the British Isles*, 3rd edn. Cambridge University Press, Cambridge.

STEP, E. 1904. *Wayside and Woodland Trees. A Pocket Guide to the British Sylva*. Frederick Warne & Co, London.

*SWANSON, R.E. 1994. *A Field Guide to the Trees and Shrubs of the Southern Appalachians*. The John Hopkins University Press, Baltimore.

SYMONDS, G.W.D. 1958; reprinted 2003. *The tree identification book: A new method for the practical identification and recognition of trees*. HarperCollins Publishers Inc, New York.

*TRELEASE, W. 1931. *Winter Botany*, 3rd edn. Dover Publications, Inc, New York.

*WARD, H.M. 1909. *Trees. A Handbook of Forest-Botany for the Woodlands and the Laboratory. Volume V. Form and Habit*. Cambridge University Press, Cambridge.

*WARD, H.M. 1910. *Trees. A Handbook of Forest-Botany for the Woodlands and the Laboratory. Volume I. Buds and Twigs*. Cambridge University Press, Cambridge.

WATTS, M.T. & WATTS, T. 1970. *Winter Tree Finder: A Manual for Identifying Deciduous Trees in Winter*. Nature Study Guild Publishers, New York.

WILLIAMS, M.D. 2007. *Identifying Trees. An All-Season Guide to Eastern North America*. Stackpole Books, Pennsylvania [contains a good selection of bark photos and other details].

WOJTECH, M. 2011. *Bark: A Field Guide to Trees of the Northeast*. University Press of New England, New Hampshire [an essential guide to those wanting to study bark].

ZOHNER, C.M. & RENNER, S.S. 2014. 'Common garden comparison of the leaf-out phenology of woody species from different native climates, combined with herbarium records, forecasts long-term change'. *Ecology Letters* **17**: 1016-25.

Electronic sources:

ANON. 2011. Go Botany: New England Wild Flower Society. Last accessed 08/8/18. https://gobotany.newenglandwild.org

COOK, W. 2016. Trees, Shrubs, and Woody Vines of North Carolina. Last accessed 18/7/17. http://www.carolinanature.com/trees [useful online resource including photos of bark].

SEILER, J. 2004. Virginia Tech Dendrology Factsheets. Last accessed 18/7/17. http://dendro.cnre.vt.edu/dendrology/factsheets.cfm [very useful online resource which includes photos and an 'Ask Dr Dendro' facility!].

THE TREE REGISTER OF THE BRITISH ISLES. 2017. The Official Champion Tree Database. Last accessed 18/7/17. http://www.treeregister.org [membership highly recommended for access to resources, including a database containing information on trees near you that you never knew existed!].

INTRODUCTION

Coverage

Over 400 taxa are covered, including all native and naturalised deciduous xylophytes (except some of the highly critical genera such as *Sorbus, Rosa* and *Rubus*) that occur in the British Isles as well as the vast majority of commonly (and many rarely) planted species from all over the temperate world. The selection includes everything from dwarf shrubs to tall trees and climbers.

Virtually every species in the key has been illustrated or photographed. Of those that aren't, some are semi-evergreen and retain at least some leaves making vegetative identification possible (although they may become deciduous during harsh winters). Other species have been added at a late stage, or differ in minor detail. It made sense to include these rarities, even though unillustrated, to assist the avid dendrologist rather than wait for a future edition. A quick online internet search in the field (how technology has changed in just a few years) will quickly display adequate photographs but be wary of misidentifications. It should be noted that the photos and illustrations are not to scale - their purpose is to highlight important identification characters and overall appearance (full measurements are given in the text).

Nomenclature

The scientific names used generally follow Stace's *New Flora of the British Isles,* 3rd edn. (2010) but since our guide contains many planted species not included, Johnson's *Tree Guide* (2004) is typically used for trees and the RHS *Plant Finder* (www.rhs.org.uk) for shrubs. English names may vary and, in a few cases, have been modified by the author.

Previous publications

This key is the first of its kind to attempt a more comprehensive identification of woody plants in the British Isles using winter characters alone. Previous books, covering far fewer species, include the classic *British Trees in Winter* (Makins 1946), followed by *A Guide to the Identification of Deciduous Broad-leaved Trees and Shrubs in Winter* (May & Panter 2000) and, more recently, *Winter Trees: a photographic guide to common trees and shrubs* (Price & Bersweden 2013). There have been a number of scholarly works on woody plants produced in Britain, Germany and North America; see the Bibliography (pp3-4) for more examples. More recently, *Geholzbestimmung im Winter* (Schulz 1999) has been revised and translated into English (Schultz 2018) and I recommend it as a useful complement to our key.

Equipment

Equipment is minimal but the following are strongly recommended:
- Hand lens (x20 preferable) - ideal for field work
- LED hand lens (x15) - ideal for desk work
- Secateurs - for taking samples and transverse and longitudinal sections to examine pith (the less squeamish could also use toenail-cutters!)
- Graticule (x10) - for accurate measuring to 0.1mm (desk work)
- Strung tags - for labelling collected twigs
- Binoculars - for observing distant twigs (and, more lazily, viewing specimen accession labels)
- Tyre tread depth gauge (optional; for measuring tree bark depth)

A normal reusable supermarket plastic bag can be used to collect and store twigs in a fridge. A camera is useful for photographing bark and silhouettes. Although a x10 lens is usually adequate, a x20 lens is recommended. A lens with a graticule (measuring loupe) can give precise measurements without the need for a microscope. Such loupes and lenses are available from www.summerfieldbooks.com.

Reference collection and cryopreservation techniques

Twigs can be dried at room temperature, however they will shrivel losing many of their characters. A fridge-freezer is useful when building up ID skills so species can be easily compared and examined at leisure. A fridge (at 2-4°C) will allow for study over weeks and a freezer (at -18°C) will permit study over months or even years. It is important that specimens are free from moisture when put into cold storage. For specimens kept in the fridge, rather than the freezer, use the salad drawers where possible (they soon fill up!) and occasionally change plastic bags (preferably use sealable freezer bags with the air pushed out) and let the specimens dry to prevent mould before re-refrigerating. Paper bags can also be an alternative as they absorb some condensation.

It is strongly recommended to keep an inventory (or at least a mental checklist) of local trees that you can revisit and study for comparison with species from elsewhere. Many public gardens and arboreta exist where you can study labelled species but note that, although the easiest means of identification is to look at the accession label, they are not always accurate so always use your judgement!

When to use the key

The key is designed for use from late autumn or early winter until early spring during the period of leaflessness and before buds begin to swell. This roughly equates from the 15th November (after most leaf fall) until the 31st March (before most bud burst), depending on the season. However, the key usually works from 1st October while leaves are helpfully still attached, and often as early as August since recognisable buds will have already developed on many species. It should be noted that in late summer and early autumn, buds and twigs are often not typically coloured (unseasoned), the buds are not near their maximum size and leaf scars are neither exposed or fully hardened. Conversely, in very late winter, leaf scars may become weathered or covered in algae reducing the visibility of bundle scars.

How to use the key

Start with the Key to Major Divisions on p17 and establish whether the buds (and leaf scars) are **alternate**, **opposite** or **whorled** on the twig. Go to the relevant Division and follow the key through. Remember to look at the end bud(s) at or near the twig tip (usually the largest) as these buds will give the majority of useful characters.

The key will usually work on any specimen (even saplings or seedlings) beyond the cotyledon stage i.e. that have shed at least one mature-type leaf and left an identifiable scar (but caution should be exercised when considering its life form).

Always remember the following four points when using the keys:
- Choose a typical twig (see notes below)
- Examine end bud(s) first (unless the key instructs otherwise)
- Read all the choices in the key carefully before making a decision
- Always use a hand lens for studying fine detail
- Check the glossary for any unfamiliar terms (or precise meanings of more common ones)

The keys will become delightfully much easier to use with experience. To gain confidence, try keying out species that you already know, e.g.:
- *Crataegus monogyna* (Hawthorn) Division **A** → Group **AC**
- *Quercus robur* (Pedunculate Oak) Division **A** → Group **AE**
- *Fagus sylvatica* (Beech) Division **A** → Group **AL**
- *Fraxinus excelsior* (Ash) Division **B** → Group **BB**
- *Aesculus hippocastanum* (Horse chestnut) Division **B** → Group **BG**
- *Acer pseudoplatanus* (Sycamore) Division **B** → Group **BH**

7

Selected groups

A few genera form natural groups that key out in more than one place. In order to prevent unnecessary repetition, keys to these groups have been removed to a 'Selected Groups' section from p124. For example, all *Betula* species are keyed out in **BET** (the first three letters being used for the group name), and the key will instruct the user to 'Go to **BET**' at the relevant points (in some cases a specific species in the group may be identified as well). If the user knows with certainty the genus of the specimen in question is *Betula*, an entry can be made immediately at **BET**.

Spot characters

Many of the keys incorporate 'spot characters' marked by ❶, ❷, etc. These indicate unusual characters, often species-specific, which act as a shortcut to identification. They should be read *before* commencing the relevant key: if one (or more) of these characters fits a specimen, the key can be circumvented and the reader can move immediately to those very few species marked with the relevant number(s). Of course, the key may also be worked through in the traditional manner.

Unusual characters

Many of the more unusual characters (some of which have been used in the keys as 'spot characters') have been compiled into an 'Unusual characters' section from p173. This enables the user to narrow down the options to a subset of taxa when a specimen cannot be put through the key due to being damaged, atypical, etc resulting in missing characters.

Appendix of additional species

A list of additional, typically much rarer, species is given from p201 along with their diagnostic characters. These species may be occasionally encountered by the serious user but could not be easily incorporated into the keys for this edition.

IDENTIFICATION

Twig morphology

A **twig** is defined as the 1st year shoot. The twig should be examined for its stoutness, colour, presence of any hairs (including the type of hair) or glands, whether round or ridged, zig-zagging, curved or straight, rigid or flexible (i.e. can it be tied in a knot?), any armature (prickles, spines or thorns) and whether the bark is splitting or peeling, etc. The twigs of some species may develop a grey 'skin' (actually a thin layer of cork) obscuring the underlying true colour. The colour of twigs (and buds) is influenced by sunlight, often becoming redder or purplish on the sunlit side.

Twig stoutness is defined as one of the following diameters (measure diameter between 2nd and 3rd internode from twig tip as a general rule):
- V slender ≤1-1.5mm diam
- Slender 1-2mm diam
- Mod slender 2-3mm diam
- Mod 3-5mm diam
- Mod stout 5-10mm diam (for comparison, a pencil is 7-8mm diam)
- Stout ≥10mm diam (much thicker than a pencil)

Stoutness is conveyed in words as well as measurements since a difference of just 1mm can make an observable difference to the stoutness of the twig.

Most species with opposite leaves have an **interpetiolar ridge** - a narrow horizontal ridge connecting two opposite leaf scars. However this interpetiolar ridge is absent in Oleaceae (e.g. *Fraxinus* (Ashes)) and from genera in several other families, so this absence is an important character. It should be noted that in opposite-budded species with round twigs, the twigs are often slightly flattened at the nodes.

The presence of **lenticels** (breathing pores in the twig bark) can be useful, particularly their shape (round lenticels may be longitudinally elongated to oval or linear), colour, and whether flat, raised or low (intermediate). Lenticels are absent from twigs with peeling bark. **Stomata** may be present instead of lenticels, as they serve a similar function, particularly on species with green twigs. Stomata are easily visible as little white dots under a hand lens.

Some woody plants may be armed with **prickles**, **spines** or **thorns** (or very rarely a combination of prickles and spines, viz *Ribes uva-crispa* (Gooseberry)) and it is crucial for identification to know the precise difference.

Prickles are an extension of the epidermis and can occur anywhere along twig internodes. *Rubus* (Brambles) and *Rosa* (Roses) are two examples, hence the classic saying "a rose between two thorns" is wrong!

Spines are modified leaves or stipules and usually occur directly <u>below</u> a leaf scar or bud. They are occasionally in pairs e.g. *Robinia* (False-acacia) or 1-3-partite in *Berberis* (Barberries) and *Ribes uva-crsipa* (Gooseberry).

Thorns, in contrast, are modified branches and thus usually occur directly <u>above</u> a leaf scar or at the end of a short branch, or collateral (adjacent) to lateral buds. They can terminate the main twig or a side twig and may have buds or leaf scars along them.

Pith is the soft parenchyma tissue filling the core of the twig. To examine pith, the twig should be cut initially crosswise (transverse section) and then again lengthways (longitudinal section) using scissors or secateurs (ideally between the 2nd and 3rd internode from the twig tip). Note the relative diameter (usually ½ diam of twig), shape (round, 3-angled, etc), colour (white, green, orange-brown, etc), whether **solid** (most species), **chambered** (ladder-like; hollow with partitions, e.g. *Juglans* (Walnuts)) or **diaphragmed** (solid but with firmer plates or partitions, e.g. *Liriodendron* (Tulip-trees)) or absent (**hollow** e.g. *Lonicera* (Honeysuckles)). Any angles in the twig are often reflected in the shape of pith. Some species often have more porous (larger celled) **spongy** or **fragmenting** (disintegrating) pith (e.g. *Ribes* (Currants, Gooseberry)) or **dense** pith (e.g. *Catalpa* (Bean-trees)).

Pith is positioned centrally within the twig, with the exception of *Tamarix* (Tamarisk) where it is off-centre (**eccentric**). The pith is smaller in branchlets, and often in sections of twigs closer to the branchlet, due to compression as the outer wood grows (hence the importance of cutting between between the 2nd and 3rd internode).

Any odour from the **inner bark** should be noticeable once the twig is cut or snapped (although the bark can be scratched as a less intrusive method). Odours are described as **aromatic** (pleasant), **fetid** (unpleasant) or **odorous** (either category depending on the olfactory sense of the person!). Rarely, inner bark may need to be chewed to confirm any distinctive taste. Few species are likely to be harmful, especially in trace amounts, but warnings are given where appropriate.

Latex may also be visible around the edge of the pith in the outer wood of twigs (contained within ducts called lactifers). However, unlike during the main growing season, latex is often sparse in winter. Latex is white in all of our species but dries black in *Rhus* (Stag's-horn Sumach) and *Toxicodendron vernicifluum* (Chinese Lacquer-tree).

Branchlets are defined as shoots that are 2-3 years old. Branchlets generally sport fewer useful characters but, occasionally, they show striae (visible ridges under the bark in *Salix cinerea* (Grey Willow)) or peeling bark that remains tight on younger twigs. Branchlets become round and eventually the same colour as the trunk, ultimately becoming branches. Shoot definitions follow this decreasing size sequence: **Trunk** > **limb** > **branch** [large > medium > small]] > **branchlet** > **twig** > **sprig**.

A typical twig is termed a **long shoot** due to its elongated internodes. Some twigs may have reduced internodes and are termed **short shoots** (or **short twigs** in this guide). In some genera, very short shoots, called **woody spurs** or spur shoots (or, technically, brachyblasts), can be present on branchlets or branches. These are stubby shoots with extremely short internodes that often grow only a few millimetres per year (usu <5mm) so the internodes are tightly congested. They are marked by dense ring-like scars left by the crowded leaf scars and bud scale scars and topped with a terminal bud. They are often the shoots that bear flowers and fruit (as it is only a short distance from the leaves supplying the nutrients). They can be curved thus occasionally resembling a cockerel's spur.

Since many species have short twigs which are somewhere between a long shoot and a spur shoot in length, the term woody spur refers only to these very short shoots to avoid any confusion.

Woody spurs are characteristic of several genera including *Betula* (Birches), *Fagus* (Beech), *Ginkgo* (Ginkgo), *Larix* (Larches) and some rosaceous genera e.g. *Malus* (Apples), *Prunus* (Cherries and Plums). Remarkably, long shoots can change to short shoots and back again to long shoots (and vice-versa), especially in *Prunus avium* (Wild Cherry).

As the terminal bud bursts, the bud scales (and any stipules) fall leaving **girdle scars** where the twig joins the 2nd year branchlet on long shoots. These are crowded and obvious in *Fagus* (Beech) and some *Acer* (Maples). Girdle scars mark the beginning of a new year's shoot thus the interval between two clusters of girdle scars indicates the amount of growth in any one year. Therefore it is possible to calculate the age of branchlets by tracing the branchlets back until the scars become covered in bark. However in *Juglans regia* (Walnut) some twigs extend in two growth bursts in the same growing season, with the location of the pause identified by close leaf scars resembling the girdle scars of a true branchlet junction.

In some shrubs, especially those in the family Caprifoliaceae e.g. *Lonicera* (Honeysuckles), *Symphoricarpos* (Snowberries), the bud scales persist on the twig as tattered papery remnants and provide a useful indication of the family. These are termed **persistent bud scales**.

Bud morphology

A **bud** contains the embryonic shoot (twig) and a usually predetermined number of leaves (usually 5-20 but some *Salix* (Willows) can have up to 50 or more) and often flowers. Buds normally occur in the leaf axil above a leaf scar (a lateral bud) or at the tip of the twigs (a terminal bud). Consequently, the distribution of buds (and leaf scars) on the twig is usually identical to that of the leaves - **alternate**, **opposite**, or **whorled**. Similarly, predominantly opposite twigs (and branchlets) indicates opposite leaves. An oddity is *Parthenocissus* (Virginia-creeper) where a bud is surprisingly absent above the leaf scar of every 3rd node. There are far fewer species with opposite buds than those with alternate buds (and even fewer species with whorled buds). This is even truer for trees than it is for shrubs.

Most species have some buds which contain both vegetative and floral parts (sometimes known as **mixed buds**). However some species have separate **leaf buds** and **flower buds**. Flower buds can usually be recognised by their much larger size or different shape to the leaf buds, such as in *Magnolia* (Magnolias), *Myrica gale* (Bog-myrtle), *Rhododendron luteum* (Yellow Azalea), *Ulmus* (Elms) and *Vaccinium corymbosum* (Blueberry). Where these two bud types occur on the same plant, the key descriptions may specifically refer to flower buds and leaf buds to distinguish between the two. Since a leaf bud actually contains many leaves and a twig, the term 'leaf bud' is a misnomer (a foliage bud would perhaps be more appropriate); similarly, a 'flower bud' usually contains several flowers.

Surprisingly, there is no consistent correlation between bud size and leaf size (or twig length, or the number of leaves on a twig). There is a reasonable correlation between bud size and twig diameter but there are frequent exceptions such as *Catalpa* (Bean-trees) in which the buds are much smaller than expected. In general, species with larger (or compound) leaves have stouter twigs since they need the strength to carry the extra weight. Climbers are often exceptions as they can afford relatively narrow stems in comparison to leaf size.

End buds

Every twig ends with either a true **terminal bud** (at the tip) or a **false terminal bud** (below the tip). A terminal bud is at the very tip of a twig and is often larger than the lateral buds. A false terminal bud is simply the uppermost **lateral bud** closest to the twig tip and described as the **end bud**, although end bud can also refer to a terminal bud i.e. the uppermost bud on any twig. In those species with a false terminal bud, a dead twig tip often extends beyond the base of the end bud (often only visible as a minute stub) or falls off leaving a small **twig-tip scar** (visible on the opposite side of the bud to the leaf scar). This scar is always absent from terminal buds. In some species, terminal buds are confined to woody spurs only e.g. *Betula* (Birches).

Those species with a terminal bud at the twig apex give rise to straight (**monopodial**) growth e.g. *Populus* (Poplars). In contrast, those with a false terminal bud (or paired end buds in the case of opposite-budded species) give rise to forked (**sympodial**) growth e.g. *Salix* (Willows), *Syringa* (Lilac). By combining monopodial and sympodial branching in one plant, many different tree architectures have evolved.

The end bud is often held more-or-less erect and this is especially noticeable in *Fraxinus* (Ashes) and *Sorbus* (Whitebeams) as the twigs have a tendency to turn up at the tips. This minimises the impact of frost which could damage the buds.

Lateral buds

Lateral buds are usually single and well-spaced along the twig. However buds may also be **clustered** at twig tips (actually 2-several lateral buds closely clustered around a single terminal bud e.g. *Prunus* (Cherries), *Quercus* (Oaks). Buds may also be **superposed** i.e. two or more buds above each other at a single leaf scar e.g. *Juglans* (Walnuts), *Lonicera* (Honeysuckles). Typically only the larger upper bud is dominant and develops into a shoot while the smaller lower bud remains dormant. *Lonicera* (Honeysuckles) are unusual in that the uppermost bud is smallest (i.e. lowest bud is dominant). When checking for superposed buds, look at both terminal and lateral positions. Buds can also be **collateral** (side-by-side with the main bud but usually smaller) e.g. *Prunus* (Plums).

In some species, buds may be **hidden** under the leaf scar membrane e.g. *Robinia* (False-acacia), *Hibiscus* (Hibiscus) or under the twig bark e.g. *Taxodium* (Swamp Cypress).

Bud shape

Bud shape is important (commonly **ovoid, globose, conical** or **lanceoloid**) and whether the bud is **acute** or **obtuse**. Buds display a wide range of different shapes and may even resemble well-known objects; the more unusual shapes are given in 'Unusual characters'. Buds can be flattened, 3-5-angled or without angles (terete). When buds are angled, the pith (and usually the twig) is similarly angled e.g. *Alnus* (Alders) have 3-angled buds, twigs and pith while *Populus* (Poplars) have 5-angled buds and pith (although the twigs can be round to 5-angled).

Buds may be **sessile** (stalkless, as in most species) or **stalked** (e.g. *Alnus* (Alders)), **spreading** from the twig (usually at an angle of 30-60° but can be up to 90°; the bud often continues the angle of the zig-zag internode below) or closely **adpressed** to the twig (at an angle of 0-15°, e.g. *Carpinus*

11

(Hornbeam)). It should be noted that adpressed buds are often flattened on the side nearest the twig. Buds may also be **oblique** to the leaf scar (i.e. tilted asymmetrically to one side) e.g. *Ulmus* (Elms), *Tilia* (Limes) instead of being positioned directly above the leaf scar as in most species.

Bud scales

Buds are usually covered in protective **scales**. There are 5-12 visible scales in the majority of species but any number from 0 (e.g. *Frangula alnus* (Alder Buckthorn)) to 30 (*Myrica gale* (Bog-myrtle)) is possible. Those buds with 0 scales are termed **naked** and are usually covered in dense hairs to provide protection. The scales are usually **overlapping**, however, in buds with 2 scales, the scales can be **valvate** (e.g. *Acer* (Maples)) or overlapping (e.g. *Alnus viridis* (Green Alder), *Cercis siliquastrum* (Judas Tree), *Hydrangea petiolaris* (Climbing Hydrangea) and *Wisteria* (Wisterias)).

A few examples of the lower and higher bud scale numbers are given in 'Unusual characters'. It is often difficult to accurately count bud scales and the number can vary (within limits) in many species. It is only the outer (visible) scales that are counted; there is no need to dissect a bud. However dissection is useful to determine the sex of the flowers in *Populus* (Poplars).

Individual bud scales are either modified leaves, modified petiole bases or modified stipules and thus they normally mirror bud and leaf scar arrangement i.e. scales alternate in alternate-leaved species and in opposite pairs in opposite-leaved (and whorled-leaved) species; however exceptions occur. In alternate-leaved species, bud scales can be **spirally arranged** (typical of most species) or **2-ranked** (distichous; in 2 rows, e.g. *Ulmus* (Elms)) or, more rarely, **4-ranked** (*Fagus* (Beech)) or **5-ranked** (*Quercus* (Oaks)). In opposite-leaved species, the scales are normally 4-ranked (i.e. decussate pairs above each other), except *Rhamnus* (Buckthorn) which has spirally arranged scales. *Juglans* (Walnuts) are unusual in that they have alternate buds with scales in opposite pairs.

It is also important to note bud scale colour, whether the surface is **hairy** (hairs are usually unicellular and adpressed but can be stellate or medifixed in some species) or **hairless**, if the margins are **ciliate** or not (ciliate margins on otherwise hairless scales <u>does not</u> qualify the bud as hairy and it is possible to have hairless, but ciliate, scales), whether **1-3-keeled**, **striate** or **smooth**, **obtuse**, **acute** or **apiculate** and if the margins are **toothed**, **gland-fringed**, **erose** or **entire**. In Rosaceae e.g. *Prunus* (Cherries, Plums), *Pyrus* (Pears), *Sorbus* (Whitebeams), at least the lower scales are keeled and 3-toothed, the tip of the keel forming the middle tooth or apiculus.

Stomata may be clearly visible as minute white dots under a x20 hand lens on the bud scales of *Hydrangea petiolaris* (Climbing Hydrangea), *Salix repens* (Creeping Willow), *Zelkova* (Zelkovas) and, occasionally, *Xanthorhiza simplicissima* (Yellowroot). Stomata are also present in *Betula* (Birches) but are obscure or confined to near the scale margins and usually demand a higher magnification (at least x60).

As mentioned earlier, some shrubs have persistent bud scales i.e. tattered papery bud scale remnants where the twig joins the branchlet (where the girdle scars would be). This is typical of Caprifoliaceae e.g. *Lonicera* (Honeysuckles), *Symphoricarpos* (Snowberries).

Leaf scars

The **leaf scar** is a mark left on the twig by a leaf after it falls. The leaf scar should be examined for shape, size (including width relative to bud width), whether it is raised or not, colour (pale or dark), and any bundle scars (see below). The width of the leaf scar is normally equal to the bud width but there are exceptions e.g. in *Betula* (Birches) the leaf scar is narrower than the bud width, while in *Rosa* (Roses) the leaf scar is much wider than the bud width. Leaf scars sometimes run down the twig (usually from the sides and occasionally the centre of leaf scars), resulting in a **ridged** or **angled** twig (check Glossary from p205 for precise definitions!). This is termed a **decurrent** leaf scar.

Some species have unusual (and occasionally amusing) shapes, such as the oft-repeated 'horseshoes' in *Aesculus*, (Horse-chestnuts, Buckeyes) and 'monkey faces' in *Juglans* (Walnuts).

In alternate-budded species, whether the leaf scars (and buds) are **2-ranked** (on opposite sides of twigs but the buds themselves are alternate) or **spirally arranged** can be a valuable character. This is known as **phyllotaxy**. However, it is not always easy to interpret and can be highly variable depending on the length of twig and whether it is growing vertically (**orthotropic**) or horizontally (**plagiotropic**). Many species with oblique buds have 2-ranked leaf scars (but not necessarily vice-versa).

In opposite-budded species, leaf scars (and buds) are in **decussate** pairs along the twig with each pair at right angles to the pair above and below i.e. the leaf scars are **4-ranked**. Naturally, there are exceptions and the plagiotropic twigs of *Metasequoia glyptostroboides* (Dawn Redwood) often twist slightly keeping all bud pairs in a horizontal plane. The 4-ranking of buds may be less pronounced on horizontal twigs of other species too.

Bundle scars

Marks within the leaf scar are called **bundle scars** and they represent the severed ends of the vascular bundles (veins) which previously connected the leaf petiole with the twig prior to abscission. The number, arrangement, shape, whether protruding or sunken are all essential characters to observe.

The majority of species have 3 bundle scars although the number is often influenced by the leaf size and complexity e.g. the leaf scars of *Aesculus* (Horse-chestnuts, Buckeyes), *Catalpa* (Bean-trees), *Fraxinus* (Ashes) are larger and have more bundle scars (because the leaves are larger and/or compound and require more vascular tissue to function effectively). Within some species there is considerable variation; bundle scars (especially the central scar) may occasionally divide, forming compound groups, termed **multiplied** in the keys. Sometimes they may fuse into one or the number is unclear. The shape of bundle scars may consist of arc(s), dots, lines, C-shapes and U-shapes. The arrangement of bundle scars is often dictated by the leaf scar shape e.g. ± circular leaf scars will have the bundle scars in a ring or scattered, while shield-shaped or U-shaped leaf scars will have them arranged in a line around the margin (resembling horseshoe nails). Some species, most notably *Ulmus* (Elms), have **sunken** bundle scars rather than the more typical protruding or flush scars.

Stipule scars

Stipule scars are left on the twig when the stipules fall off. Stipules are bracts, often leaf-like, that occur in pairs (one on each side) on the twig at the base of the petiole, or on the petiole itself. It is important to note that, just because a species has stipules, it doesn't automatically mean it has stipule scars. For example, many genera in Rosaceae have the stipules attached to the petiole not the twig, so no stipule scar is left on the twig when the leaf falls.

Stipules normally exist only to protect the young unfurling leaf so are soon redundant and have usually dropped by mid-summer. However, as previously mentioned, stipules may also be modified into bud scales protecting the young bud.

Determining the presence, or absence, of stipule scars is a requirement in using the key (and perhaps one of the most daunting steps for a newcomer). Although initially difficult, it becomes very easy with practice. Familiarising yourself with common examples is the best way to learn. Stipule scars are normally small and situated adjacent to the upper edge of the leaf scar (either adjoining the leaf scar or slightly separate from it). Stipule scars, although in pairs, are often unequal in size or shape and, rarely, only one is visible. Occasionally, stipule scars form a closed ring or partial ring around the twig (e.g. *Platanus* (Planes) and *Fagus* (Beech) respectively) which may not be immediately recognised as a stipule scar, however the key and illustrations will guide you.

Rarely, minute vascular bundle scars may be visible within stipule scars. In some species, the stipules or their remnants may persist e.g. *Cotoneaster* (Cotoneasters), *Laburnum* (Laburnums).

Life form: tree, shrub or woody climber

A **tree** can be defined as a woody plant with typically a <u>single</u> trunk at least 7cm in diameter, a defined **crown** and a height of at least 4m at maturity. A **shrub** is distinguished from a tree by its <u>multiple</u> narrow stems from the base (or more inclined to branch near the base) and shorter height (usually <4(6)m tall). Shrub stems are continually replaced between 2-15 years and the twigs often have more spongy, rather than dense, pith compared to trees but this is not a reliable character. Johnson (2004) defines a tree as *"any plant which commonly grows to 3m on a single stem at least 20cm thick"*. Use your judgement!

Some species may grow into either shrubs or trees, depending on their growing conditions. While size can be one way that can help to separate the two, this is not the determining factor and some trees, such as *Acer palmatum* (Japanese Maple) and *Betula nigra* (River Birch), can have multiple trunks like shrubs. A few shrubs can be less than 10cm tall and are then termed **dwarf shrubs** e.g. *Genista pilosa* (Hairy Greenweed), *Salix herbacea* (Dwarf Willow). The term **subshrub** is often used interchangeably but specifically refers to a dwarf shrub that is woody only at the base.

A **climber** is a woody plant that uses other plants or objects for support. Climbers use either **tendrils** (modified stems in the species contained within this key), **twining stems** (either **clockwise-** or **anticlockwise-twining** but can be **ambidextrous** in *Solanum dulcamara* (Bittersweet)) or **adventitious roots** e.g. *Hydrangea petiolaris* (Climbing Hydrangea). With twiners, there is a limit to the diameter of the support they can circumvent thus rarely found around large trunks.

The stems of climbers possess little or no ability to bear any weight (so often easily compressed) but instead are very flexible with considerable tensile strength (i.e. an ability to resist pulling and twisting).

In addition to true climbers, there are **scramblers** e.g. *Rubus fruticosus* agg (Brambles) which have arching stems that sprawl over other plants or structures for support (often using prickles). Unusually, *Solanum dulcamara* (Bittersweet) can be a scrambler or a twiner.

Bark

Bark is the outermost non-living protective layers of twigs, branchlets, branches and trunks. Identification by trunk bark can be important on the rare occasion when twigs and buds do not provide a conclusive identification e.g. some *Magnolia* (Magnolias) and *Catalpa* (Bean-trees).

Bark can be **smooth, peeling, flaking, fissured** or **furrowed** (note depth). It may also have distinctive lenticels, colours, patterns, etc. Generally only look at the bark of fully grown mature trees as younger bark is usually smoother and may be a different colour. However younger bark can have unique characters absent when older e.g. the diamond-shaped lenticels on *Populus alba* (White Poplar) and *Salix caprea* (Goat Willow). Unless stated, the descriptions in the key refer to the bark of a mature tree viewed at eye level.

Smooth bark is thin and relatively unbroken but can be **striated** (vertically striped or lined with a contrasting colour giving rise to '**snake bark**') as in *Acer davidii* (Père David's Maple) and other Snakebark Maples. **Lenticels** may create 'tiger stripes' on otherwise smooth bark such as in *Prunus avium* (Wild Cherry) or wart-like lumps in *Ficus* (Fig).

Peeling bark curls off in thin horizontal papery strips or rolls e.g. *Betula pendula* (Silver Birch). Strongly peeling bark may be called **shreddy** e.g. *Betula nigra* (River Birch). **Shaggy** refers to bark that peels in longitudinal curved strips loose at both ends e.g. *Carya ovata* (Shagbark Hickory).

Flaking bark can be shed as either **plates** or **scales,** which are loose pieces of bark. This may result in a mottled appearance with a varied colour pattern caused by the exposed underbark. **Plates** are generally larger flat separate pieces of bark which rarely overlap (e.g. *Platanus* (Planes)) while **scales** are generally small flattish pieces of overlapping bark (e.g *Cotinus coggygria* (Smoke-tree)). However these definitions aren't sharply defined.

Fissured bark has shallow longitudinal splits or cracks, often irregular and some may develop 'ski run' patterns such as *Quercus rubra* (Red Oak) and its close allies.

Furrowed bark (or 'ridged and furrowed' bark) is deeply vertically grooved, the ridges separated by more-or-less regular deep furrows. Ridges are usually **intersecting** forming diamond-shaped furrows (e.g. *Acer platanoides* (Norway Maple)) but they may be **broken horizontally** (e.g. *Tilia* (Limes), *Pyrus* (Pears)) or, rarely, **uninterrupted** (e.g. *Toona sinensis* (Chinese Mahogany)). The pattern close-up may even resemble cracked paint e.g. *Robinia pseudoacacia* (False-acacia).

In intersecting bark, the size and shape of furrows may vary from small diamond-shaped furrows to large ones depending on the distance between each intersection. The ridges may even appear fibrous and **rope-like** in *Robinia* (False-acacia) or deeply furrowed bark may become **blocky,** such as the base of over-mature *Betula pendula* (Silver Birch) trunks, and may even resemble charcoal briquettes e.g. *Diospyros* (Date-palm) or crocodile-skin e.g. *Nyssa* (Tulepo).

The fissuring and furrowing of bark can loosely be defined using depth where the bark shows a regular depth pattern around the circumference. Measure from the top of the ridge to the bottom of the furrow:

* Smooth 0mm deep
* Fissured ≤4mm deep
* Shallowly furrowed 4-10mm deep
* Furrowed 10-15mm deep
* Deeply furrowed >15mm deep

These categories aren't always clear-cut and are given as guidance only. The variations on furrowed are best lumped into a single term. Bark can be intermediate between smooth and fissured and appear 'cracked' where it is generally smooth with a few irregular fissures. Even as a mature tree, *Fraxinus excelsior* (Ash) is smooth in early maturity but becomes furrowed later on.

Identifying a tree by its bark is challenging and takes practice. Bark is also difficult to describe succinctly so is best learnt by observation - even photographs can be confusing.

Some examples of bark types for common trees (and some rarer species with unique bark) are given in 'Unusual characters'. For those wishing to learn more, refer to the books by Godet (2011), Schwankl (1956), Williams (2007) and Wojtech (2011) in the Bibliography (pp3-4), as well as the online resources.

Tree shape (silhouette)

The trunk, branches and crown (composed of 'sprays') give rise to the overall shape (outline or silhouette) of a tree, which is often diagnostic in many species, albeit hard to put into words. The crown is simply the the collective branches, branchlets and twigs of a tree or shrub, excluding the trunk, i.e. the 'head' of the tree or shrub. To describe the crown, 2-dimensional shapes of the silhouette are used (e.g. ovate) rather than the geometrically correct 3-dimensional ones (e.g. ovoid). Crown shape can be similar in separating otherwise similar trees, especially between some *Populus* (Poplars), *Catalpa* (Bean-trees) and *Quercus* (Oaks).
Simplified, there are two fundamental types of architecture: trees with an unbranched trunk continuous to the tree tip (an **excurrent** growth habit) resulting in a **pyramidal** or **conical** crown *e.g. Alnus glutinosa* (Alder), *Populus tremula* (Aspen); and trees with a branched non-continuous trunk (a

decurrent or deliquescent growth habit) usually developing a **rounded** or **oval** crown. The latter includes the vast majority of trees with *Acer* (Maples), *Fraxinus* (Ashes) and *Sorbus* (Whitebeams, Rowans) being common examples.

Within these two growth habits, there are various categories of shapes of which the most obvious include **fastigiate** (usually excurrent), **weeping** (usually decurrent) and **vase-shaped** (usually decurrent). See 'Unusual characters' for examples.

The shape varies according to many factors, particularly whether the tree is young or mature and whether it is growing in an open or closed canopy. The upper crown of trees tends to flatten out as it matures. Urban trees are often pollarded, cut back or pruned, which alters their natural shape. Also there are fastigiate and weeping cultivars of many tree species.

With practice one can recognise a number of commoner trees at a distance, even from a moving vehicle (making being a passenger on a long journey more enjoyable). However in most cases you usually need more information to confirm scarcer species.

Phenology

The relative dates of bud burst (and subsequent leafing) is largely constant across the temperate zone of Europe and North America. Although there can be 2-3-week interyear shifts in bud burst dates, **early bursting** is considered as bud burst before the end of March (excluding flower buds which may precede leaf buds by several weeks), while **late bursting** is from the middle of April to the middle of May (exceptionally early June). Most species burst in the first two weeks of April and are termed **moderate bursting**.

Northern England may be 1-2 weeks behind the south and northern Scotland perhaps a further 1-2 weeks behind (depending on the species).

Bud burst is primarily controlled by three main factors; cold winter temperatures (**chilling period** i.e. the number of days below a specific temperature between 0-10°C), warm spring temperatures (**forcing**) and day length (**photoperiod**). The impact of each of these factors depends on the species and many different combinations can result in bud burst. In addition, genetics, origin (particularly in relation to planted species) and microclimate also play a role in individual variation of bud burst date.

The leafing of early bursting species is usually linked to warm spring temperature as they have a minimal chilling period and no photoperiod requirement. In contrast, late bursting species are usually controlled by the winter chilling period and/or photoperiod.

Some of the very earliest species are *Lonicera periclymenum* (Honeysuckle) and *Sambucus nigra* (Elder) followed by (in alphabetical order) *Chaenomeles* spp ('flowering quinces'), *Fuchsia magellanica* (Fuchsia), *Hypericum androsaemum* (Tutsan), *Kerria japonica* (Kerria), *Leycesteria formosa* (Himalayan Honeysuckle), *Lycium* spp (Teaplants), *Ribes sanguineum* (Flowering Currant), *Rosa* spp (Roses), *Rubus fruticosus* agg (Brambles), *Spiraea japonica* (Japanese Spiraea), *Sorbaria sorbifolia* (Sorbaria) and *Viburnum* x *bodnantense* (Bodnant Viburnum).

In contrast, some of our latest species are *Carya ovata* (Shagbark Hickory), *Castanea sativa* (Sweet Chestnut), *Catalpa* spp (Bean-trees), *Fagus sylvatica* (Beech), *Fraxinus excelsior* (Ash), *Genista aetnensis* (Mount Etna Broom), *Ginkgo biloba* (Ginkgo), *Gleditsia triacanthos* (Honey-locust), *Gymnocladus dioicus* (Kentucky Coffeetree), *Hibiscus syriacus* (Hibiscus), *Juglans regia* (Walnut), *Morus nigra* (Black Mulberry), *Paulownia tomentosa* (Foxglove-tree), *Populus* x *canadensis* 'Serotina' (Late Hybrid Black-poplar), *Populus tremula* (Aspen), *Quercus* spp (Oaks), *Rhamnus cathartica* (Buckthorn), *Rhododendron luteum* (Yellow Azalea), *Tilia cordata* (Small-leaved Lime), *Ulmus minor* (Field Elm) and *Vitis vinifera* (Grape-vine). The sequence varies from year-to-year.

A few species have wide phenophases (phenological stages) and can be early to late bursting. *Acer pseudoplatanus* (Sycamore) is a common example as buds can burst between the end of March and mid-May.

Documentation for many species is lacking in the literature but Zohner & Renner (2014) and Panchen et al (2014) include much novel data. Recording the sequence (and date) of leaf burst, particularly of the late bursting species, is a fun and instructive experiment that anyone can do in the spring.

Rather unexpectedly, the latest species to burst are often the first to have fully formed buds in the summer. There is no correlation with date of leaf fall in the autumn (which is caused by reduced day length, cooling temperatures, drought and strong winds), although the earliest species to lose their leaves include many *Populus* (Poplars) and *Gymnocladus dioicus* (Kentucky Coffeetree) (*Gymnocladus* means 'naked branch') while *Alnus cordata* (Italian Alder) is one of the last. Although the autumn colours prior to leaf fall are attractive, they are of comparatively little use for identification. As a very general rule, the leaves of most European species turn yellowish while many species from North America and East Asia turn red (with those from East Asia often turning last).

EPILOGUE

Exhausted? Me too! However with a little time spent observing the above characters, it all becomes quite easy. Good luck!

Key to Major Divisions

(Based upon arrangement of buds and lf scars)

Key works best between 15th Nov (after most lf fall) and 31st March (before most bud burst depending on season) but usu works from 1st Oct when lvs are still attached

Ideally collect entire 1st yr twig and examine crown shape, bark and characters of branchlets (but key usu works with terminal portion of twig only). Check 'Unusual characters' from p173 (inc odour, pith, etc) if specimen doesn't key out readily. The first-time user should read the Introduction (p5 onwards) before proceeding with the key

All the taxa in Division C are keyed out with full descriptions in Division B, however Division C has been created as a rapid ID shortcut for whorled species

■Buds and lf scars alt...A
■Buds and lf scars opp or subopp (rarely 3(6)-whorled)...B
■Buds and lf scars 3(6)-whorled..C

Key to Groups in Division A

(Buds and lf scars alt)

■Twigs armed with prickles, spines or thorns (look carefully, some thorny spp may appear unarmed)
Prickles present (emerging from internodes along twigs)...**AA**
Spines present (usu <u>below</u> lf scar or bud), occ in prs or 1-3-partite...**AB**
Thorns present (usu <u>above</u> lf scar or at end of shoot, occ collateral to buds, always single).......**AC**
■Twigs unarmed (some thorny spp may key out here if apparently unarmed)
Climber, occ sprawling..**AD**
Tree or shrub (occ dwarf shrub <30cm)
At least some buds clustered (≥3) at twig tip or base of twig, rarely stalked or hidden..............**AE**
At least some buds superposed (one bud above the other at same node) at lateral or terminal
positions on twig, occ v small or partly hidden in bark, stalked or sessile................................**AF**
All buds single (occ 1-2 collateral, or hidden below bark or lf scar), stalked or sessile
Buds naked (usu densely hairy) OR with 1 scale, >2mm..**AG**
Buds with 2-3 scales, >2mm
At least some buds on a >1mm stalk (beware woody spurs)..**AH**
All buds sessile (occ short-stalked <1mm)..**AI**
Buds with ≥4 scales OR <2mm (occ hidden under bark or lf scar) (occ obscured by hairs in
Laburnum, Malus, Populus alba and *Pyrus salicifolius,* by scales in *Elaeagnus* and by
stipules in *Potentilla fruticosa*)
Twigs green (beware unseasoned twigs, or twigs developing grey skin).............................**AJ**
Twigs not green
Stipule scars present on twigs, usu adjacent to (or adjoining) lf scars (look at several nodes
carefully, occ linear or ± encircling twig, occ obscure, or on 1-side only, but not covered by
woolly hairs) (*Populus* and some other spp key out in both **AK** & **AL**)
Lateral buds (±) adpressed to twig...**AK**
Lateral buds spreading from twig..**AL**
Stipules persisting, not falling or leaving scars (*Colutea arborescens, Cotoneaster,*
Potentilla fruticosa, Rubus)...**AM**
Stipule scars (and stipules) absent
Lf scars absent or present as a shrivelled stub in *Rubus* (branchlet scars occ present in
Tamarix and *Taxodium*), OR lf scars present with 1 bundle scar (occ a short arc).......**AN**
Lf scars with 2 bundle scars (*Ginkgo biloba*)..**AO**
Lf scars with 3 bundle scars (typical of most spp)..**AP**
Lf scars with 5 bundle scars (rarely mixture of 3, 4 and 5) (mostly *Sorbus* subgen
Sorbus)..**AQ**
Lf scars with 7-30 bundle scars (*Ailanthus, Carya, Paeonia, Toxicodendron, Xanthorhiza*)
....**AR**

Group AA – *Twigs armed with prickles (look carefully inc nr base). Stipule scars absent*

■Lf scars shrivelled on persistent raised petiole bases (narrowly crescent-shaped when visible), spiralling, shortly decurrent; bundle scars 3, rarely visible, middle scar long-protruding. Buds often superposed, usu spreading, occ adpressed; scales keeled (at least lower). Stipules occ persisting, ± linear, not falling leaving scars. Pith white to orange-brown. Shrub, often trailing. Often suckering ....(*Rubus*) Go to **RUB**

■Lf scars distinct, not raised. Suckering

Twigs stout (10-15mm diam). Bundle scars 25-40, in 1 row, protruding

Twigs pale grey, prickly, round, with stout white adpressed (strigose) hairs nr tip; prickles to 7mm, slender, straight; pith white, >>¾ diam, round. Lf scars narrowly U-shaped, extending ½ way around twig. Terminal bud 6-15mm, conical, bluntly acute; scales 3-5, grey-brown, hairless, papery, erose. Lateral buds smaller, set well above lf scar. Trunk 1-5(10)m, erect, unbranched, prickly. Shrub or small tree. Also known as 'Devil's Walking-sticks' Remnant lfts hairless exc for occ bristles on main veins below. PL 5 ....*Japanese Angelica-tree* **Aralia elata**

Remnant lfts densely softly hairy below ....(not illustrated) *Chinese Angelica-tree* **Aralia chinensis**

Twigs slender to mod (2-5mm diam). Bundle scars 3

Terminal bud spindle-shaped, 4-10mm; scales 6-12, white, turning brown. Twigs occ with bristle-like prickles; pith white or green. Shrub. PL 27…(see **AB**) *Gooseberry* **Ribes uva-crispa**

Terminal bud ovoid, (1.5)3-7mm; scales 3-5, green or red, 1(3)-keeled, with 3-toothed tip or apiculus, hairless, not ciliate but usu minutely gland-fringed. Lateral buds similar, often set slightly above lf scar (not touching lf scar), spreading at 45-90°. Twigs green to red, round, with stomata; prickles occ in prs below nodes; pith ¾ diam, white, round. Lf scars v narrow, line-like, >> bud width (extending ≥½ way around twig), weakly decurrent. Shrub. Suckers usu more prickly. Frs are generally required for identification (many fertile hybrids and additional spp occur)

Prickles v unequal and straight. Twigs not zig-zagging, v prickly. Erect, non-climbing

Twigs mod (4-5mm diam), grey-brown, densely hairy (± woolly), often with stout glandular hairs; longer prickles to 6mm, straight or slightly reflexed, hairy at least nr base; shorter prickles c2mm. Buds 5-7mm; scales red. To 2m. PL 27..........*Japanese Rose* **Rosa rugosa**

Twigs slender (1.5-3mm diam), reddish-brown, hairless but short stiff glandular hairs esp nr tip; longer prickles 5-10mm, scattered, slender, straight (or slightly reflexed), broad-based; shorter prickles 0.5-3mm, abundant. Buds 2-3mm; scales red. Usu 0.2-1(2)m. Mostly coastal or planted. PL 27...*Burnet Rose* **Rosa spinosissima**

Prickles (±) equal or not (may have acicles (needle-like prickles)), at least some strongly curved. Twigs zig-zagging or not, hairless. Erect or arching, climbing or not

Twigs purple, usu pruinose, 2-3mm diam, ± wavy; prickles sparse, 4-7mm, slender (1mm width at midpoint), broad-based (6mm width at base). Buds 3-5mm; scales red. PL 27 ....*Red-leaved Rose* **Rosa ferruginea**

Twigs green to reddish (esp on sunlit side), not pruinose, v variable. PL 27 ....(inc sect *Rosa* and *Caninae*) *Rose* **Rosa spp**

Aralia elata
Japanese Angelica-tree

Rosa rugosa
Japanese Rose

Rosa spinosissima
Burnet Rose

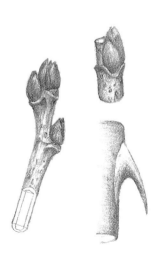

Rosa ferruginea
Red-leaved Rose

Rosa canina
Dog-rose

Group AB – *Twigs armed with spines at nodes (usu <u>below</u> a lf scar). Stipule scars absent*

■Tree to 30m. Buds hidden under lf scar membrane

Spines (actually thorns) usu 3-partite (with 2 short branches nr base), occ 2-partite or simple, 5-8cm, vicious, shiny reddish-brown; present on twigs, branchlets and trunk; those on trunk often longer and more branched. PL 14...........................(see **AF**) *Honey-locust* **Gleditsia triacanthos**

Spines (modified stipules) in prs, (2)5-20mm, broad-based, ± laterally flat, slightly upcurved, persisting several yrs, absent from older or slow-growing twigs. Twigs slender to stout (1.5-5mm diam), usu zig-zagging, reddish-brown, hairless, 5-angled, brittle; lenticels low, round to longitudinal, small, pale; inner bark smelling of fresh green beans; pith ½ diam, white, 5-angled. Buds (when visible) all lateral, 2-5 superposed, minute, naked, brown-hairy, on vigorous twigs a bud above lf scar may develop into a weak twig (soon falling leaving scar). Lf scars spiralling, irreg triangular or 3-lobed, large, covered by membrane split between 3 obscure bundle scars, rupturing as underlying buds develop; bundle scars in 3 groups. Bark deeply furrowed with broad intersecting ridges, like cracked paint on close inspection, brown, later rope-like. Trunk occ leaning, often short; crown oblong, open; branches ascending, twisted, slender. Often suckering. Late bursting. PL 27...*False-acacia* **Robinia pseudoacacia**

■Medium shrub >1m. Buds 2-8mm, ovoid

Twigs 4-angled, green with white ridges, occ brown or covered in grey skin, mod slender (2-3mm diam), weakly zig-zagging, hairless, with persistent bud scale remnants at join with branchlet; lenticels absent; stomata obscure; inner bark green, odorous; pith ½ diam, green, ± round, fragmenting. Branchlets occ with woody spurs. Buds all lateral, adpressed, occ collateral, 4-8mm, ovoid, acute; scales 3-4, pale grey-brown, papery, loose, 3-veined, hairless, not ciliate. Spines (modified stipules) in prs, c5mm, thread-like, upright to spreading, occ broken or absent. Lf scars spiralling, v raised, circular, decurrent; bundle scar 1. Bark smooth, with lenticels, greenish. PL 7 ....*Siberian Pea-shrub* **Caragana arborescens**

Twigs 5-9-ridged, not green, slender (2mm diam), not zig-zagging, hairless; lenticels absent; inner bark (and wood) yellow, odourless; pith ½-⅔ diam, white, round. Branchlets without woody spurs; bark finely fissured. Buds all lateral, spreading, occ collateral; scales 6-8, brown, acute or acuminate, apiculate, often recurved, outermost clearly modified petiole bases. Spines at c90°. Lf scars often crowded (if lvs were in fascicles) at top of persistent lf bases, raised, semi-circular or elliptical, small, << bud width, blackish; bundle scars 3, minute, often indistinct. Bark weakly peeling in longitudinal strips. Often suckering. Other taxa also occur

Spines mostly 3-partite, often simple or absent nr twig tip and 5-partite nr twig base, 3-12mm, yellow-brown. Twigs mod 5-7-ridged, dull orange-brown to greyish. Branchlets grey-white to grey-brown. Buds 3-6mm. PL 5...*Barberry* **Berberis vulgaris**

Spines mostly 1 (simple), occ 2-3-partite nr twig base, 4-16mm, purplish-red. Twigs strongly 5-9-ridged, bright orange-brown to purplish-red. Branchlets purplish-brown. Buds 2-3mm. PL 5 ....*Thunberg's Barberry* **Berberis thunbergii**

■Low shrub to 1m. Buds 4-10mm, spindle-shaped

Twigs mod slender (2-4mm diam), whitish to brown, often bleached or straw-coloured, hairless to minutely hairy or bristly, occ with bristle-like prickles, round or angled nr tip, with persistent bud scale remnants at join with branchlet; inner bark weakly odorous; pith ½ diam, white or green, often turning brown, round, soon fragmenting. Branchlets with splitting bark, occ with woody spurs. Terminal bud usu single, occ paired, acute; scales 6-12, white, turning brown, obtuse, apiculate, weakly 3-veined, keeled (esp lower), (woolly-) ciliate (esp inner), loose. Lateral buds ± adpressed to spreading. Spines 1-3-partite, at 90°, 8-15mm, reddish-brown to whitish. Lf scars weakly raised, angled crescent-shaped, >> bud width (extending c½ way around twig), weakly decurrent; bundle scars 3. Bark ± peeling in longitudinal strips. Branches often drooping. Occ suckering. PL 27..*Gooseberry* **Ribes uva-crispa**

Gleditsia triacanthos
Honey-locust

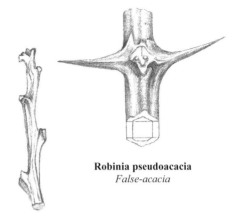

Robinia pseudoacacia
False-acacia

Caragana arborescens
Siberian Pea-shrub

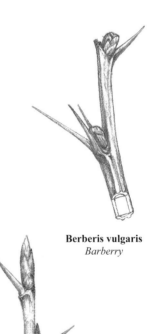

Berberis vulgaris
Barberry

Berberis thunbergii
Thunberg's Barberry

Ribes uva-crispa
Gooseberry

Group AC – *Twigs armed with thorns (look carefully), rarely absent. Thorns usu directly above a lf scar or at the end of a short branch (unlike spines), usu at 90° to branchlet.* ❶ *Twigs with odorous inner bark.* ❷ *Buds with tuft of buff or golden-yellow hairs at tip (2 entries).* ❸ *Twigs (and buds) with peltate scales (2 entries).* ❹ *Latex present.* ❺ *Stipule scars ± circular*

■End bud usu >2mm (*Chaenomeles* may key out here if buds >2mm)

Lateral buds adpressed. Bundle scars 3

Twigs with odorous inner bark. Terminal bud rarely present. Lateral buds (2)4-6mm, ovoid-conical, acute, talon-like, dark or blackish-brown, hairless, often subopp. Stipule scars present. ❶. PL 26...(see **BB**) Buckthorn **Rhamnus cathartica**

Twigs with inner bark odourless. Terminal bud absent. Lateral buds 2-5mm, flattened-ovoid, obtuse, red- to purplish-brown, buff-woolly at tip. Stipule scars present. ❷. PL 11 ....(see **AI**) Quince **Cydonia oblonga**

Twigs with inner bark odourless. Terminal bud 3-8mm, ± ovoid, ± sharply acute, usu white-woolly or -hairy at least at base or tip. Lateral buds 2-5mm, flattened-ovoid, obtuse, shiny reddish-purple, ± woolly to hairless, ciliate. Stipule scars absent....(*Malus sylvestris*) Go to **MAL**

Lateral buds usu spreading (but occ adpressed and flattened esp on vigorous shoots)

Twigs with bronze peltate scales at least nr tip. Bundle scar 1. Stipule scars absent

Twigs mod slender (2-4mm diam), angled; pith c½, brown, round to ± 3-angled. Thorns to 1cm. Buds all lateral, occ collateral, 2-5mm, obovoid, obtuse, densely covered with minute bronze peltate scales; those of female plants with 2(4) scales, heart-shaped; those of male plants with 6(8) scales. Lf scars spiralling, rarely opp (without interpetiolar ridge), raised, crescent-shaped to semi-circular or elliptical, small; bundle scar flat arc, not sunken. Bark fissured. Suckering shrub, rarely small tree. ❸. Often coastal and invasive, esp sand dunes. PL 14 ....Sea-buckthorn **Hippophae rhamnoides**

Twigs white-felted at least nr tip. Bundle scars 3, not sunken. Stipule scars absent. Terminal bud 6-12mm ....(*Pyrus elaeagnifolia*) Go to **PYR**

Twigs hairy at least nr tip. Bundle scars 3

Stipule scars present. Twigs minutely hairy to hairless; inner bark weakly odorous. Bundle scars not sunken. Terminal bud absent. Lateral buds 2-5(6)mm ....(*Prunus domestica*) Go to **PRU**

Stipule scars absent. Twigs adpressed-hairy (or woolly) at tip; inner bark odourless. Bundle scars often sunken. Terminal bud (2)3-6mm. PL 19......(see **AP**) Medlar **Mespilus germanica**

Twigs usu hairless. Bundle scars 3. Stipule scars absent

Twigs usu mod (3-5mm diam), olive- to orange- or reddish-brown, not zig-zagging; pith white or green. Buds not red; scales often ciliate. Bark in square or rectangular scales. Tree; crown pyramidal to round. Often ❷..(*Pyrus*) Go to **PYR**

Twigs slender to mod (1.5-4mm diam), shiny dark reddish-brown, often zig-zagging; round; lenticels few, flat, oblong to longitudinal, small, pale; pith ½ diam, white, round. Branchlets with woody spurs 3-8mm. Terminal bud occ with 1 collateral bud, ovoid to globose, acute to obtuse; scales 4-8, shiny dark red to reddish-brown, hairless, not ciliate, minutely gland-fringed to erose, occ keeled, occ apiculate or with remnants of 3-toothed tip, lowermost bulging out. Lateral buds similar, (1)2-4(6)mm, occ with 1(2) collateral buds. Lf scars spiralling, weakly raised, crescent-shaped to semi-circular, not or weakly decurrent. Thorns occ absent, occ with bud(s) along length. Bark smooth red-brown when young, later grey-brown and fissured into long rectangular scaly strips (>5x as long as wide). Shrub or small tree; crown round

Thorns 0.5-1.5cm, ± curved. Terminal bud 2-5mm. Lateral buds 2-3(4)mm. Twigs slender (1.5-2mm diam)

Frs all with 1 style and stone. PL 11...................................*Hawthorn* **Crataegus monogyna**

Frs with mixture of 1-2 styles and stones. *C. laevigata x monogyna* ....(not illustrated) Hybrid Midland Hawthorn **Crataegus x media**

Frs all with 2 styles and stones.......(not illustrated) Midland Hawthorn **Crataegus laevigata**

Hippophae rhamnoides
Sea-buckthorn

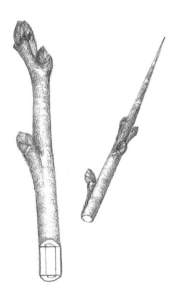

Crataegus monogyna
Hawthorn

Thorns 2-4cm, straight or ± curved. Frs with (1)2(3) styles and stones. Terminal bud 3-6(8)mm. Twigs slender to mod (2-4mm diam). PL 11
....*Broad-leaved Cockspurthorn* **Crataegus persimilis**
Thorns 3-6cm. Frs with (3)5 styles and stones. Terminal bud 6-8mm
....*Downy Hawthorn* **Crataegus mollis**
Thorns 5-9cm. Frs with 1-2(3) styles and stones. Terminal bud 3-6mm. PL 11
....*Cockspur Hawthorn* **Crataegus crus-galli**
■All buds usu 1-2mm (rarely to 3mm in *Chaenomeles*) (*Crataegus* may key out here)
  Bundle scar 1
    Twigs with silvery to bronze peltate scales. Tree or shrub to 5(7)m. Stipule scars absent. ❸
    ....(see **AN**) **Elaeagnus** spp
    Twigs hairless. Arching shrub to 2m
      Stipule scars obscure, oval. Twigs slender (1-2mm diam), zig-zagging, grey-brown, round; pith ½ diam, white, round; <u>latex white</u>. Thorns c1cm, curved, orange-brown. Buds all lateral, partly sunken in bark, 1mm, globose, occ collateral; scales c5, obscure, reddish-brown or same colour as twig, hairless, not ciliate. Lf scars 2-ranked, semi-circular to triangular; bundle scars several ± fused into 1, obscure, in ellipse. Bark fissured, brown with orange in the cracks. Small tree; crown round. ❹. PL 17...........................*Osage-orange* **Maclura pomifera**
      Stipule scars absent. Twigs slender (1.5-3mm diam), curved, greyish-white, occ purplish, 3-5-lined, ± brittle, at 90° to branchlets; pith ½-⅔, green, round, fragmenting, occ hollow. Buds usu collateral to thorns, often obscure, 1mm, ± globose, soon bursting exposing young green lvs; scales several, indistinct, pale brown. Lf scars spiralling, weakly raised, occ clustered at nodes, crescent-shaped, small, decurrent; bundle scar round. Thorns 0.5-3cm, occ with lf scars. Suckering. Early bursting
        Lvs lanc (widest nr middle). PL 17......................*Duke of Argyll's Teaplant* **Lycium barbarum**
        Lvs narrowly ovate or rhombic (widest below middle). PL 17
        ....(not illustrated) *Chinese Teaplant* **Lycium chinense**
    Twigs adpressed-hairy. Low erect shrub to 0.5m
      Stipule scars absent. Twigs slender (1mm diam), grey, ridged; bark soon peeling; pith c½ diam, ± round, <u>green</u>. Buds naked (actually young green lvs). Lf scars v raised on dark peg, minute; bundle scar indistinct. Thorns 1-3cm, recurved, simple, v rarely branched, ridged, occ green, hairless. Semi-evergreen (usu), with fasicles of lvs. Early bursting
      ....*Petty Whin* **Genista anglica**
  Bundle scars 3. Twigs occ hairy at least nr tip
    Stipule scars triangular to linear. Buds terminal or lateral, occ collateral, 1-2mm, pale or dark reddish-brown...............................(*Prunus cerasifera, domestica, spinosa*) <u>Go to</u> **PRU**
    Stipule scars ± circular, small. Lf buds all lateral, single or with <u>1-2(3) collateral buds</u>, 1-2(3)mm, ovoid to globose, obtuse to acute; scales (2)3-7, dark or reddish-brown, usu hairless, occ ciliate, loose, later parting revealing pinkish-red inner scales. Fl buds clustered on branchlets. Thorns 1-2cm, occ absent, slender, with lf scars along length, usu 2 collateral buds at base. Twigs slender (c2mm diam), often ± zig-zagging, dull red- to purplish-brown or brown to grey, round or ± angled; lenticels few, flat, oblong, pale; pith c½ diam, white, round. Branchlets soon dark or grey-brown, blackish-brown when old; bark fissured. Lf scars spiralling, <u>raised</u>, small, crescent-shaped to triangular or elliptical, <u>decurrent</u>; bundle scars <u>often sunken</u>. Bark smooth but with raised lenticels. Arching shrub to 2.5m. Early bursting. The hybrid (*C. x superba*) is perhaps the most common taxon but is inseparable from *C. japonica*. Collectively known as 'Flowering Quinces'
      Twigs shortly hairy or becoming hairless and minutely warty due to raised hair bases. ❺. PL 8
      ....*Japanese Quince* **Chaenomeles japonica**
      Twigs hairless, not warty. PL 8.................................*Chinese Quince* **Chaenomeles speciosa**

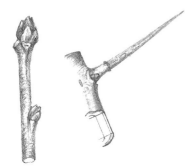

Crataegus persimilis
Broad-leaved Cockspurthorn

Crataegus mollis
Downy Hawthorn

Maclura pomifera
Osage-orange

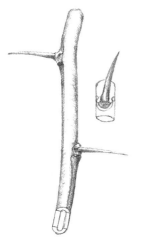

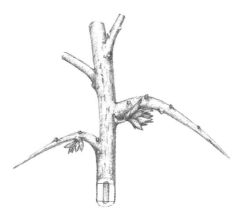

Lycium barbarum
Duke of Argyll's Teaplant

Genista anglica
Petty Whin

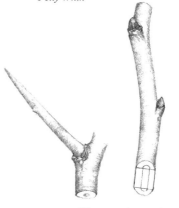

Chaenomeles japonica
Japanese Quince

Chaenomeles speciosa
Chinese Quince

Group AD – *Climber, occ scrambling. Terminal bud absent. Buds all lateral. Pith round (when present).* ❶ *Twigs with fetid inner bark.* ❷ *Ochrea present (fused stipules surrounding twig)*

■Tendrils present or falling leaving scars, occ shrivelled (remnant panicles of *Solanum dulcamara* occ resemble tendrils but keys out below under 'Tendrils (and scars) always absent')
   Twigs mod stout (4-10mm diam), occ zig-zagging, ± round, rarely angled, striate, swollen at nodes, tip usu dying back; lenticels absent; pith usu <u>orange-brown</u>, rarely white, with dark woody partitions at each node, ½-¾ diam, solid, occ chambered adjacent to nodes. Tendrils (or scars) opp lf scars, <u>absent from every 3rd node</u>, forked, not swollen at tips. Buds <u>at every node</u>, occ ± oblique to lf scar, occ 1 collateral bud, 4-6mm, conical-ovoid to ± globose; scales 2, reddish-brown, broad. Lf scars ± 2-ranked, semi-circular to crescent-shaped, with irreg surface; bundle scars several, occ in 3 groups, usu indistinct. Stipule scars linear, ± equal. Bark peeling
     Bud tip and inner scales white-woolly. Twigs greenish to reddish-brown, hairless. Late bursting. PL 37 ....*Grape-vine* **Vitis vinifera**
     Bud tip and inner scales usu brown-woolly. Twigs reddish-brown, sparsely white-woolly to hairless. PL 37...*Crimson-glory-vine* **Vitis coignetiae**
   Twigs mod slender (≤4mm diam), not zig-zagging; pith <u>green</u>, occ fragmented or hollow, c½ diam
     Twigs green, 5-angled, slender (2-3mm diam), hairless, tough fibres when cut; pith soon hollow. Tendrils coiled, unbranched, <u>on same side as lf scars</u>, on raised base, at every node. Buds 1mm; scales few, brown, loose. Lf scars spiralling, raised, ± circular, decurrent; bundle scars 3-5, obscure. Stipule scars circular to linear. Bark smooth, green. Usu semi-evergreen
     ....(not illustrated) *Passion-flower* **Passiflora caerulea**
     Twigs grey-brown, round, swollen at nodes, hairless; lenticels raised, oblong, small, pale or same colour as twig; pith occ fragmented or splitting into diaphragms. Tendrils (or scars) opp lf scars, <u>absent from every 3rd node</u> (at intervening nodes to buds), often falling off, with 5-12 branches ending in shrivelled adhesive pads. Branchlets with circular scars from falling twigs. Buds <u>only at every 3rd node</u>, spreading, occ with 1 small collateral bud, oblique to lf scar, globose-conical, obtuse to acute; scales 2-3(4), pale orange-brown, reddish before bursting, hairless, not ciliate. Lf scars 2-ranked, raised, ± circular, sunken with raised rim (crater-like); bundle scars 7-12, ± indistinct (later covered by a corky layer), in an ellipse. Stipule scars ± linear, curved, ± equal. Bark not peeling, grey-brown, aerial roots occ present
       Tendrils 5-15cm. Twigs with long internodes (mostly >5cm), mod slender (2-3(4)mm diam). Buds (2)3-7mm. PL 20....................................*Virginia-creeper* **Parthenocissus quinquefolia**
       Tendrils 1-2cm. Twigs with short internodes (often 3-5cm), slender (1.5-2mm diam). Buds 1-2mm. PL 20...*Boston-ivy* **Parthenocissus tricuspidata**
■Tendrils (and scars) always absent. Twigs slender to mod (1.5-5mm diam)
   Inner bark fetid. Pith fragmenting or hollow. Buds spreading. ❶
     Ambidextrous twining (clockwise or anticlockwise) or scrambling semi-woody per. Twigs woody at least nr base, often dying back in winter, ± slender (2-3mm diam), pale grey or greenish or dark purple-brown and finely mottled, hairy to hairless, ± 3(5)-angled, occ adventitious buds sunken in bark (occ mistaken for lenticels); lenticels few, raised, round, pale; pith ⅔ diam, green or white (or mottled). Buds 1-2mm, ± globose; scales 4-5, brown, obtuse, hairy, loose. Lf scars spiralling, v raised on short peg, at 90° to twig, ± circular or elliptical; bundle scar 1, U-shaped, occ broken into 3. Stipule scars absent. Remnant panicle with dried berries often persistent, occ opp lf scars, occ mistaken for tendrils (esp when remnant fr discs present). PL 31...*Bittersweet* **Solanum dulcamara**
   Inner bark odourless
     Pith chambered
       Twigs usu mod stout (3-7mm diam), not zig-zagging, brown, brown-hairy to hairless, rough with minutely raised hair bases, round; lenticels raised, oval, pale; pith chambers crowded (20-30 per cm), buff, ⅔ diam. Buds sunken under bark above lf scar, 1-3mm when breaking through, globose, densely buff-hairy; scales obscured by hairs. Lf scars spiralling, v raised on short peg, at 90° to twig, swollen, large, circular, sunken with raised rim (crater-like); bundle

29

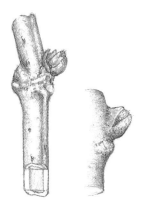

Vitis vinifera
Grape-vine

Vitis coignetiae
Crimson-glory-vine

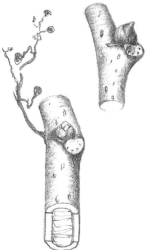

Parthenocissus quinquefolia
Virginia-creeper

Parthenocissus tricuspidata
Boston-ivy

Solanum dulcamara
Bittersweet

AD

scar 1, involute U-shaped, in lower ½ of scar. Stipule scars absent. Anticlockwise-twining.
Other spp grown. PL 3..*Kiwifruit* **Actinidia deliciosa**
Pith not chambered (may be fragmented or hollow in *Fallopia baldschuanica*)
 Buds adpressed
  Twigs mod (3-5mm diam), ± angled, green to whitish-grey, hairy to hairless; lenticels usu
  absent; pith ½-⅔ diam, white or brown, round. Buds 5-8mm, oblong-conical, acute; scales 2,
  overlapping, often nearly surrounded by outer scale, (green-) dark purple-brown, loose,
  hairless but silky inner scale hairs occ visible. Lf scars spiralling, raised, elliptical to ±
  circular, shortly decurrent, often with a wart-like swelling each side or occ with a spine-like
  projection each side and appearing 2-horned; bundle scar 1 or indistinct and appearing as a
  fibrous mass. Stipules occ persisting, linear; stipule scars elliptical to short-linear. Bark
  smooth, grey. Old trunks grooved and muscle-like, resembling *Carpinus betulus*
   Clockwise-twining. PL 37...*Japanese Wisteria* **Wisteria floribunda**
   Anticlockwise-twining...........................(not illustrated) *Chinese Wisteria* **Wisteria sinensis**
 Buds spreading (at c60° to twig but c90° in *Celastrus*)
  Twigs (±) round
   Lf scars raised, obscure, with extra-floral nectary (small pit) on lower side (occ mistaken for
   lf scar), spiralling, occ remnants of ochrea (fused stipules surrounding twig); bundle scars
   obscure. Twigs slender (1.5-2.5mm diam), grey (-brown), ± round (usu angled at tip),
   striate, hairless, with persistent bud scale remnants at join with branchlet; lenticels
   obscure; pith ½-⅔ diam, green to white, soon hollow; surrounding wood v porous with
   minute hollows (distinctly ring-porous). Branchlets solid. Buds occ with 1 collateral bud,
   2-6mm, ovoid-conical, ± acute; scales c7, brown, hairless, not ciliate, loose, ragged.
   Clockwise-twining, trailing to 30m. ❷. PL 12.............*Russian-vine* **Fallopia baldschuanica**
   Lf scars v raised on green peg (lvs deciduous slightly above petiole base), half-elliptical,
   occ twisted, spiralling; bundle scars 5-6, in an ellipse, reduced to 3 if peg removed. Twigs
   slender (1.5-2(3)mm diam), green to olive-brown, hairless, round; lenticels few, raised,
   oblong, pale; pith c½ diam, white. Buds occ with 1 collateral bud, 1.5-4mm, ovoid, ± acute;
   scales 6-12, ovate, apiculate, green to brown, hairless. Clockwise-twining. Occ semi-
   evergreen. PL 4..*Chocolate-vine* **Akebia quinata**
  Twigs 5-lined at least nr tip
   Twigs green, slender (2-3mm wide), hairless; lenticels absent. PL 15
   ....(see **AJ**) *Yellow Jasmine* **Jasminum humile**
   Twigs reddish-brown, slender (2mm diam), hairless, often ringed by transverse lines;
   lenticels many, low, round, orange; pith ½-⅔ diam, white. Buds rarely superposed, at c90°,
   1-2mm, ± globose-conical, sharply acute; scales 3-5 prs, same colour as twig, apiculate,
   keeled. Lf scars spiralling, weakly raised, ± circular, ± sunken; bundle scar involute U-
   shaped (1-many scars fused). Stipule scars obscure, rarely visible, occ persistent
   resembling stiff hairs. Clockwise-twining or scrambling. Roots orange. PL 8
   ....*Staff-vine* **Celastrus orbiculatus**

31

AD

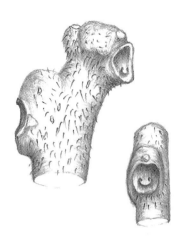

Actinidia deliciosa
Kiwifruit

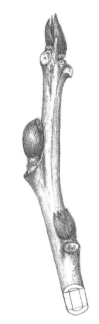

Wisteria floribunda
Japanese Wisteria

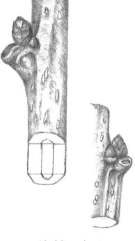

Akebia quinata
Chocolate-vine

Fallopia baldschuanica
Russian-vine

Celastrus orbiculatus
Staff-vine

Group AE – *Buds clustered (only 1 true terminal bud, the surrounding buds are actually lateral buds; all lateral in* Hippocrepis emerus*). Lf scars spiralling and twigs not zig-zagging (exc* H. omerus *which has zig-zagging twigs with 2-ranked lf scars).* ❶ *Buds short-stalked (2 entries).* ❷ *Pith orange-brown.* ❸ *Buds usu hiddon*

■Bundle scar 1. Stipules 1mm, persistent or falling leaving scars. PL 14

....(see **AJ**) *Scorpion Senna* **Hippocrepis emerus**

■Bundle scars 3 (occ multiplied)

    Stipule scars present (occ obscure in *Prunus*)

        Pith 5-angled. Buds occ sticky or balsam-scented. Lateral buds with lowest scale directly above lf scar (a 'thumb nail' as wide as bud and usu 2-4-lobed). Inner bark with astringent taste ....(*Populus*) <u>Go to</u> **POP**

        Pith (±) round. Buds never sticky or balsam-scented. Lateral buds with scales not as above. Inner bark with weak bitter almond odour....................................(*Prunus*) <u>Go to</u> **PRU**

    Stipule scars absent. Pith round

        Pith buff, chambered. Tree. ❶. PL 24........(see **AF**) *Caucasian Wingnut* **Pterocarya fraxinifolia**

        Pith white, soon fragmenting, ½ diam. End buds usu 3-5-clustered at twig tip or nodes of each yrs growth, 3-7mm, soon short-stalked. Lf scars >> bud width. Shrub. Often ❶

        ....(*Ribes nigrum, rubrum, spicatum*) <u>Go to</u> **RIB**

        Pith orange, solid, ½-⅔ diam. End buds c5-clustered, 1.5-4mm, ovoid, acute; scales 1(2) prs, dark purple to green-black, hairless, ciliate. Lateral buds similar, single, spreading, 1-2mm, flattened-ovoid. Lf scars raised on persistent blackish petiole base (bud slightly sunken behind lf scar), semi-circular to ± heart-shaped, with raised rim, small, equal to bud width; bundle scars 3, or 3 groups of 3. Twigs mod (3-4mm diam), purple-brown to orange, often <u>pruinose nr tip</u>, minutely patent-hairy or hairless, round; lenticels low, round, small, pale orange; sap ± sticky, aromatic (soap-scented). Bark becoming scaly, dark grey to black. Shrub or small tree. ❷. PL 10..*Smoke-tree* **Cotinus coggygria**

■Bundle scars 4, in a diamond shape, often v obscure. Stipules or scars present

    End buds partly or entirely hidden within flat-topped circular pads above lf scar, (3)4-7-clustered, white-woolly with branched hairs. Lateral buds similar. Twigs mod slender (2-3mm diam), whitish-grey, v sparsely to densely <u>stellate-hairy</u>, ridged; lenticels same colour as twig; pith ½ diam, white or green, ± round. Branchlets with woody spurs. Lf scars v raised, peg-like, half-circular to ± circular. Stipules to 5mm, thread-like, persistent or leaving small raised round scars. Bark smooth, pale. Bark fissured. Shrub or small tree. Late bursting. ❸. PL 14........*Hibiscus* **Hibiscus syriacus**

■Bundle scars 7-12, scattered or in an ellipse, occ obscure. Stipules or scars present. Twigs slender to mod stout (2-5mm diam), weakly 5-angled, often several twigs radiating from end of previous yrs branchlet, olive to reddish-brown, often with grey skin; lenticels low, ± round, small, pale; pith ½ diam, white, <u>5-angled</u>. End buds usu (3)4-5-clustered, ± ovoid, ± 5-angled; scales 5-ranked. Lateral buds single, spreading, occ oblique to lf scar. Lf scars raised, semi-circular to kidney-shaped. Branches twisted, often with scars of cast twigs. Tree; lower branches often with dead lvs persisting (marcescent). Late bursting

    End buds with persistent long (10-25mm) narrow twisted whisker-like stipules (occ obscuring bud cluster, rarely falling). Twigs minutely grey stellate-hairy. Buds 2-6mm, obtuse, grey stellate-hairy; scales <12, reddish-brown. Bark furrowed into rectangular or hexagonal islands, dark grey, <u>with orange in furrows</u>. PL 25..*Turkey Oak* **Quercus cerris**

    End buds without stipules. Twigs hairless. Stipule scars unequal, small, triangular

        Bud scales entire, ciliate. Bark furrowed into rectangular or hexagonal islands, grey to brown, rarely with orange in furrows. The hybrid of *Q. petraea* x *robur* (*Q.* x *rosacea*) commonly occurs

        Buds (±) hairless, 3-8mm, ovoid, ± obtuse to ± acute; scales usu <20, <u>reddish-brown</u>, with pale or dark margins. PL 26....................................*Pedunculate Oak* **Quercus robur**

        Buds hairy, 5-15mm, ovoid, ± acute; scales usu >20, dull <u>pale grey-brown</u>, usu with dark margins. Trunk usu straighter and longer with more symmetrical crown than *Q. robur*. PL 26

        ....*Sessile Oak* **Quercus petraea**

Cotinus coggygria
Smoke-tree

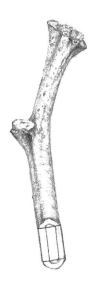

Hibiscus syriacus
Hibiscus

Quercus cerris
Turkey Oak

Quercus robur
Pedunculate Oak

Quercus petraea
Sessile Oak

Bud scales (esp lower) usu notched or split at tip, usu <20, wide dark margins, usu cilliate. Bark
with shallow fissures like 'ski tracks' when young (at least around head height), eventually
furrowed into rectangular or hexagonal islands, grey-brown to blackish, usu with orange in
fissures

Buds ± conical, acute, <u>dark reddish</u>-brown. Lvs lobed ≤½ way to midrib

Buds (4)5-9mm, usu white- or buff-hairy nr tip, occ hairless. Trunk usu short; lower branches
stout and usu at 90° to trunk; crown round, without pin-like branchlets. PL 26
....*Red Oak* **Quercus rubra**

Buds ovoid, obtuse to ± acute, <u>pale brown</u>, occ reddish-brown. Lvs lobed ≥½ way to midrib

Buds (4)5-7(8)mm, white- or buff-hairy nr tip. Trunk rapidly tapering from swollen base;
crown pyramidal when young, later rounded, with many dead branches; lower branches
often persisting at 90° to trunk, without dead stubs. PL 25....*Scarlet Oak* **Quercus coccinea**

Buds 2-5mm, hairless (occ a few hairs at tip). Trunk straight, with stubs of dead branches;
crown remaining pyramidal, distinctive with lower branches <u>drooping</u>, middle branches
horizontal and upper branches ascending; branches with <u>many stubby pin-like branchlets</u>
(often dead) resulting in a spiny appearance. PL 25...................*Pin Oak* **Quercus palustris**

Quercus rubra
Red Oak

Quercus coccinea
Scarlet Oak

Quercus palustris
Pin Oak

Group AF – *Buds superposed (the upper bud larger).* ❶ *Pith chambered.* ❷ *Buds stalked (6 entries).* ❸ *Buds naked (2 entries).* ❹ *Pith orange-brown (2 entries).* Alnus glutinosa, Daphne mezereum, Elaeagnus, Ostrya, Liriodendron *and* Liquidambar *may v rarely key out here*

■Twigs >5mm diam; pith chambered, odorous (chemical smell). Stipule scars absent. Tree. ❶ Terminal bud(s) stalked to 10mm, 1-3 superposed, <u>naked</u> (actually young folded lvs shaped like folded fan), 10-20mm inc stalk, <u>reddish-brown with dense minute scale-like hairs</u>, sparse minute yellow glands. Lateral buds <u>set well-above lf scar</u>, with 0-2 superposed buds, sunken in bark, 0-5mm. Twigs mod stout (6-8mm diam), olive-green to grey, round; lenticels low, round, small, buff; pith chambers crowded (c15 per cm), buff, ½ diam, angled. Lf scars elliptical or heart-shaped, large, not or weakly raised, whitish; bundle scars 3, U-shaped, occ divided. Bark soon furrowed with broad intersecting ridges. Suckering. ❷❸. PL 24..........*Caucasian Wingnut* **Pterocarya fraxinifolia**
Terminal bud sessile, usu single; scales 1-2 prs, ± valvate (occ parted). Lateral buds smaller, usu with 1 superposed bud. Twigs mod stout, round but ridged nr tip. Lf scars spiralling, large, usu wider than lateral buds, weakly raised, broadly Y-shaped or angled heart-shaped, whitish, resembling a 'monkey face'; bundle scars in 3 U-shaped groups. Crown round. Not suckering
   Twigs usu hairless, occ minutely buff-hairy (hairs never glandular), 5-10mm diam, olive-grey to purplish-brown, occ green; lenticels flat, oval, small, pale; pith chambers well-spaced (8-12 per cm), buff. Terminal bud 5-10mm, broadly ovoid; scales 1(2) prs, occ more visible, dark grey to blackish, minutely scurfy or hairy. Lateral buds smaller, 3-5mm, occ set well above lf scar, spreading; scales 1-3 prs. Preformed young male catkins may be confused with lateral buds (but have >100 small 'scales'). Bark pale grey and smooth when young, later with intersecting ridges. Trunk short. Late bursting. PL 15....................*Walnut* **Juglans regia**
   Twigs minutely white- or buff-hairy (hairs occ glandular), 5-8mm diam, olive- or reddish-brown to grey; lenticels ± raised, oval, small, buff; pith chambers crowded (14-18 per cm), brown. Terminal bud 5-10mm, broadly oblong, obtuse, ± 3-angled; scales 2 prs but appearing naked due to short woolly hairs, pale grey. Lateral buds 2-4mm, ovoid, grey-hairy. Bark brown to greyish-black, furrowed, with intersecting scaly ridges, with <u>dark chocolate-brown</u> underbark. Trunk tall. Late bursting. PL 15.......................*Black Walnut* **Juglans nigra**
■Twigs <5mm diam (or if >5mm diam, pith not chambered); pith solid, odourless. Stipule scars (or stipules in *Rubus*) often present
   Lf scars shrivelled. Pith white to orange-brown, large. Stipules persistent. Occ ❹(*Rubus*) <u>Go to</u> **RUB**
   Lf scars distinct
      Buds stellate-hairy, <5mm. Twigs hairless or with occ stellate hairs, round, zig-zagging
         Twigs slender (1-2mm diam), orange-brown; lenticels absent or obscure; pith ½ diam, green, round. Branchlets with fissured bark. Buds all lateral, adpressed, short-stalked to 1mm, 4-5mm, with 1 smaller (2mm) superposed bud, ovoid-oblong, obtuse, naked, cream (occ rusty) stellate-hairy. Lf scars 2-ranked, weakly raised, broad crescent-shaped; bundle scar 1, U-shaped. Stipule scars absent. Bark smooth, grey-brown, later with orange-brown in fissures. Trunk ± grooved, muscle-like. ❷. PL 34................*Japanese Snowbell-tree* **Styrax japonicus**
      Buds stellate-hairy, >5mm. Twigs often stellate-hairy at least nr tip, round or (±) 3-angled nr tip, ± zig-zagging; pith green, ≤½ diam, ± 3-angled
         Twigs whitish-grey or rusty-brown with dense stellate hairs, mod slender (2-3mm diam); lenticels few or obscure, low, oval, buff; bark <u>finely fissured</u>. Terminal bud on 4-10mm stalk, with 1(2) superposed buds, (6)10-15mm, scalpel-shaped or oblong, ± flattened; scales 2, soon falling off (so bud often naked or with 1 scale), pale brown, occ dark or rusty-brown. Lateral buds <u>oblique to lf scar</u>, ± adpressed, sessile to short-stalked, usu with 1(2) superposed buds. Lf scars 2-ranked, ± raised, semi-circular to ± 3-lobed, equal to bud width, <u>blackish</u>, <u>deciduous</u> (easily removed or falling in spring); bundle scars 3, often divided. Stipule scars triangular to linear, usu unequal, pale to dark brown. Bark (±) smooth or slightly scaly, grey to grey-brown, often mottled; inner bark purple. Small tree or shrub, occ suckering. ❷❸
         Fl buds lateral, in groups of 3-12 on short recurved stalks, globose. Fls spring or autumn. PL 14..*Witch-hazel* **Hamamelis spp**
         Fl bud terminal, single. Fls spring, frs persisting on upright spikes. Terminal bud not as flattened as *Hamamelis*......................(not illustrated) *Mountain Witch-alder* **Fothergilla major**

Pterocarya fraxinifolia
Caucasian Wingnut

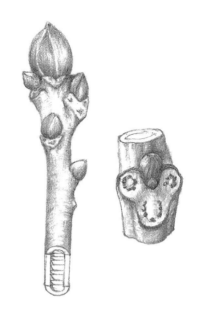

Juglans regia
Walnut

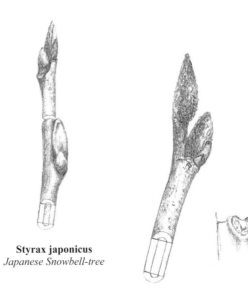

Styrax japonicus
Japanese Snowbell-tree

Juglans nigra
Black Walnut

Hamamelis sp
Witch-hazel

Twigs olive-brown, often stellate-hairy nr tip, slender to mod (1.5-4mm diam); lenticels low, oblong, buff; bark not fissured. Terminal bud with 1 superposed bud, on 1-3(5)mm stalk, 5-8mm, ovoid-oblong, ± flattened or lopsided; scales 2, ± overlapping, appearing ± naked, dark (blackish-) brown, often 2-tone if 1 scale fallen, scurfy with dark stellate hairs. Lateral buds ± oblique to lf scar, ± spreading, smaller, sessile or short-stalked. Fl buds globose. Lf scars 2-ranked, ± raised, semi-circular or triangular, small, < bud width, blackish; bundle scars 3, occ , often fused or forming a U or ring or flat arc. Stipule scars triangular to linear, unequal, pale to dark brown. Bark smooth, brown, <u>flaking</u> in patches revealing paler underbark. Small tree; crown round or vase-shaped. ❷. PL 20....................................*Persian Ironwood* **Parrotia persica**
Buds densely brown silky-hairy, <5mm. Twigs hairless, zig-zagging. Stipule scars absent
Twigs mod (4-5mm diam), shiny dark reddish-brown, round, <u>brittle</u>; lenticels low, oval to longitudinal, pale or same colour as twig; inner bark odorous; pith ½ diam, white, round. Buds all lateral, 3-6mm, with 3(4) closely superposed buds usu appearing as one, globose to conical, naked, concealed by petiole base until lf fall (even after lfts fallen). Lf scars 2-ranked, weakly raised, ± encircling bud; bundle scars (3)5(7). Bark smooth, often wrinkled, grey. Crown wide, usu low-branched. Small tree. PL 9.........................*Kentucky Yellowwood* **Cladrastis kentukea**
Buds hairless or sparsely hairy at tip, often ≤5mm. Twigs hairless, zig-zagging
Twigs mod slender (2-3mm diam), dark red-brown or blackish, ± round; lenticels low, round, buff; pith ½ diam, white, occ pinkish, round. Branchlets with bark not splitting. Buds all lateral, often of 2 sizes (fl and lf buds separate). Lf buds adpressed, usu with 1 superposed bud (lower smaller and occ resembling a bud scale), sessile, 3-5mm, narrowly ovoid, flattened, acute; scales 2, overlapping, dark reddish-brown to ± black, often keeled, hairless, not ciliate. Fl buds lateral, often with 1 superposed bud, occ collateral or clustered, 5-8mm, usu swollen, usu adpressed, ± <u>stalked</u> (concealed by bud scales); scales 5-7, occ buff-ciliate esp nr tip. Lf scars 2-ranked, raised, triangular to heart-shaped, <u>dark</u>, <u>upper margin with reddish hair fringe</u>, weakly decurrent; bundle scars 3, U-shaped, occ fused. Stipule scars <u>linear, on auricle-like projections above corners of lf scar</u>, often obscure. Bark smooth, orange, later blocky and purplish to dark grey, occ with red-brown patches and orange in the cracks. Small tree; trunk short, twisted, often with clusters of fl buds (cauliflory). Occ ❷. PL 8................*Judas Tree* **Cercis siliquastrum**
Twigs v slender (0.5-2mm diam), red to reddish-brown, sparsely hairy to hairless, round to ± 5-lined; lenticels absent; pith ½ diam, white to <u>orange-brown</u> (esp in branchlets), round. Branchlets occ with grey skin; <u>bark splitting</u>. Buds all lateral, spreading, usu with 1(2) superposed buds, slightly stalked, (1)2mm, ovoid; scales usu (2)4, reddish, hairless or sparsely hairy at tip, occ ciliate. Lf scars usu 2-ranked, low, semi-circular, small, often shortly decurrent; bundle scars 3, occ ± fused. Stipule scars peg-like, protruding from sides of lf scar. Low or ground-covering shrub, with wide-spreading (60-90°) arching branches. ❷❹. PL 34
....*Stephanandra* **Stephanandra incisa**
Buds hidden, sunken under lf scar. Twigs hairless, zig-zagging. Stipule scars absent
Pith salmon-pink, ½ diam, round. Twigs 8-10mm diam, brown; lenticels flat, round, white. Buds all lateral, v small, <2mm, ± sunken in bark, naked, dome-shaped, densely golden-hairy with white tuft at tip, with 1(2) superposed buds (uppermost largest). Lf scars flat, heart-shaped; bundle scars 3 or 5. Trunk with large branches but without smaller branches. Late bursting (and lvs early deciduous). PL 14.....................................*Kentucky Coffeetree* **Gymnocladus dioicus**
Pith white, ½ diam, round. Twigs mod stout (4-5mm diam), <u>swollen at nodes and tip ('knobbly')</u>, shiny reddish- to greyish-brown or greenish; lenticels low, oval to longitudinal, orange, rarely same colour as twig. Branchlets with splitting bark. Buds all lateral, v small, partly or completely concealed below buff membrane covering lf scars (later rupturing revealing several green inner scales), with 1-3(5) superposed buds (uppermost bud occ <u>set well-above lf scar</u> and sunken in bark); scales several, brown, thin, hairless. Lf scars spiralling, raised or not, U- or shield-shaped, orange-edged; bundle scars 3. Bark smooth, grey-brown with horizontal lenticels when young, later fissured into long narrow curling plates free at one edge, revealing orange underbark. Trunk usu short, dividing nr ground into stout upright branches, further dividing into long slender horizontal branches; crown wide, open, often flat-topped. Medium tree. Late bursting. PL 14.....................*Thornless Honeylocust* **Gleditsia triacanthos** var **inermis**

Cladrastis kentukea
Kentucky Yellowwood

Parrotia persica
Persian Ironwood

Cercis siliquastrum
Judas Tree

Stephanandra incisa
Stephanandra

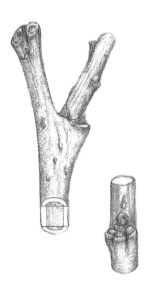

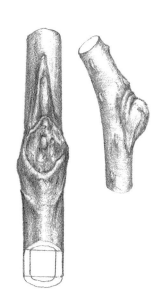

Gymnocladus dioicus
Kentucky Coffeetree

Gleditsia triacanthos var **inermis**
Thornless Honeylocust

AG

Group AG – *Buds naked or with 1 scale, >2mm* (*Parrotia* persica *may key out here if superposed bud overlooked).* ❶ *Twigs with white latex (3 spp).* ❷ *Twigs with strongly odorous inner bark (3 entries)*

■Buds naked, densely hairy

Twigs >5mm diam; latex white, drying black; pith solid. Stipule scars absent

Twigs stout (8-15mm diam), densely brown-hairy (fuzzy like deer antlers in velvet), round; lenticels raised, small, orange, usu obscured by hairs; pith >¾ diam, orange-brown, round. Branchlets olive- or grey-brown, ± hairless. False terminal bud ≤ laterals. Lateral buds 3-6mm, conical, obtuse, densely pale buff-hairy, partly sunken in lf scar. Lf scars spiralling, weakly raised, U-shaped forming an almost closed ring around bud, dark; bundle scars 9-18, in 1 row. Bark smooth, orange horizontal lenticels, eventually ± scaly. Small tree; trunk short; crown v open; branches widely forked. Suckering. Late bursting. ❶. PL 26....*Stag's-horn Sumach* **Rhus typhina**

Twigs mod stout (6-10mm diam); pith ⅔ diam, white, round. Terminal bud 6-10mm, conical, acute; scales 2 prs but may appear naked, densely pale buff-hairy. Lf scars not raised, ± circular, pale; bundle scars 15-30, ± scattered. Late bursting. ❶. Caution! Sap is a caustic contact-poison. PL 36..(see **AR**) *Chinese Lacquer-tree* **Toxicodendron vernicifluum**

Twigs >5mm diam; latex absent; pith chambered. Stipule scars absent. ❷. PL 24 ....(see **AF**) *Caucasian Wingnut* **Pterocarya fraxinifolia**

Twigs <5mm diam; latex absent; pith solid

Stipules and scars absent. Twigs usu with occ white adpressed stellate hairs. Buds white stellate-woolly. PL 7.............................(see **AN**) *Alternate-leaved Butterfly-bush* **Buddleja alternifolia**

Stipules and scars absent. Twigs hairless. Buds densely brown-hairy. PL 9 ....(see **AF**) *Kentucky Yellowwood* **Cladrastis kentukea**

Stipules (or remnants) often present (stipule scars oval to linear). Twigs usu with yellowish adpressed hairs. Buds densely yellowish-hairy..(*Cotoneaster*) Go to **COT**

Stipule scars small, oval, dark, occ obscured by hairs. Twigs buff-hairy at tip, slender (2mm diam), dark (violet-) brown, angled nr tip; lenticels many, low, pale; inner bark strongly odorous; pith c½ diam, white with yellow outer ring. Branchlets occ subopp, often with short twigs. Terminal bud 3-7mm, ± ovoid, (orange-) brown-hairy, with next season's stipules occ visible as black linear appendages. Lateral buds adpressed, 2-5mm, uppermost often just below terminal bud. Lf scars raised, ± semi-circular, equal bud width, dark, weakly decurrent; bundle scars 3. Bark smooth, with lenticels, occ fissured. Small tree. Late bursting. ❷. PL 13...*Alder Buckthorn* **Frangula alnus**

■Buds with 1 scale, densely hairy to hairless

Stipule scars small or absent, not encircling twig. Buds all lateral, ≤12(15)mm........(*Salix*) Go to **SAL**

Stipule scar a line encircling twig from top of lf scar

Terminal bud usu 10-50mm, densely hairy to hairless. Twigs slender to stout (2-10mm diam); pith c½ diam, white; inner bark aromatic. Bundle scars ≥(5)9. ❷.......................(*Magnolia*) Go to **MAG**

Terminal bud (10)12-25mm, hairless, conical, acuminate, often curved; scale 1, wrapped around inner scale (scales actually stipules), green, occ orange nr tip, striate, ciliate, falling leaving scar encircling twig. Lateral buds often with 1 collateral bud, spreading, 2-6mm (fl buds nr max size), globose; scales 2-5. Twigs stout (c10mm diam), not zig-zagging, green- to olive-brown, minutely hairy to hairless, round to ridged nr tip; lenticels more obvious nr nodes, low, round to longitudinal, pale; inner bark weakly coconut scented; pith ⅔ diam, bright white, round, dense; latex white. Lf scars spiralling, not raised, ± circular, ± large; bundle scars many, in an ellipse or involute U-shape. Bark smooth, silvery- to brown-grey, ± warty with raised round lenticels. Small tree; crown v wide. Late bursting. ❶. PL 12..*Fig* **Ficus carica**

Terminal bud absent. Lateral buds 5-10mm, all ± equal size, hairless, spreading, conical, ± twisted or curved, ± acute; scale cap-like (fused stipules), shiny reddish or purplish, striate to grooved. Twigs mod (3-5mm diam), zig-zagging, reddish- to olive-brown, occ wool at nodes, weakly ridged nr tip, rigid; lenticels low, oval, small, buff; pith ½ diam, green, round. Lf scars usu 2-ranked, ± raised, collar-shaped, ± encircling bud, narrowed between bundle scars. Bundle scars 5(9), occ divided and grouped in 3(5)s. Bark smooth, grey-brown, flaking revealing pale underbark (mottled 'camouflage' bark). Fallen lvs decay-resistant (often blown some distance from tree)

Lvs lobed to ½ way. Buds often 5-7mm, reddish. PL 21.......*London Plane* **Platanus x hispanica**

Lvs lobed >⅔ way. Buds often 7-10mm, purplish. PL 21.........*Oriental Plane* **Platanus orientalis**

Rhus typhina
Stag's-horn Sumach

Toxicodendron vernicifluum
Chinese Lacquer-tree

Frangula alnus
Alder Buckthorn

Ficus carica
Fig

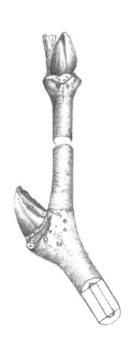

Platanus x hispanica
London Plane

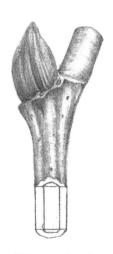

Platanus orientalis
Oriental Plane

Group AH – *Buds with 2-3 scales, stalked. Tree (shrub in* Ribes*). (Betula keys out here in error if woody spurs mistaken for stalks).* ❶ *Twigs and/or buds with aromatic yellow glands*

■Stipule scars absent. Pith white, soon fragmenting, ½ diam. Shrub. ❶.....*(Ribes nigrum)* Go to **RIB**

■Stipule scar a line encircling twig and forming a 'V-neck' opp lf scar. Pith white, solid but diaphragmed with firm green partitions (15-20 per cm). Terminal bud resembling a duck's bill

Twigs mod (3-5mm diam), not zig-zagging, shiny reddish-brown (rarely grey or brown), often pruinose, hairless, round; lenticels few, low, oval, pale; inner bark odorous (soapy), bitter-tasting; pith c½ diam, round. Terminal bud 8-20 x 5-9mm, on 2-4mm stalk, oblong, usu much wider than twig, flattened, obtuse; scales 2, valvate, green when young, usu pruinose, hairless, white- or yellow-dotted. Lateral buds 1-8mm, occ superposed or absent; the lower v small, globose, sessile. Lf scars spiralling, ± not raised, ± circular, large, pale; bundle scars 7-10(15), scattered or in an ellipse, often indistinct. Trunk continuous to tree tip; crown pyramidal when young, later oblong; lower branches often drooping with upturned twig tips. Tree

Buds purplish. Bark grey, later furrowed with intersecting rounded or flat ridges with white in furrows (resembling powdery white lichen or dust), the ridges cracked, resembling parallel mountain ridges with gullies in their sides. PL 17...................*Tulip-tree* **Liriodendron tulipifera**

Buds yellowish. Bark pale yellow-grey, remaining ± smooth. PL 16
....*Chinese Tulip-tree* **Liriodendron chinense**

■Stipule scars small. Pith green at least initially, solid

Twigs and/or buds blackish stellate-hairy nr tip. Pith remaining green. Lateral buds ± oblique to lf scar. Keys out here if superposed bud overlooked or absent. PL 20
....(see **AF**) *Persian Ironwood* **Parrotia persica**

Twigs (and buds) often scurfy with small whitish to reddish resin glands (similar to *Betula*) nr tip, usu mod slender (2-3mm diam), weakly zig-zagging, shiny reddish-brown to dark olive-brown or ± black, (±) 3-angled nr tip; lenticels low, oval, small, orange; pith ⅓-½ diam, quickly turning orange-brown, 3-angled. Branchlets with short twigs. Terminal bud often ± lopsided; scales 2(3), valvate or overlapping, often unequal, stuck together, margins occ obscure, occ faintly plicate, ciliate. Lateral buds ± equal to terminal bud, spreading, not oblique to lf scar. Lf scars usu 2-ranked, raised, triangular to elliptical, ± decurrent; bundle scars 3, middle scar occ divided into 3. Stipule scars narrowly triangular, often ± equal. Bark (±) smooth with horizontal lenticels when young. Wood turns orange when exposed to air (red in *A. rubra*). Catkins often present at end of twigs (esp late winter). Fr a persistent small woody 'cone' (actually female catkin)

Twigs densely minutely grey-hairy at least nr tip

Buds ellipsoid, 'club-shaped', ± 3-angled, usu obtuse, purplish, 6-10mm, on 2-4mm hairy stalk, with resin glands, minutely grey-hairy (hairs becoming sparse to absent). Bark smooth, even at maturity, grey. Small tree or shrub. Often suckering. PL 4.............*Grey Alder* **Alnus incana**

Twigs hairless (rarely sparsely hairy in *A. rubra*)

Buds ± globose (occ ovoid or ellipsoid), pale green turning reddish-purple

Buds on 3-10mm stalk, 4-7(10)mm, obtuse, dotted red-brown with resin glands. Bark with many lenticels, later fissured, dark grey-brown. Tree; crown broadly pyramidal; lower branches spreading. Lvs late-deciduous. PL 4............................*Italian Alder* **Alnus cordata**

Buds ellipsoid, 'club-shaped', ± 3-angled (*A. viridis* (**Al**) rarely keys out here but buds with stalk ≤1mm)

Buds purplish to ± bluish-grey, 6-10mm, on 2-8mm hairless stalk, usu obtuse, rarely ± acute, dotted with resin glands, hairless, occ superposed. Bark dark purplish-brown, eventually fissured into rectangular scales. Tree, occ multi-trunked; trunk(s) often with epicormic shoots nr base; crown pyramidal; lower branches spreading. PL 4.....*Alder* **Alnus glutinosa**

Buds reddish at least on sunlit side (often greenish below esp early winter), (8)10-13mm, on (2)4-5mm stalk, obtuse to acute, usu dotted with resin glands, rarely sparsely hairy. Twigs rarely sparsely hairy. Bark grey to greyish-brown, later breaking into rectangular plates esp nr base; inner bark turning red. Tree; crown broadly pyramidal; lower branches drooping. PL 4..*Red Alder* **Alnus rubra**

Liriodendron tulipifera
Tulip-tree

Liriodendron chinense
Chinese Tulip-tree

Alnus incana
Grey Alder

Alnus cordata
Italian Alder

Alnus glutinosa
Alder

Alnus rubra
Red Alder

Group AI – *Buds with 2-3 scales, sessile. (Cotinus coggygria may key out here if clustered buds overlooked. Populus may key out here if lateral buds examined in error).* ❶ *Stipules persistent (3 entries).* ❷ *Pith orange-brown (5 entries).* ❸ *Twigs with white latex (3 entries).* ❹ *Buds like 'boxing gloves' (2 entries).* ❺ *Twigs white-woolly at least nr tip (3 entries).* ❻ *Pith 5-angled (2 entries)*

■Buds with 2 scales only (valvate or overlapping)

Stipules persistent (not falling leaving scars). Bundle scar 1. Shrub. ❶❷. PL 23
....(see **AM**) *Shrubby Cinquefoil* **Potentilla fruticosa**

Stipule scar a line encircling twig at top of lf scar. Bundle scars many
  Bud scales overlapping. Pith white, solid. Inner bark with coconut odour. (Rarely keys out here if 2nd scale showing but actually 1 wrap-around scale). ❸. PL 12.....(see **AG**) *Fig* **Ficus carica**
  Bud scales valvate. Pith white, solid but diaphragmed with firm green partitions (15-20 per cm). Inner bark with soapy odour. Terminal bud 8-20mm, on 2-4mm stalk, oblong, resembling a duck's bill, hairless. Tree
    Buds purplish. PL 17...(see **AH**) *Tulip-tree* **Liriodendron tulipifera**
    Buds yellowish. PL 16.............................(see **AH**) *Chinese Tulip-tree* **Liriodendron chinense**

Stipule scars present but not encircling twig
  Twigs (±) round
    Twigs bristly-hairy, rough with raised hair bases, mod (3-4mm diam), ± zig-zagging, dull (reddish-) brown; pith ½ diam, white, round; <u>latex white</u>. Buds all lateral, spreading, 3-5mm, conical-ovoid, acute; scales overlapping, striate, the outer red-brown, the inner green, white-hairy but often buff hairy at tip. Lf scars occ opp or 3-whorled, not raised, ± circular; bundle scars 4-6, obscure, in ellipse or involute U-shape. Stipule scars ± linear, unequal. Bark ± smooth but with shallow intersecting fissures, grey or yellowish. Crown round; branches brittle. Small tree, occ suckering. ❸. PL 6.................*Paper Mulberry* **Broussonetia papyrifera**
    Twigs crisped-hairy to hairless, often rough (due to swollen reddish resin glands, lenticels and hair bases), slender (1-2mm diam), ± zig-zagging or not; pith ⅓ diam, <u>green</u>, <u>3-angled</u>. Buds 4-7mm, narrowly ovoid; scales shiny reddish- to orange-brown, some yellow-green. Bundle scars 3 (or groups of 3). Stipule scars short-linear, ± equal. Bark <u>v shreddy</u>. Tree
    ....(*Betula nigra*) Go to **BET**
    Twigs usu hairless, occ stellate- or long-hairy, smooth, slender (1-3mm diam), zig-zagging; pith c½ diam, white (occ pink or yellow), round. Buds 3-10mm, ovoid but <u>lopsided</u> (like 'boxing gloves'), oblique to lf scar; scales green to red. Bundle scars 3, occ multiplied. Stipule scars triangular to linear, unequal. Tree. ❹.............................(*Tilia* esp *T. cordata*) Go to **TIL**
    Twigs hairless, smooth, mod slender (2-3mm diam), zig-zagging; pith c½ diam, white, occ pinkish, round. Buds 3-5mm, narrowly ovoid, flattened; scales dark reddish-brown to ± black. Lf scars dark, upper margin with <u>reddish hair fringe</u>. Bundle scars 3. Stipule scars linear, <u>on auricle-like projections</u> above corners of lf scar, often obscure. Small tree. PL 8
    ....(see **AF**) *Judas Tree* **Cercis siliquastrum**
  Twigs (±) 3-angled at least nr tip
    Twigs stellate-hairy at least nr tip, slender to mod (1.5-5mm diam), ± zig-zagging. Bundle scars 3. PL 20.....................................(see **AF**) *Persian Ironwood* **Parrotia persica**
    Twigs usu white-woolly nr tip, otherwise often hairless, (mod) slender (1.5-3mm diam), ± zig-zagging, shiny dark olive-green to dark reddish-brown (± blackish), flexible; lenticels many, raised, round, orange (esp on branchlets); pith ½ diam, white, round. Thorns rarely present, with 1-2 buds at base. Buds all lateral, adpressed, 2-6mm, flattened-ovoid, obtuse; scales 2-3, usu overlapping, tips breaking, red- to purplish-brown, buff-woolly at tip. Lf scars spiralling, ± raised, broadly crescent-shaped to oval, small, equal to bud width, weakly decurrent; bundle scars 3. Stipule scars oval to ± linear, often ± equal. Bark dark reddish-brown, streaked by lines of lenticels, finally ± flaking. Small tree; crown round; branches crooked. ❺. PL 11
    ....*Quince* **Cydonia oblonga**
    Twigs hairless, occ scurfy with small whitish to reddish resin glands nr tip, mod slender (2-3mm diam), ± zig-zagging, orange- to red-brown, often with grey skin, ± flexible; lenticels low,

Broussonetia papyrifera
Paper Mulberry

Cydonia oblonga
Quince

oval, small, orange; pith ⅓ diam, green, <u>turning brown</u>, 3-angled. Branchlets ± with woody spurs. Terminal bud present. Lateral buds spreading, <u>oblique to lf scar</u>, (8)10-14mm, narrowly ovoid, asymmetric, twisted spirally, acuminate, occ hooked at tip, sessile or short-stalked (≤1mm), <u>sticky</u> (occ exuding yellow resin); scales 2-3, overlapping, dark red, hairless. Lf scars spiralling, raised, semi-circular to kidney-shaped; bundle scars 3. Stipule scars small, narrowly triangular, often ± equal. Bark (greenish-) grey with wart-like lenticels; inner bark red. Shrub or small tree. Occ suckering. Catkins absent, appearing after leafing (unlike other *Alnus*). Fr persistent small woody 'cone' (actually female catkin). PL 4
....*Green Alder* **Alnus viridis**
  Stipule scars absent
    Tree. Twigs ≥4mm diam. Bundle scars ≥3
      Pith chambered, buff. Inner bark odorous (chemical smell). Twigs mod stout (5-10mm diam).
      PL 15.................................(see **AF**) *Walnut* **Juglans regia**
      Pith solid, orange-brown. Inner bark fetid (smelling of mice). Twigs stout (8-15mm diam). ❺.
      PL 4.................................(see **AR**) *Tree-of-heaven* **Ailanthus altissima**
      Pith solid, white, c½ diam. Inner bark odourless. Twigs mod (4-5mm diam), ± zig-zagging, brown, hairless or shortly hairy, angled nr tip; lenticels raised, orange-brown, round. Buds all lateral, partly sunken above lf scar, spreading, 3-4mm, broadly ovoid (teardrop-shaped), acute; scales valvate, dark (reddish-) brown, adpressed-hairy to hairless, ciliate with cilia forming hair tuft at tip. Lf scars v raised, triangular to shield-shaped, ± large, with a raised outer rim, <u>blackish</u>, occ weakly decurrent; bundle scars in 3 groups. Bark brown to grey, with flat ridges with orange-brown fissures. Tree, often small; crown round to vase-shaped, untidy.
      PL 15.................................*Pride-of-India* **Koelreuteria paniculata**
    Tree. Twigs usu ≤3mm diam. Bundle scar 1
      Twigs not zig-zagging, olive- to grey-brown, ± slender (2-3mm diam), hairless, round; lenticels low, linear, pale; pith usu solid, occ weakly diaphragmed with lace-like partitions, green, later white. Buds all lateral (dead twig tip often >> end bud), adpressed, partly sunken behind lf scar, 4-6mm, conical; scales overlapping, dark red-black, hairless but buff-hairy inner scales occ exposed (or tuft at tip), not ciliate. Lf scars raised, ± circular to heart-shaped; bundle scar U-shaped. Bark grey-brown with orange in fissures when young, later blackish forming deep square blocks reminiscent of charcoal briquettes. Small to medium tree; crown round; branches crooked, often drooping. PL 12.................................*Date-plum* **Diospyros lotus**
      Twigs usu zig-zagging, orange-brown, occ with grey skin, slender (2mm diam), hairless, round to ± flattened; pith ½ diam, green. Branchlets with fissured bark. Terminal bud 8-12mm, lanc (>2.5x as long as wide), flat, <u>knife-like</u>, acute; scales 2-4, overlapping, orange-brown, silky-hairy, ciliate, acute, keeled. Lateral buds spreading. Lf scars raised, semi-circular to crescent-shaped; bundle scar U-shaped. Bark smooth, grey, brown and green, mottled, flaking revealing orange underbark ('camouflage' bark). Small tree; trunk short; crown pyramidal to round. PL 34.................................*Deciduous Camellia* **Stewartia pseudocamellia**
  Shrub (occ low). Twigs usu ≤3mm diam. Bundle scar 1
    Twigs reddish-brown, not warty, finely to strongly lined, not zig-zagging......(*Spiraea*) <u>Go to</u> **SPI**
    Twigs green or purplish, warty with raised stomata, (±) round, zig-zagging. PL 36
    ....(see **AN**) *Blueberry* **Vaccinium corymbosum**
    Twigs green, not warty but with stomata, strongly 3-5-ridged, ± zig-zagging, slender (1.5-2mm diam), hairless; pith ⅔ diam, green, ± round. Branchlets round, reddish-brown when older. Buds all lateral, ± adpressed, 1.5-3(4)mm (uppermost on twig largest), conical-ovoid, acute; scales valvate (occ parted exposing 2-4 inner scales on upper buds), pale green, hairless, not ciliate. Lf scars raised, semi-circular to crescent-shaped, small, ≤ bud width, brown, decurrent. Low rhizomatous shrub to 0.5m. PL 36.................................*Bilberry* **Vaccinium myrtillus**
■Buds with (2)3 scales (overlapping)
  Stipule scars absent. Twigs not green
    Bundle scar 1. Twigs hairless; pith green. Small tree. PL 34
    ....(see above) *Deciduous Camellia* **Stewartia pseudocamellia**

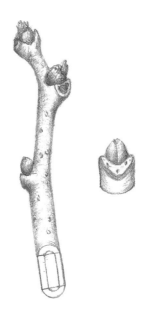

Alnus viridis
Green Alder

Koelreuteria paniculata
Pride-of-India

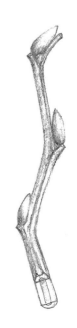

Diospyros lotus
Date-plum

Stewartia pseudocamellia
Deciduous Camellia

Vaccinium myrtillus
Bilberry

Bundle scar 1. Twigs silvery to bronze with peltato scales; pith usu orange-brown, occ white. ❷
....(see **AN**) **Elaeagnus** spp
Bundle scars 3 (*Malus* rarely keys out here esp if scales obscured by hairs)
Tree. Terminal bud <2.5x long as wide. Bundle scars often sunken. Pith solid but <u>diaphragmed</u> <u>with firm green partitions</u> (10-20 per cm). Inner bark odourless.

Branchlets with woody spurs
Terminal bud 2-3mm, dome-shaped, acute to obtuse; scales 3(4) (modified petiole bases), obtuse, green to purplish, hairless to sparsely hairy at tip, ciliate. Lateral buds minute, spreading. Lf scars weakly raised, heart-shaped to semi-circular, with a raised outer rim. Twigs mod (3-4mm diam), green to purplish-brown, sparsely hairy nr tip to hairless, round; lenticels few, low, round, pale; pith c½ diam. Bark furrowed, not blocky. Trunk continuous to tree tip; crown pyramidal; branches usu 90° to trunk. Usu by water. PL 20
....*Water Tupelo* **Nyssa aquatica**
Terminal bud 3-5(7)mm, ovoid to conical, often curved; scales (3)4-6(7). Bark furrowed, blocky, like 'crocodile-hide' when older. PL 20...................................(see **AP**) *Tupelo* **Nyssa sylvatica**
Shrub. Terminal bud >2.5x long as wide. Bundle scars not sunken. Pith solid, not diaphragmed. Inner bark with weak almond odour.................(see **AP**) *Chokeberry* **Aronia** spp
Bundle scars 5
Tree. Twigs usu mod (3-5mm diam); inner bark with fetid cherry odour. Lf scars on a late-deciduous raised red-black petiole base..............................(see **AQ**) **Sorbus** subgen **Sorbus**
Stipule scars present (look carefully), or occ with stipule remnants in *Colutea*, *Laburnum* and *Potentilla* (*Populus* may key out here if lateral buds examined in error)
Twigs with white latex, slender to mod stout (2-6mm diam), ± zig-zagging. Buds occ oblique to lf scar; scales 3-5. Bundle scars >7. Tree. ❸
Buds 5-10mm. Twigs mod to ± stout (3-6mm diam). PL 19
....(see **AL**) *Black Mulberry* **Morus nigra**
Buds 2-5mm. Twigs slender (2-3mm diam). PL 19..........(see **AL**) *White Mulberry* **Morus alba**
Twigs without latex
Twigs mod to mod stout (3-6mm diam), 5-angled. Tree
Twigs not zig-zagging, olive- to red-brown or greyish, hairy to hairless, <u>rough</u> (due to minute whitish resin granules), rigid; lenticels obvious, raised, small, round, white; pith c½ diam, green, <u>5-angled</u>. Buds all lateral, spreading, <u>oblique to lf scar</u>, (4)5-8(10)mm, false terminal bud usu largest, ovoid, often asymmetric, obtuse to ± acute; scales (2)3, reddish-orange to purplish (often greenish nr base), often notched, occ adpressed-hairy. Lf scars ± raised, heart-shaped to ± circular, decurrent; bundle scars (3)5-7(9), usu scattered, occ in arc or 3 groups. Stipule scars triangular to linear, unequal (1 occ obscure). Bark developing intersecting furrows, often spiralling, grey-brown. Crown broadly ovate; lower branches often twisted, occ horizontal or descending; upper branches ascending. Late bursting. ❻. PL 7..*Sweet Chestnut* **Castanea sativa**
Twigs usu slender to mod (1-4mm diam)
Bundle scars (3)5. Twigs 3-5-lined, hairless; pith orange-brown. Shrub. ❷. PL 21
....(see **AK**) *Atlantic Ninebark* **Physocarpus opulifolius**
Bundle scars 3. Twigs unlined. Tree (occ shrub in *Alnus viridis*)
Twigs white-felted, not zig-zagging, flexible. Buds ovoid. ❺❻...(*Populus alba*) <u>Go to</u> **POP A**
Twigs usu white-woolly nr tip, ± zig-zagging, flexible; lenticels orange; pith white. Buds all lateral, adpressed, flattened-ovoid, red- to purplish-brown, buff-woolly at tip. Bark dark reddish-brown, with many raised orange lenticels. ❺. PL 11
....(see above) *Quince* **Cydonia oblonga**
Twigs not white-felted or woolly (may be densely hairy)
Buds ovoid but lopsided (like 'boxing gloves'), never acuminate, oblique to lf scar, all lateral, green to red. Twigs green to red, zig-zagging, flexible; pith white. ❹
....(*Tilia*) <u>Go to</u> **TIL**

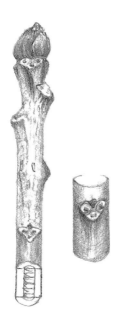

Nyssa aquatica
Water Tupelo

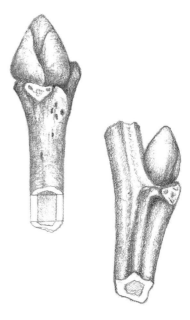

Castanea sativa
Sweet Chestnut

Buds ovoid or narrowly so, not lopsided, occ acuminate, occ oblique to lf scar
Twigs green, mod (3-4mm diam), rigid, zig-zagging or not; pith white. Terminal bud
ovoid, ± obtuse, not twisted. Lateral buds (if present) not oblique to lf scar. Stipules (or
remnants) often present. Bark with diamond-shaped lenticels, green
....(see **AJ**) *Laburnum* **Laburnum** spp
Twigs not green, ± slender (1-3mm diam), flexible, zig-zagging or not, often with resin
glands; inner bark rarely with antiseptic odour; pith green, <u>not</u> turning brown. Terminal
bud only on woody spurs (if present). Lateral buds narrowly ovoid, acute, not twisted,
occ oblique to lf scar. Bark often peeling in horizontal strips, usu white or (red-) brown
....(*Betula*) <u>Go to</u> **BET**
Twigs not green, slender (2-3mm diam), ± flexible, ± zig-zagging, occ with resin glands;
inner bark odourless; pith green, <u>turning brown</u>. Terminal bud narrowly ovoid,
acuminate, spirally twisted. Lateral buds similar, oblique to lf scar. Bark with wart-like
lenticels, (greenish-) grey. PL 4.....................(see above) *Green Alder* **Alnus viridis**
Bundle scar 1. Stipules (or remnants) present. Shrub
Twigs green; pith green. ❶. PL 9................(see **AM**) *Bladder-senna* **Colutea arborescens**
Twigs reddish-brown; pith orange-brown. ❶❷. PL 23
....(see **AM**) *Shrubby Cinquefoil* **Potentilla fruticosa**

51

Laburnum anagyroides
Laburnum

Colutea arborescens
Bladder-senna

Potentilla fruticosa
Shrubby Cinquefoil

AJ

Group AJ – *Twigs green, with or without visible stomata.* ❶ *Buds black and hidden in pit above lf scar.* ❷ *Tree with drooping twigs*

■Twigs mostly ≥3mm diam

Buds 8-12mm, sparsely hairy to hairless. Tree

Twigs mod (3-4mm diam), with v unequal internodes, green to red, occ pruinose, hairless, round; inner bark with <u>sweet aniseed odour</u> (like *Magnolia salicifolia*); pith ⅔ diam, white, round. Branchlets green. Terminal bud 8-12mm, broadly ovoid, ± acute; scales 4-7 (the outermost smallest), (yellow-) green, occ purplish-brown tinge, obtuse. Lateral buds <1mm, globose. Lf scars spiralling not or weakly raised, semi-circular to broadly crescent-shaped; bundle scar a short line, occ ± broken into 3. Stipule scars absent. Bark furrowed, grey-brown; inner bark orange. Suckering. PL 31...*Sassafras* **Sassafras albidum**

Buds 5-15mm, hairless (may be ciliate). Tree. PL 16

....(see **AP**) *American Sweetgum* **Liquidambar styraciflua**

Buds 5-10mm, minutely scurfy hairy. Tree. PL 15...........................(see **AF**) *Walnut* **Juglans regia**

Buds 3-5mm, with at least some silky hairs. Small tree

Twigs mod (3-4mm diam), zig-zagging or not, olive-green, occ with grey skin, round, without visible stomata; lenticels flat, small, round, whitish; pith ½ diam, white, ± round. Branchlets with woody spurs, remaining green for several yrs. Terminal bud 3-5mm, ovoid, ± obtuse, surrounded by several green petiole bases occ bearing stipules; scales (3)4, green, sparsely to densely silky-hairy. Lateral buds similar, often aborted, spreading, (flattened-) ovoid. Lf scars spiralling, raised on persistent green petiole bases, crescent-shaped to semi-circular, small; bundle scars 3, nr centre, ± fused or indistinct. Stipules (or remnants) often persistent at corners of lf scars, green, acute; stipule scars, if present, oval to linear. Bark smooth, with diamond-shaped lenticels, green, eventually greyish with splits. Crown ± vase-shaped, with few arching branches

Petiole bases (lowest bud scales) adpressed-hairy. Twigs usu adpressed-hairy at least nr tip, rarely hairless. Fr pod densely hairy; upper suture with low keel <1mm

....*Laburnum* **Laburnum anagyroides**

Petiole bases (lowest bud scales) usu hairless. Twigs usu hairless, occ adpressed-hairy nr tip. Fr pod sparsely hairy; upper suture keeled to 1mm; <u>seeds often few or ill-developed</u>. PL 16

....(not illustrated) *Hybrid Laburnum* **Laburnum x watereri**

Petiole bases (lowest bud scales) hairless. Twigs usu hairless, occ sparsely adpressed-hairy nr tip. Fr pod hairless; upper suture winged 1-2mm, forming a knife-like edge

....*Scottish Laburnum* **Laburnum alpinum**

Buds 1-2mm, ± hidden behind peg (petiole base), silky-hairy. Shrub

Twigs mod slender (2-4mm diam), rush-like, not zig-zagging, flexible, with long internodes, round with 20-50 fine striations (rough to touch when dry), with stomata; pith >¾ diam, white, round. Branchlets often opp or subopp. Buds all lateral, flattened-globose; scales obscure. Lf scars often opp or subopp, raised on green peg, tiny, circular, brown; bundle scar 1, usu indistinct. Stipule scars absent. PL 33..................................*Spanish Broom* **Spartium junceum**

Buds hidden (in pit above lf scar), black-woolly. Tree

Twigs mod (3mm diam), not zig-zagging, sparsely minutely hairy or hairless, round, usu angled nr tip, brittle, without visible stomata; lenticels raised, oval, orange; inner bark <u>odorous</u>; pith ½ diam, green, round. Branchlets green for several yrs. Buds all lateral, several, obscure. Lf scars spiralling, v raised, sunken in middle, with swelling above, V-shaped, narrowed between bundle scars; bundle scars 3. Stipule scars small, oval. Bark furrowed, grey-brown, reddish-brown in furrows. ❶. PL 34...*Pagoda Tree* **Styphnolobium japonicum**

■Twigs ≤3mm diam

Bundle scars 3. Shrub

Twigs round, slender (1-2.5mm diam), not zig-zagging, with stomata; pith ½ diam. Buds all lateral, 1-2mm, usu adpressed. Lf scars spiralling, raised, <u>± circular</u> to semi-circular, v small, decurrent, occ hair-fringed. Stipule scars <u>obscure</u>, oval to linear

....(*Prunus cerasifera*) <u>Go to</u> **PRU**

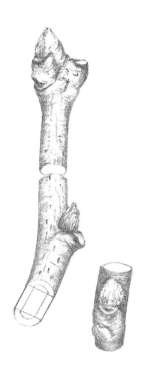

Sassafras albidum
Sassafras

Laburnum anagyroides
Laburnum

Laburnum alpinum
Scottish Laburnum

Spartium junceum
Spanish Broom

Styphnolobium japonicum
Pagoda Tree

Twigs round to 5-lined (occ v weak), slender (1-2mm diam), usu <u>zig-zagging</u>, hairless, usu brittle, with stomata; pith <u>>¾ diam</u>, white, round. Buds all lateral, usu spreading, occ collateral, 2-5(6)mm, ovoid, acute to obtuse; scales (3)4-7, green, often brown-margined, occ purplish, hairless, ciliate, obscurely 3-toothed at tip. Lf scars usu 2-ranked (on zig-zagging twigs), weakly raised, triangular to angled crescent-shaped, weakly decurrent from sides and middle; bundle scars along upper margin. Stipule scars <u>short-linear, brown, often obscure or ± absent</u>. Arching, suckering. Early bursting. PL 15..*Kerria* **Kerria japonica**
Twigs 5-8-ridged, slender (1-3mm diam), not zig-zagging, green at least nr tip, soon pale orange- or grey-brown, hairless, scurfy, occ salt-encrusted, with stomata often obscure; inner bark with weak resin odour; pith ½ diam, white, weakly 5-8-angled. Buds all lateral, spreading, c1mm, ± globose, encased in hard greenish resin, soon bursting into minute green leaves; scales 2-4. Lf scars spiralling, weakly raised, angled crescent-shaped, decurrent from sides and middle (forming ridges); bundle scars sunken. Stipule scars <u>absent</u>. Erect, suckering. Often semi-evergreen. Early bursting. PL 5....................*Tree Groundsel* **Baccharis halimifolia**
Bundle scar 1, often indistinct or obscure
  Twigs zig-zagging at least nr tip, flexible or not. Bundle scar distinct. Shrub
    Twigs round or angled, hairy or hairless, <u>warty</u> with raised stomata. Erect, to 2m. PL 36
    ....(see **AN**) *Blueberry* **Vaccinium corymbosum**
    Twigs 4-angled (green with white ridges), hairless, not warty. Stipules <u>spine-like</u>, occ broken or absent. PL 7......................................(see **AB**) *Siberian Pea-shrub* **Caragana arborescens**
    Twigs 3- or 5-ridged, hairless, not warty. Erect, to 0.5m. PL 36
    ....(see **AI**) *Bilberry* **Vaccinium myrtillus**
    Twigs 5-ridged, hairless, not warty, slender (2-3mm diam), with stomata, with persistent bud scale remnants at join with branchlet; lenticels absent; pith ¾ diam, white, round. Buds all lateral, spreading, 2-5mm, globose-ovoid, obtuse; scales 3 prs (paired scales unusual for spp with alt buds), green, with purple-brown margins, obtuse, weakly keeled, hairless, minutely ciliate (occ buff). Lf scars spiralling, raised, semi-circular, small, ± equal to bud width, brown, v decurrent; bundle scar flat arc or involute U-shaped. Stipule scars absent. Erect or climbing, to 2m. Occ semi-evergreen. PL 15......................................*Yellow Jasmine* **Jasminum humile**
    Twigs strongly 7-ridged, sparsely adpressed-hairy or hairless, not warty, v slender (1-1.5mm diam), with stomata; lenticels absent; pith ½ diam, round, white, occ firmer white partitions. Buds all lateral, 1-4 collateral, 1-2(3)mm, ovoid; scales (3)4, reddish-brown, inner green and adpressed-hairy. Lf scars 2-ranked, v raised, ± circular; bundle scar distinct. Stipules 1mm, triangular, green or reddish, persistent or falling leaving short linear scars. Erect, to 1.5(2)m. Early bursting. PL 14..*Scorpion Senna* **Hippocrepis emerus**
  Twigs not zig-zagging, flexible; pith white, round. Lf scars spiralling, < bud width
    Tree, 2-6m. Terminal bud absent. Bundle scar indistinct or obscure
      Twigs round, with 10-15 obscure grooves, slender (1-1.5mm diam), drooping, usu hairless, occ minutely hairy in grooves, without visible stomata; pith c½ diam. Buds <1mm, silky, behind lf scar, often not visible. Lf scars raised on green peg, minute, triangular, brown, without auricles. Stipules scars absent. Bark greenish, later furrowed. Late bursting. ❷. PL 13...*Mount Etna Broom* **Genista aetnensis**
    Medium shrub, usu 0.5-3m, often arching. Terminal bud absent. Bundle scar indistinct or obscure
      Twigs hairy (hairs occ minute or obscure in furrows) (*Colutea* rarely keys out here)
        Twigs round with 8-10 shallow ridges (branchlets with 10-15 shallow ridges), obscurely adpressed-hairy in furrows, slender (1-1.5mm diam), curved; inner bark odourless; pith ¾ diam. Buds 1mm, globose-ovoid; scales 2-4, green, ± hairless. Lf scars raised on green peg, minute, brown, with small acute auricles each side. Stipule scars absent. Bark striate. PL 11...*Hairy-fruited Broom* **Cytisus striatus**
        Twigs 8-10-furrowed (shallow nr twig tip but deep nr base), adpressed hairs obscure visible as white in furrows, 1mm diam, curved, without visible stomata; inner bark <u>odorous</u>; pith c½ diam. Buds 1mm, globose-ovoid, often hidden behind auricles; scales c3, obscure,

Kerria japonica
Kerria

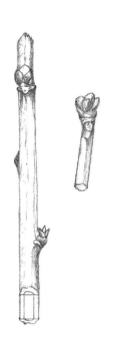

Baccharis halimifolia
Tree Groundsel

Jasminum humile
Yellow Jasmine

Hippocrepis emerus
Scorpion Senna

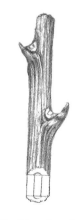

Genista aetnensis
Mount Etna Broom

Cytisus striatus
Hairy-fruited Broom

green, sparsely hairy. Lf scars raised on short green peg, minute, circular, with small <u>spanner-like</u> obtuse auricles each side. Stipule scars absent
....*White Broom* **Cytisus multiflorus**
Twigs minutely hairy, round or obscurely ridged, turning brown nr tip, slender (1.5-2mm diam). Buds sunken behind peg, 1mm, ovoid-globose, v obtuse; scales green, adpressed-hairy. Lf scars raised on green peg, ± large, circular, without auricles. Stipule scars absent. PL 11..*Black Broom* **Cytisus nigricans**
Twigs hairless
Twigs with 20-50 fine striations. PL 33........(see above) *Spanish Broom* **Spartium junceum**
Twigs with (4)5 deep ridges, ± narrowly winged, slender (1.5-2mm diam), <u>± rough</u> due to minute rounded bumps, dark green, usu curved, usu dying back from tip, with stomata; inner bark <u>odorous</u>; pith ¾ diam (exc twig ridges). Buds all lateral, partly behind auricles, adpressed, 1-2mm, globose-ovoid, obtuse; scales 2-4(6), green, obtuse, hairless, not ciliate, loose. Lf scars raised on green peg, tiny, triangular, brown, with small rounded auricles each side. Stipule scars absent. Bark smooth, greenish with reddish stripes, later shallowly fissured. PL 11...*Broom* **Cytisus scoparius**
Low shrub, <0.5m, often much less. Bundle scar indistinct or obscure
Twigs (4)5-7-ridged, slender (1.5mm diam), occ pruinose, usu curved, hairless, rarely occ adpressed hairs, with stomata; pith ¾ diam. Buds all lateral, adpressed, 0.5-1(2)mm, globose-ovoid; scales 2-3, green, obtuse, sparsely hairy nr tip. Lf scars raised on short green peg, elliptical, tiny, < bud width. Stipules c1mm, <u>spine-like</u>, adpressed, green to translucent nr tip, persistent. Arching to trailing, to 0.5m high. PL 13
....*Lydian Broom* **Genista lydia**
Twigs striate to weakly angled, v slender (0.5-1mm diam), adpressed-hairy. Buds <1mm, hidden by swollen lf bases, naked (actually young green lvs), silky-hairy. Lf scars with small rounded auricles each side. Stipule scars absent. Trailing subshrub, to 0.1m high. VR. PL 13...*Hairy Greenweed* **Genista pilosa**

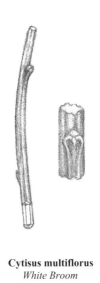

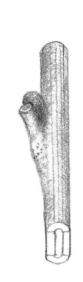

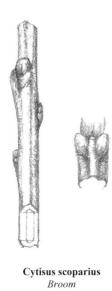

Cytisus multiflorus
White Broom

Cytisus scoparius
Broom

Cytisus nigricans
Black Broom

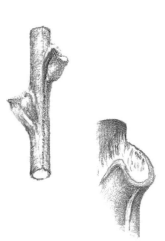

Genista lydia
Lydian Broom

Genista pilosa
Hairy Greenweed

Group AK – *Stipule scars present. Lateral buds (±) adpressed to twig.* ❶ *Twigs white-felted.* ❷ *Bundle scars >5 and twigs with white latex (2 entries).* ❸ *Pith orange-brown (3 entries).* ❹ *Twigs with strongly odorous inner bark.* ❺ *Bud scales striate or obscurely so (3 entries)*

■Lateral buds with lowest scale directly above lf scar (a 'thumb nail' as wide as bud, 2-4-lobed), never oblique to lf scar, 3-25mm. Twigs hairless to white-felted; pith 5-angled. Occ ❶

....*(Populus)* Go to **POP**

■Lateral buds with lowest scale not directly above lf scar (not forming a 'thumb nail'), OR lateral buds absent (all buds terminal). Twigs never white-felted; pith not 5-angled

Bundle scars >5. Twigs with white latex. Tree ❷

Buds 5-10mm, ovoid. Twigs 3-6mm diam. PL 19...............(see **AL**) *Black Mulberry* **Morus nigra**

Buds 2-5mm, ± globose. Twigs 2-3mm diam. PL 19..........(see **AL**) *White Mulberry* **Morus alba**

Bundle scars (3)5 (unequal, lowest scar largest, uppermost 2 occ obscure so only 3 visible)

Stipule scars linear, on slight projections above corners of lf scar, occ obscure. Terminal bud usu present. Lateral buds 5-8mm, ovoid-oblong to ± conical, acute; scales (3)5, reddish-brown, papery, occ hairy, loose, free at tips, margins ragged, the lower keeled. Twigs mod slender (2-3mm diam), occ ± zig-zagging, orange- or reddish-brown, hairless, 3-5-lined, often twisted; bark soon splitting; lenticels absent; pith ⅔ diam, orange-brown, round. Lf scars spiralling, raised, angled crescent-shaped to ± 3-lobed, ± small, often shrivelled, decurrent. Bark peeling in longitudinal strips. Arching shrub to 2.5m. ❸. PL 21

....*Atlantic Ninebark* **Physocarpus opulifolius**

Bundle scars 3 (occ obscure, multiplied or fused into 1). Tree

Inner bark odorous. Lateral buds with 3-8 scales. ❹

Inner bark with fetid almond odour; pith white. Buds 7-11mm..........*(Prunus padus)* Go to **PRU**

Inner bark with antiseptic 'germolene' (oil-of-wintergreen) odour; pith green. Buds 5-7(8)mm.

❺..*(Betula alleghaniensis, lenta)* Go to **BET**

Inner bark odourless

Lateral buds with 8-16 scales. Buds 6-12mm

Buds all lateral, adpressed or incurved, end bud occ strongly kinked (c45°) away from lf scar, occ spreading, not or weakly oblique to lf scar, ovoid-conical, ± 4-angled, acute; scales 4-ranked, pale or reddish-brown, often green nr base, v obscurely striate, hairy nr tip. Fl buds larger, swollen, often spreading. Twigs slender (1.5-2mm diam), ± zig-zagging, dark olive- to blackish-brown, minutely hairy, often sparse longer ± adpressed hairs to 1.5mm (persisting until 2nd yr), round; lenticels flat, oval, pale; pith ⅓ diam, green, obscurely 5-angled. Lf scars 2-ranked, raised, elliptical to crescent-shaped, small, ≤ bud width; bundle scars occ multiplied. Stipule scars triangular-linear, ± equal. Bark smooth, grey, *Fagus*-like. Trunk grooved, muscle-like; crown ± round but the upright cultivar 'Fastigiata' often planted; lower branches often with dead lvs persisting (marcescent). ❺. PL 7

....*Hornbeam* **Carpinus betulus**

Lateral buds with ≤6 scales

All buds 3-15mm; scales often green with brown margins (to dark purple-brown), often sticky or coated in dry resin, at least obscurely striate with many parallel veins. Terminal bud with c7 scales. Lateral buds usu with 3-4 scales, occ oblique to lf scar, adpressed to spreading, ovoid, acute, weakly 3-4-angled to flattened, often slightly incurved (or to 1-side) at tip. Twigs slender (1-2.5mm diam), dark brown, flexible; pith ⅓ diam, green, (±) 3-angled. Branchlets with woody spurs. Lf scars small, < bud width. Catkins usu present. ❺

....*(Betula)* Go to BET

All buds 3-5mm; scales pale brown to purplish, not sticky, without resin, not striate. Terminal bud absent (fl buds of *Cercis* key out here if superposed bud absent or overlooked)

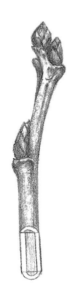

Physocarpus opulifolius
Atlantic Ninebark

Carpinus betulus
Hornbeam

End bud, if kinked, ≤45° away from lf scar. Buds not oblique to lf scar, v adpressed, ovoid, flat only on side of twig (appearing humped), 4-angled, ± acute to obtuse; scales 5-7, spiralling, dull <u>pale brown</u>, occ minutely hairy, <u>long white-ciliate</u>. Twigs v slender (1-1.5mm diam), not zig-zagging, ± shiny olive- to reddish-brown, minutely hairy to hairless; lenticels flat, oval, pale; pith solid, ½ diam, green. Lf scars ± 2-ranked, raised, semi-circular, ± with rim, ≤ bud width; bundle scars often fused into 1 or obscure, not protruding. Stipule scars short-linear, ± equal, occ obscure (as ± same colour as twig), stipules occ persisting. Bark fissured into rectangular flaking plates, grey-brown. Crown narrowly oval, with branchlets often drooping. Tall tree. PL 20..*Roble* **Nothofagus obliqua**

End bud strongly kinked 45-90° away from lf scar. Buds not oblique to lf scar, v adpressed, conical-ovoid, ± flattened; scales 4-5(6), <u>2-ranked</u>, <u>reddish-brown to purplish</u> (often 2-tone), buff-hairy, usu short to long <u>buff-ciliate</u>. Twigs slender (1-2mm diam), occ zig-zagging, dark (olive-) brown, wavy-hairy; lenticels raised, oval, pale; pith usu <u>chambered or diaphragmed esp nr nodes</u>, ½ diam, white. Lf scars 2-ranked, raised, < bud width, half-elliptical; bundle scars with middle scar occ divided, occ all joined in U-shape. Stipule scars oval to linear, small, occ obscure. Bark pale grey, smooth but developing wart-like lenticels and horizontal wrinkles. Crown wide, round. Medium tree. PL 8 ....*European Nettle-tree* **Celtis australis**

All buds 2-3(4)mm, shiny reddish-brown, occ sticky, with yellow resin, not striate. Terminal bud absent. PL 20.....................................(see **AL**) *Antarctic Beech* **Nothofagus antarctica**

Nothofagus obliqua
Roble

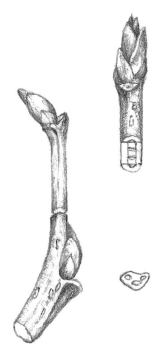

Celtis australis
European Nettle-tree

Group AL – *Stipule scars present. Lateral buds (±) spreading from twig. Tree (shrub in* Corylus avellana*).* ❶ *Twigs white-felted.* ❷ *Bud scales striate or obscurely so (4 entries).* ❸ *Bundle scars >5 and twigs with white latex.* ❹ *Twigs with inner bark strongly odorous (3 entries)*

■Lateral buds with lowest scale directly above lf scar ('thumb nail' as wide as bud, 2-4-lobed), never oblique to lf scar, 3-25mm. Twigs hairless to white-felted; pith 5-angled. Occ ❶ ....*(Populus)* Go to **POP**

■Lateral buds with lowest scale not directly above lf scar (not forming a 'thumb nail'), OR lateral buds absent (all buds terminal). Twigs never white-felted; pith not 5-angled

  Buds usu 9-25mm

    Twigs mod (4-5mm diam). Buds (6)7-12mm, not oblique to lf scar, ovoid, with tuft of buff hairs at tip; scales 8-10, shiny reddish-brown, 3-toothed at tip, gland-fringed or erose ....*(Prunus serrulata)* Go to **PRU**

    Twigs (±) slender (1-3mm diam) (*Carpinus betulus* may rarely key out here)

      Lateral buds 15-25mm, oblique to lf scar, spreading at c60°, spindle-shaped (c5x as long as wide), acute, narrowed to base, occ appearing slightly stalked; scales c20, at least lower 4-ranked, shiny reddish-brown with darker margins, usu pale-tipped with white or buff silky hairs, ciliate. Terminal bud similar, often absent. Twigs slender (2-3mm diam), zig-zagging, (±) shiny reddish- to olive-brown, occ densely hairy or cottony nr tip, round; lenticels low, round to longitudinal, orange to grey; pith ⅓ diam, green, round. Branchlets with woody spurs; girdle scars many, crowded (more so than other woody taxa). Lf scars usu 2-ranked, occ spiralling, weakly raised, triangular to heart-shaped or elliptical, ± small; bundle scars 3(5), middle scar occ divided, occ multiplied. Stipule scars linear, extending around twig and overlapping but not joined. Bark smooth, grey, occ mottled or with woody nodules. Crown round; lower branches occ with dead lvs persisting (marcescent). Fr husks often persisting. Late bursting. PL 12...*Beech* **Fagus sylvatica**

      Lateral buds 9-15mm, occ oblique to lf scar, adpressed to spreading, often slightly incurved (or to 1-side) at tip, weakly 3-4-angled to flattened), often sticky or coated in dry resin; scales 3-4, spiralling but lowest 2 scales forming V-shape above lf scar, often green with brown margins, at least obscurely striate, hairy to hairless, ciliate. Terminal bud only on woody spurs (if present); scales c7. Twigs mod slender (2-2.5mm diam), dark brown, flexible; pith ⅓ diam, green, (±) 3-angled. Lf scars usu spiralling, < bud width. Bark usu peeling. Catkins usu present. ❷...*(Betula papyrifera, utilis)* Go to **BET**

      Lateral buds 9-15mm, oblique to lf scar, spreading at 45-60°, oblong, 4-angled (grooved, like a Phillips screwdriver head!), ± acute; scales c12, 4-ranked, reddish-orange, obtuse, obscurely striate, hairless, occ shortly sparsely ciliate, usu ± sticky (esp inner). Terminal bud absent. Twigs slender (1-2mm diam), weakly zig-zagging, dark olive-brown, usu long-hairy, round; lenticels low, oval, pale; pith ½ diam, white, round. Lf scars 2-ranked, not raised, triangular; bundle scars 3, occ multiplied, protruding or not. Stipule scars small, oval to short-linear, unequal, stipules occ persisting. Bark ± smooth, grey. Crown pyramidal. ❷. PL 19 ....*Rauli* **Nothofagus alpina**

  Buds usu <9mm

    Buds ± flattened (or lopsided), green (with brown scale margins) to purplish (often still green on lower side) or dark brown, 4-10mm, all lateral, ± curved or tilted to side; scales spiralling, ovate, obtuse. Fl buds ± globose. Twigs mod slender (2-3mm diam), ± zig-zagging, hairless or minutely hairy, occ long glandular hairs, round; pith c½ diam, ± round, soon ± chambered. Lf scars usu 2-ranked, occ spiralling, raised, semi-circular to triangular or kidney- to heart-shaped, small, ≤ bud width, dark, not decurrent; bundle scars 3 or multiplied, occ obscure. Stipule scars triangular to linear, equal or not. Catkins often present (esp late winter), often not at ends of twigs. (*Morus alba*, *Prunus serotina* & *Ulmus* (esp *U. procera*) rarely key out here if buds slightly flattened)

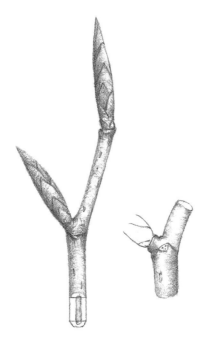

Fagus sylvatica
Beech

Nothofagus alpina
Rauli

Shrub. Buds oblique to lf scar or not, 4-8mm, single, broadly ovoid (-globose), flattened, often 'boxing glove'-like, (±) <u>obtuse;</u> scales (5)7-8(10), green (with brown scale margins) to purplish (often still green on lower side), hairy to hairless, long-ciliate, minutely reddish gland-fringed. Twigs pale or olive-brown, flexible; lenticels low, round to longitudinal, pale orange; bark weakly or obscurely fissured, not corky; pith usu <u>white,</u> usu <u>buff in branchlets.</u> Bark pale greyish brown, occ ± shiny, smooth, peeling in c3-5yrs into <u>intersecting net-like pattern,</u> finally smooth again

 Buds dark purple, 5-8mm. PL 10...............*Purple-leaved Filbert* **Corylus maxima 'Purpurea'**
 Buds usu green, 4-6mm. V common. PL 10......................................*Hazel* **Corylus avellana**
Tree; trunk continuous to tree tip; crown pyramidal. Buds oblique to lf scar, 5-8(10)mm, occ 1 small collateral bud, ovoid, ± flattened, usu ± <u>acute;</u> scales 4-6, reddish- or brownish-green (brown nr tip) to <u>dark brown,</u> usu hairy, usu ciliate. Twigs pale <u>whitish-</u>brown, brittle; lenticels usu absent; bark soon <u>fissured or corky</u> (esp branchlets); pith <u>brown.</u> Bark <u>whitish-</u>grey, flaking in small scales revealing orange-brown underbark. PL 10.........*Turkish Hazel* **Corylus colurna**
Buds not flattened (or weakly so), never wholly green
 Bundle scars 7-20, ± in a ring with some scattered, occ clustered into 3 groups, ± protruding
  Twigs usu zig-zagging, short-hairy to hairless, round; lenticels low, elongate, buff; inner bark weakly odorous, ± sweet-tasting, thin fibres present when broken; latex white; pith ½-⅔ diam, white, round. Branchlets occ at 90°. Buds usu all lateral, rarely with 1 collateral bud, occ oblique to lf scar; scales 3-4(5), 2-ranked, hairless, ciliate. Lf scars ± spiralling, ± raised, ± <u>circular,</u> sunken with raised rim (crater-like). Stipule scars oval to linear, unequal. Bark orange-brown when young. Small tree. Late bursting. ❸, rarely ❹
   Buds 5-10mm, ± spreading, ovoid, acute; scales dark reddish-brown, occ green nr base, usu darker margined. Twigs <u>mod to mod stout</u> (3-6mm diam), reddish-brown. Bundle scars 10-20. Bark fissured into long scales, orange to brown. Trunk <u>leaning;</u> branches stout, spreading; crown v broad. Not suckering. PL 19.......................*Black Mulberry* **Morus nigra**
   Buds 2-5mm, <u>± addressed</u> to ± spreading, <u>± globose,</u> ± flattened, obtuse; scales dark or <u>pale brown,</u> occ lacking dark margins. Twigs <u>mod slender</u> (2-3mm diam), white-grey to orange-brown, occ with white skin. Bundle scars usu 7-10. Bark furrowed, grey, orange inner bark visible in furrows. Rarely suckering. PL 19................*White Mulberry* **Morus alba**
 Bundle scars 3, <u>sunken</u> (look at uppermost scars) (unarmed *Chaenomeles* may key out here)
  Buds not oblique to lf scar. ❹..(*Prunus serotina*) <u>Go to</u> **PRU**
  Buds oblique to lf scar. Twigs often zig-zagging; bark peeling back when twig broken; pith white. Branchlets occ with corky wings. Buds usu of 2 kinds; ± ovoid lf buds nr twig tips and ± globose fl buds towards twig base. Lf bud scales 2-ranked, 6(10), usu notched, often with some reddish hairs...(*Ulmus*) <u>Go to</u> **ULM**
Bundle scars 3 (rarely split into 5 or fused into 1), not or rarely sunken, often protruding. Buds oblique or not. (Unarmed *Chaenomeles* may key out here)
 Lateral buds usu with ≤4 scales, usu 5-8mm, occ oblique to lf scar, often ± resinous, at least obscurely striate with many parallel veins. Twig inner bark odourless; pith ⅓ diam, green, (±) 3-angled. Lf scar < bud width. Tree. Catkins usu present. ❷...............(*Betula*) <u>Go to</u> **BET**
 Lateral buds with 4(5) scales, 2-4mm, oblique to lf scar, usu resinous (occ sticky) with yellow resin, end bud often kinked; ovoid-globose, obtuse; scales spiralling, shiny reddish-brown, obtuse, sparsely hairy to hairless, ciliate or not. Terminal bud absent. Twigs slender (1mm diam), zig-zagging, reddish-brown, minutely hairy to hairless, round; lenticels flat, oval, white; pith ½ diam, white, round. Branchlets herringbone-like. Lf scars ± 2-ranked, weakly raised, triangular to elliptical, small, < bud width; bundle scars occ ± fused. Stipule scars ± linear, ± equal, stipules occ persisting. Bark fissured into long rectangular plates. Tree. PL 20..*Antarctic Beech* **Nothofagus antarctica**
 Lateral buds usu with >4 scales (occ 4 in some *Prunus*). Pith round, white, brown or green

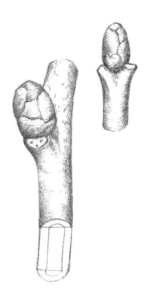

Corylus maxima 'Purpurea'
Purple-leaved Filbert

Corylus avellana
Hazel

Corylus colurna
Turkish Hazel

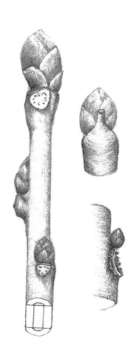

Morus nigra
Black Mulberry

Morus alba
White Mulberry

Nothofagus antarctica
Antarctic Beech

Buds not oblique to lf scar. Twigs with inner bark weakly to strongly odorous (bitter almonds); pith ½ diam, white to brown, round. Tree or shrub. Occ ❹....(*Prunus*) Go to **PRU**

Buds oblique to lf scar (occ v weakly so in *Zelkova*). Twigs with inner bark odourless. Tree (*Corylus colurna* keys out here if buds not flattened)

Buds 5-8mm, all lateral, end bud not kinked, v rarely superposed, ovoid-oblong, acute to ± obtuse, sticky when crushed; scales 6-8(9), spiralling, green at least in lower ½ and brown above, faintly striate, hairy, ciliate. Twigs slender (1.5-2mm diam), weakly zig-zagging, brown, with minute or longer ± adpressed hairs, round; lenticels low, round, buff; pith ⅓ diam, green, obscurely angled or ± round. Lf scars 2-ranked, raised, semi-circular to elliptical, small, < bud width; bundle scars rarely 5. Stipule scars small, triangular to linear, unequal. Bark cracked into scales, grey-brown. Trunk usu slender; crown round; lower branches often drooping but branchlets curving up. Catkins often present at ends of twigs. ❷. PL 20..........................*Hop-hornbeam* **Ostrya carpinifolia**

Buds 1-3mm, all lateral, end bud often kinked, occ with 1 small collateral bud, ovoid-globose, obtuse (to ± acute); scales 3-5 prs, 4-ranked, reddish-brown, obtuse, hairless, usu minutely pale-dotted with stomata (x20). Twigs slender (1-2mm diam), weakly zig-zagging, grey-brown, round; bark peeling back when twig broken; lenticels flat, oval, orange; pith ½ diam, white, round. Lf scars 2-ranked, weakly raised, crescent-shaped to elliptical, small, equal to bud width; bundle scars occ ± fused. Stipule scars triangular-linear, ± equal. Bark smooth, grey-brown, with pink-orange lenticels, later with flaking scales exposing orange underbark. Trunk short, dividing into many upright branches; crown vase-shaped

Twigs hairless. Buds 2-3mm; scales pale reddish-brown, not or obscurely ciliate. PL 38 ....*Japanese Zelkova* **Zelkova serrata**

Twigs hairy. Buds 1-2mm; scales dark reddish-brown, ciliate. PL 38 ....*Caucasian Zelkova* **Zelkova carpinifolia**

67

Ostrya carpinifolia
Hop-hornbeam

Zelkova serrata
Japanese Zelkova

Zelkova carpinifolia
Caucasian Zelkova

Group AM – *Stipules persisting, not falling or leaving scars. (*Nothofagus *spp may rarely key out here esp early winter.* Caragana arborescens *may rarely key out here if green twigs completely covered in grey skin and stipules non-spiny).* Papery scale lvs of Tamarix *and* Taxodium *occ mistaken for stipules but stipules are always in prs)*

■Stipules whitish, papery, <5mm, remnants usu persistent on corners of lf scar

Twigs slender (1-2mm diam), green to whitish-grey, usu minutely adpressed-hairy (x20), angled, brittle, with persistent bud scale remnants at join with branchlet; pith ⅓ diam, green, round. Buds all lateral, 2-3mm, adpressed, globose-ovoid, occ ± flattened, almost hidden behind raised lf scar; scales 2-4, green but usu obscured by grey papery loose outer scales, hairless. Lf scars v raised, elliptical, orange gland-fringed, decurrent; bundle scar 1 (occ divided into 3, 5 or 7 scars in a line). Bark splitting into longitudinal strips. Fr an inflated bladder-like pod, often persistent. Shrub to 2m. PL 9..*Bladder-senna* **Colutea arborescens**

■Stipules brown, papery, <12mm, persisting on sides of leaf scar (shrivelled stub on persistent petiole base). Pith ¾ diam, white or orange-brown, round.....................................*(Rubus)* Go to **RUB**

■Stipules reddish-brown, papery, lanc, usu long, (5)7-10mm, extending well beyond lf scar

Twigs v slender (1mm diam), reddish-brown, (sparsely) long-hairy, rough (minutely warty) due to raised hair bases, round, each node with a persistent 3-veined long slender clasping lf base with remnants of stipules at tip (and occ a persistent petiole) covering at least lower part of bud and occ hiding the twig; bark soon splitting, peeling in longitudinal strips; pith ⅓ diam, brown, round. Buds all lateral, obscured by stipules, adpressed, 3-6mm, oblong; scales 2-4, reddish-brown, papery, striate, hairless to silky-hairy (esp inner). Lf scars easily overlooked, v raised on long lf base, v small, round; bundle scar 1. Low shrub to 1m. PL 23 ....*Shrubby Cinquefoil* **Potentilla fruticosa**

■Stipules red or green, not papery, ≤8mm, at top of lf scar. Pith c½ diam, white, round. Buds naked but next season's stipules may be visible and resemble scales. Bundle scars 3. Hairs often yellowish...*(Cotoneaster)* Go to **COT**

Colutea arborescens
Bladder-senna

Potentilla fruticosa
Shrubby Cinquefoil

Group AN – *Stipule scars absent. Lf scars absent (*Taxodium, Tamarix*) or present as a shrivelled stub (*Rubus*), or If scars distinct with 1 bundle scar.* ❶ *Lf scars absent or obscure (4 entries).* ❷ *Twigs with inner bark odorous but not pine-scented (2 entries).* ❸ *Twigs with peltate scales.* ❹ *Twigs with occ stellate hairs nr tip*

■Tree (conifer); trunk continuous to tree tip; crown ± pyramidal. Twigs without lenticels; inner bark resinous with pine odour; pith ≤⅓ diam

Twigs unridged, slender (1-2mm diam), pale to reddish-brown, hairless; pith green, ± 3(5)-angled. Branchlets without woody spurs, usu forked. Lf scars absent (no bundle scar) but flat circular branchlet scars present (resembling If scars but not immediately below buds), spiralling, with 1 protruding false 'bundle scar'. Terminal bud absent. End buds 1-3 (single unless developing into green catkin-like fl clusters), 1-3mm, ± globose, occ resinous; scales 7-15, green to brown, acute, keeled. Lateral buds hidden below bark or scarcely breaking through (occ obscured by scale lvs which may resemble fused stipules), <1mm, brown but green as bursting. Bark fibrous, often peeling in longitudinal strips. Trunk often widened and grooved nr base, often surrounded by large conical 'knees' (pneumatophores) emerging from roots (in wet places only). Branches alt to ± whorled. ❶. PL 35...*Swamp Cypress* **Taxodium distichum**
Twigs ridged, usu mod slender ((1)2-3mm diam), occ pruinose; pith white or green, ± round. Branchlets with woody spurs; woody spurs occ opp, with rings of If scars. Lf scars spiralling, peg-like, obliquely raised, triangular to diamond-shaped, small, < bud width, decurrent. Terminal bud hairless. Lateral buds spreading at 45-90°. Bark with flaking scales, often revealing reddish-brown underbark. Branches irreg whorled

Terminal bud (of both long shoots and woody spurs) with scales apiculate to whisker-tipped, 3-5mm, ovoid-globose; scales 7-10, pale brown, not resinous or waxy, triangular-ovate, keeled, not ciliate. Lateral buds 2-3mm; scales c7, not ciliate. Twigs usu reddish-brown, occ yellow-brown, hairless. Woody spurs usu 10-35mm (growing 2-3mm/yr), often broader at tip. Branches horizontal to ascending; branchlets occ slightly drooping at tips. Cones shattering, leaving a central stalk. PL 24...*Golden Larch* **Pseudolarix amabilis**
Terminal bud (of long shoots) with scales obtuse (lower rarely long-apiculate but soon breaking off), 1-3mm, globose; scales 7-12, dark reddish-brown or same colour as twig, often slightly resinous (occ dried and wax-like), ovate, keeled (esp lower), not ciliate. Terminal bud (of woody spurs) with >20 recurved non-apiculate usu ciliate scales. Lateral buds 1-2mm. Woody spurs mostly <5mm, cylindrical. Cones not shattering

Twigs yellow-brown, hairless. Branches downswept, ascending nr ends but branchlets (and twigs) strongly drooping. Cones with scales not recurved. PL 16
....*European Larch* **Larix decidua**
Twigs dark reddish- or purplish-brown, occ sparse minute hairs nr base. Branchlets (and twigs) not drooping

Cones with scales weakly recurved. *L. decidua* x *kaempferi*. PL 16
....*Hybrid Larch* **Larix x marschlinsii**
Cones with scales strongly recurved...........(not illustrated) *Japanese Larch* **Larix kaempferi**
■Shrub (or small tree in *Elaeagnus angustifolia* and occ *Tamarix gallica*) (non-conifer)

Mtns (usu). Twigs v slender (1mm diam); lenticels absent

Terminal bud present. Lateral buds adpressed, 2mm, ovoid, obtuse; scales 2 (4 if outer pr parted), reddish, hairless. Twigs not zig-zagging, reddish-brown, occ with grey skin, hairless, ± angled; bark flaking revealing brighter reddish-brown underbark; pith ⅓ diam, white, 3-angled. Lf scars spiralling, raised, circular, tiny; bundle scar 1. Trailing subshrub to 0.2m. Dead lvs often persisting (marcescent), red or brown, rugose. PL 5
....*Arctic Bearberry* **Arctostaphylos alpinus**
Terminal bud absent. Lateral buds spreading, all lateral, 1mm, ovoid, acute; scales 2(4) (outer pr slightly parted), shiny purplish, acute, keeled, hairless. Twigs zig-zagging, pale grey to orange-brown, turning dark grey- to red-brown, minutely patent-hairy (<0.1mm) to hairless,

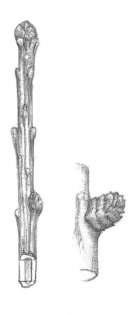

Taxodium distichum
Swamp Cypress

Pseudolarix amabilis
Golden Larch

Larix decidua
European Larch

Arctostaphylos alpinus
Arctic Bearberry

Larix x marschlinsii
Hybrid Larch

round, with persistent bud scale remnants at join with branchlet; bark peeling in longitudinal strips; pith c½ diam, green, round. Lf scars spiralling, raised, semi-circular; bundle scar 1. Low shrub to 0.5m, decumbent or erect. PL 37.........................*Bog Bilberry* **Vaccinium uliginosum**
Lowlands. Twigs slender to stout (≥1.5mm diam)
  Twigs bristly hairy or with rough hair bases remaining
    Twigs ± whorled at ends of branchlets, usu mod (3-4mm diam), reddish-brown, ± round, brittle; inner bark weakly odorous; pith ½ diam, green, round. Terminal fl bud 12-20mm, with 2-several tiny lateral lf buds ± whorled around base, ovoid, acute; scales 9-12(15), yellow-green to orange-purple, obtuse to acute, <u>apiculate</u> (often <u>v long</u> on lower scales), keeled, hairless, shortly ciliate, brown gland-fringed. Lateral lf buds c1mm, often crowded nr twig tip, lower ill-developed; scales 2-3. Lf scars not raised, shield-shaped, ≤ terminal bud width, > lateral bud width, pale; bundle scar 1, central or in upper ½, occ involute or divided. Shrub. Late bursting. ❷. PL 26..*Yellow Azalea* **Rhododendron luteum**
  Twigs silvery to bronze with peltate scales
    Twigs ± slender (1.5-2.5mm diam), not zig-zagging, round, occ angled nr tip; pith ⅔ diam, usu <u>orange-brown</u> (esp in branchlets), occ white, round. Branchlets shiny bronze, occ thorny. Terminal bud present. Lateral buds often collateral, v rarely superposed, ± spreading, 3-5mm, oblong, obtuse; scales 3-5, silvery to bronze. Lf scars ± raised, semi-circular, small, ≤ bud width, dark; bundle scar 1. Bark smooth, grey, later furrowed. ❸
      Twigs with silvery scales only. Tree to 5(7)m, occ multi-trunked, rarely shrub. Rarely suckering. PL 12..*Russian-olive* **Elaeagnus angustifolia**
      Twigs with silvery and occ bronze scales. Shrub to 3(5)m. Often suckering
      ....*Spreading Oleaster* **Elaeagnus umbellata**
      Twigs with bronze scales only. Shrub to 2(4)m. Often suckering. PL 12
      ....*Silverberry* **Elaeagnus commutata**
  Twigs warty (raised stomata), densely hairy to hairless
    Twigs slender (1-3mm diam), usu zig-zagging esp nr tip, green or purplish (esp above), round or weakly ridged to ± flattened nr tip; pith ½ diam, green, round. Buds all lateral, often of 2 sizes (fl and lf buds separate), one or mixture of both types on each twig. Fl buds (usu end and upper buds) 4-8mm, broadly ovoid; scales 6-9, green but soon pink to reddish-brown, often multi-coloured, (long-) apiculate, often with papery brown tips, weakly keeled, hairless, not ciliate. Lf buds (any position but often lower) adpressed or spreading, 2-6mm; scales 1(2) prs, valvate to overlapping, (long-) acuminate. Lf scars raised, semi-circular to crescent-shaped, small, < fl bud width; bundle scar 1. Bark peeling in longitudinal strips, grey- to reddish-brown. Erect shrub to 3m. PL 36........................*Blueberry* **Vaccinium corymbosum**
  Twigs not warty, with occ stellate hairs nr tip
    Twigs v slender (1-1.5mm diam), long, curved, orange-brown, c5-ridged, brittle; lenticels absent; pith ½ diam, white, round. Buds 1(2)mm, naked, actually pr of young white stellate-woolly lvs. Lf scars v raised, peg-like, minute, shrivelled; bundle scar 1, usu obscure. Bark peeling in longitudinal strips, grey-brown. Arching shrub. Occ ❶, ❹. PL 7
    ....*Alternate-leaved Butterfly-bush* **Buddleja alternifolia**
  Twigs not warty, with simple hairs or hairless
    Twigs >4mm diam
      Lf scar with persistent petiole base appearing as a shrivelled stub; bundle scars obscure. Stipules remnants occ present. ❶...............*(Rubus* esp *R. odoratus, parviflorus)* <u>Go to</u> **RUB**
    Twigs <4mm diam *(Colutea arborescens* and unarmed *Lycium* rarely key out here)
      Twigs brittle, round, finely to strongly lined, slender (0.5-3mm diam), usu reddish-brown. Buds 1-5mm; scales 2-12, usu keeled. Erect to arching shrub, 0.3-3m....*(Spiraea)* <u>Go to</u> **SPI**
      Twigs brittle, round to ± flattened, unlined, slender (2mm diam), orange-brown, occ with grey skin; pith ½ diam, green. Terminal bud 8-12mm, lanc, flat, knife-like; scales 2-4, orange-brown, silky-hairy, keeled. Small tree. PL 34
      ....(see **Al**) *Deciduous Camellia* **Stewartia pseudocamellia**

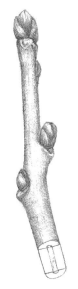

Rhododendron luteum
Yellow Azalea

Vaccinium uliginosum
Bog Bilberry

Elaeagnus angustifolia
Russian-olive

Elaeagnus umbellata
Spreading Oleaster

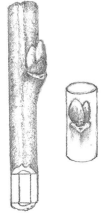

Vaccinium corymbosum
Blueberry

Buddleja alternifolia
Alternate-leaved Butterfly-bush

Elaeagnus commutata
Silverberry

Twigs often flexible, round, striate, slender (0.5-2mm diam) with wispy tip, orange- to purple-brown, curved, hairless; lenticels flat, small, round, pale; pith to 1-side (eccentric), ⅓ diam, white, ± round. Branchlets deciduous, falling in autumn leaving circular scar. Buds all lateral, single or with 1-2 collateral buds, ± spreading, often partially hidden behind papery scale lvs (bracts) or remnants of their widened bases, 1mm, ovoid-globose; scales 1-2 prs, often obscure, pale brown, occ reddish, not keeled, hairless, not ciliate. Lf scars absent (no bundle scars) but raised circular branchlet scars present on older branchlets (resembling lf scars but not immediately below buds), spiralling, with 1 large circular false 'bundle scar'. Bark smooth with elongated lenticels, brown, later fissured into rectangular blocks. Trunk usu curved. Shrub or small tree to 4m. Often coastal. ❶. PL 35.....*Tamarisk* **Tamarix gallica**

Twigs flexible, tough, round or ± 4-angled, mod slender (2-3mm diam), pale grey-brown, black-speckled, occ sparsely adpressed-hairy; inner bark odorous; pith c½ diam, green, ± round. Terminal lf bud 7-12mm, conical, acute. Lateral fl buds similar, often clustered nr tip. Lateral lf buds 2-4mm, occ superposed or collateral, ovoid, obtuse. All bud scales 4-6, green to purple-black, obtuse but apiculate, keeled, hairless, ciliate. Lf scars 4-ranked (view from above), occ opp, not raised, crescent-shaped to elliptical, small. Low shrub to 0.5(1)m. ❷. All parts poisonous and handling fresh twigs can cause irritation. PL 11
....*Mezereon* **Daphne mezereum**

Group AO – *Stipule scars absent. Bundle scars 2*

■Twigs slender to mod (2-4mm diam), zig-zagging, reddish-brown to pale grey, hairless, round, rigid; bark soon splitting; pith ⅓ diam, yellow, 3-angled; inner wood with mucus canals. Woody spurs on branchlets spreading at 60-90°, 5-10mm, ± cylindrical. Terminal bud 2-4mm, dome-shaped, ± obtuse; scales 3-5, brown, v obtuse, loose, occ with recurved tips, thickened, rough (minutely sculptured), hairless, not ciliate. Lateral buds spreading at c45°. Lf scars spiralling (on woody spurs) or 2-ranked (on long shoots), ± raised, horizontally elliptical, equal to bud width, upper margin occ hair-fringed. Bark fissured, pale grey (-brown), later furrowed. Tree; trunk continuous to tree tip; crown ± conical; branches stout, irreg, the upper branches ascending at c45°. Late bursting. PL 14...*Ginkgo* **Ginkgo biloba**

75

Tamarix gallica
Tamarisk

Daphne mezereum
Mezereon

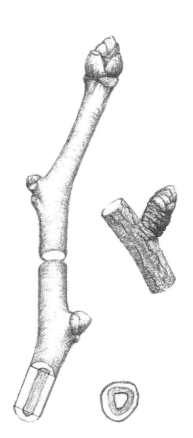

Ginkgo biloba
Ginkgo

AP

Group AP – *Stipule scars absent. Bundle scars 3. (Robinia* pseudoacacia *keys out here if unarmed. Sorbus* subgen Sorbus *keys out here if bundle scars miscounted).* ❶ *Pith orange-brown or chambered (4 spp).* ❷ *Bundle scars visible as 3 white rings.* ❸ *Bundle scars often sunken (4 spp).* ❹ *Twigs white-felted or woolly at least nr tip.* ❺ *Buds 'pea-like'*

■Twigs and/or buds with scattered sessile yellow disc-like aromatic glands. Shrub

Lf scars >> lateral bud width, not raised, crescent-shaped. Twigs with splitting and peeling bark
....*(Ribes nigrum)* Go to **RIB**

Lf scars ≤ bud width, raised, broadly crescent-shaped to ± triangular, small, spiralling. Twigs slender (1.5-2mm diam), clustered to ± whorled nr ends of branchlets, hairy, round; bark not splitting; lenticels few, flat, v small, round, white; pith ⅓ diam, <u>green</u>, ± angled. Lateral buds spreading. Erect, suckering

Terminal bud absent. Lateral buds usu of different size and shape (fl and lf buds separate). Fl buds nr twig tip, different on male and female plants. Male fl buds 5-8 x 3mm, narrowly ovoid to cigar-shaped (often >2.5x long as wide), ± acute, > lf scar width; scales 20-25(30), ± 5-ranked, bronzy reddish-brown, often with darker centres, with whitish waxy margins, hairless, occ sparsely ciliate. Female fl buds 2-3 x 1-2mm, ovoid; scales 8-15. Lf buds lower on twig, c2mm, ovoid, obtuse to acute, equal to lf scar width; scales 6-8. Twigs purple-brown. Usu bogs. PL 19
....*Bog-myrtle* **Myrica gale**

Terminal bud similar to lateral buds. Lateral buds all similar, ± equally distributed along twig, 1.5-3mm, ± globose, v obtuse; scales 4-8, in prs, purple, without waxy margins, hairless, not ciliate. Twigs green to reddish-brown. PL 19.............................*Bayberry* **Myrica pensylvanica**

■Twigs and buds without aromatic glands

Buds >2.5x long as wide. Branchlets often with short twigs, occ with woody spurs

Twigs with splitting and peeling bark (esp branchlets in 2nd yr); lenticels <u>absent</u>; pith c½ diam, white or green, soon fragmenting. Lateral buds often short-stalked. Lf scars ≥ lateral bud width. Shrub, rarely suckering...*(Ribes alpinum, sanguineum)* Go to **RIB**

Twigs without splitting or peeling bark, dark olive- or red-brown, developing grey skin, round; lenticels few, low, oval, buff. Lateral buds sessile, smaller or absent. Lf scars 2-ranked or spiralling, weakly raised, crescent-shaped, narrowed between bundle scars, weakly decurrent. Terminal bud with scales ± 1(3)-keeled (weakly 3-veined), 3-toothed or apiculate. Rarely suckering

Terminal bud green turning purplish on sunlit side, with 2nd scale ≤½ bud length, 8-14mm, spindle-shaped, 3-4x long as wide, acute, often smaller lateral bud just below terminal; scales 2-ranked, c6, increasing in size upwards, ± thin, hairless, long-ciliate. Lateral buds (±) adpressed, incurved, rarely with extra pr of basal scales fused and appearing short-stalked. Twigs slender (1.5-2mm diam), ± zig-zagging, hairless; inner bark with almond odour; pith ⅓ diam, white or green, ± round. Lf scars equal to bud width. Bark smooth, green, striped with 'snake bark' pattern. Small tree. PL 4..............................*Juneberry* **Amelanchier lamarckii**

Terminal bud shiny dark red, with 2nd bud scale ≥½ bud length, 5-10mm, oblong to ± conical, <u>± flattened</u>, (2)3x long as wide, acute, often curved; scales 2-ranked, 3-5, ± thick, <u>glandular-ciliate</u>. Lateral buds adpressed, curved. Twigs slender (1.5-3mm diam), densely adpressed-hairy or woolly nr tip to ± hairless; inner bark with <u>weak</u> almond odour; pith ½ diam, white, round. Lf scars usu > bud width, occ fringed with long brown glands. Bark smooth, with lenticels, reddish-brown, later peeling into diamond pattern. Shrub, erect, occ arching with frs

Old frs red. Lateral buds to 8mm; scales 3-4. Terminal bud to 11mm, ± hairless. Twigs 2-3mm diam. To 3m. PL 5.................................*Red Chokeberry* **Aronia arbutifolia**

Old frs dark purple. Intermediate between parents. *A. abutifolia* x *melanocarpa*. PL 5
....*Purple Chokeberry* **Aronia x prunifolia**

Old frs black. Lateral buds 1-5mm; scales 1-3. Terminal bud to 5mm, hairless. Twigs 1.5-2mm diam. To 1.5m. PL 5.......................................*Black Chokeberry* **Aronia melanocarpa**

Buds <2.5x long as wide

Pith orange-brown OR brown and chambered ❶

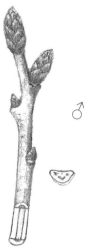

Myrica pensylvanica
Bayberry

Amelanchier lamarckii
Juneberry

Myrica gale
Bog-myrtle

Aronia x **prunifolia**
Purple Chokeberry

Aronia arbutifolia
Red Chokeberry

Aronia melanocarpa
Black Chokeberry

Tree. Pith chambered, odorous (chemical odour). PL 15...........(see **AF**) *Walnut* **Juglans regia**
Tree. Pith solid, fetid (mice odour). PL 4.............(see **AR**) *Tree-of-heaven* **Ailanthus altissima**
Shrub or small tree. Pith solid, aromatic (soapy odour). PL 10
....(see **AE**) *Smoke-tree* **Cotinus coggygria**
Shrub. Pith solid, odourless, ¾ diam. Twigs mod to stout (4-7mm diam), ± zig-zagging, pale
(reddish-) brown to grey, hairless, round; lenticels flat, round, grey. Buds all lateral, collateral
buds developing as buds burst, spreading, (3)4-9mm, ovoid, obtuse; scales c4, usu green,
occ reddish, turning dark purple-brown, hairless, minutely ciliate, margins jagged. Lf scars
spiralling, flat or slightly sunken, shield-shaped, large, > bud width, same colour as twig or
paler; bundle scars protruding, nr outer margin. Suckering. Early bursting. Other spp may
occur. PL 32...*Sorbaria* **Sorbaria sorbifolia**
Pith usu white (occ green, brown or purple), not chambered (but diaphragmed in *Davidia* and
Nyssa). Lf scars spiralling. (*Celtis* keys out here if stipule scars overlooked)
  Bundle scars visible as pale or white rings around dark centres (occ exuding resin). Branchlets
  with woody spurs. Tree
    Terminal bud 5-15mm, ovoid to conical, acute, ± sticky, aromatic when crushed; scales (3)6-
    8, shiny green to orange- or reddish-brown, darker margins, obtuse, apiculate, hairless, buff-
    or white-ciliate. Lateral buds similar, 5-10mm, usu spreading, rarely collateral, occ short-
    stalked, occ small and adpressed. Twigs mod (3-5mm diam), shiny yellow-green to reddish-
    brown, hairless, weakly 5-angled or flattened nr tip; lenticels low, oval, buff; sap aromatic,
    sticky; pith ½ diam, white, ± 5-angled. Branchlets with fissured bark, often with corky wings
    (3-4 wings on upper side of horizontal branches and all around vertical ones). Lf scars
    raised, semi-circular or triangular, decurrent. Bark smooth but warty when young, greyish-
    brown, later furrowed. Trunk usu continuous to tree tip; crown ± pyramidal when young;
    branches usu at 90°. ❷. PL 16.......................*American Sweetgum* **Liquidambar styraciflua**
  Bundle scars often sunken (at least on some lf scars). Branchlets with woody spurs (exc
  Baccharis). Tree, occ small (shrub in *Baccharis*)
    Terminal bud 7-10mm, ovoid, ± sharply acute; scales c6, shiny dark purple, v narrow pale
    margins, broad, v obtuse but lower apiculate or notched, not keeled, v rarely with sparse
    adpressed hairs, occ minutely ciliate. Lateral buds 0-10mm, sessile or on woody spurs,
    spreading, larger buds similar to terminal. Twigs mod (4-5mm diam), ± zig-zagging, dark
    brown, hairless, round; lenticels ± raised, small, round, pale; pith c½ diam, white, round,
    solid but diaphragmed with indistinct white partitions (c15 per cm, occ only extending part
    way). Branchlets with woody spurs. Lf scars weakly raised, half-elliptical or 3-lobed, pale,
    weakly decurrent; bundle scars large. Bark smooth, pale grey-brown, later dark orange-
    brown with small flaking scales revealing purplish underbark. Tree, often small; crown
    broadly conical, later v wide. ❸. PL 11.................................*Dove-tree* **Davidia involucrata**
    Terminal bud 3-5(7)mm, ovoid to conical, often curved at tip, acute; scales (3)4-6(7) (modified
    petiole bases), green to reddish-brown or purplish (esp on sunlit side), obtuse, (white-) buff-
    hairy nr tip, rarely hairless, ciliate. Lateral buds smaller, spreading. Twigs slender (2-3mm
    diam), green to reddish-brown, hairless or sparsely hairy nr tip, round; lenticels few, low, round,
    pale; pith solid but diaphragmed with firm green partitions (10-20 per cm), c½ diam.
    Branchlets with slender curved woody spurs. Lf scars weakly raised on orange base (exc on
    woody spurs), crescent-shaped to semi-circular, surrounded by narrow raised rim. Bark
    furrowed, later blocky like 'crocodile-hide'. Tree; trunk continuous to tree tip; crown
    pyramidal; branches usu 90° to trunk. ❸. PL 20.................................*Tupelo* **Nyssa sylvatica**
    Terminal bud (2)3-6mm, ovoid, often 1(2) collateral buds, ± obtuse to sharply acute; scales
    5-9(12), reddish-brown, obtuse, short- to long-apiculate, at least lowest hairy, ciliate.
    Lateral buds similar, usu smaller, ± spreading. Twigs mod ((2)3-5mm diam), densely
    adpressed-hairy (or woolly) at tip (or base of bud), reddish-brown, round, occ ridged;
    lenticels raised, ± round, orange or same colour as twig; pith <½ diam, white, ± round.
    Thorns occ present, to 15mm, slightly curved. Lf scars raised, crescent-shaped, narrowed
    between bundle scars, often > bud width; bundle scars nr top of lf scar. Bark later flaking in

79

Sorbaria sorbifolia
Sorbaria

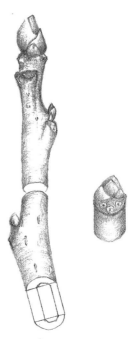

Liquidambar styraciflua
American Sweetgum

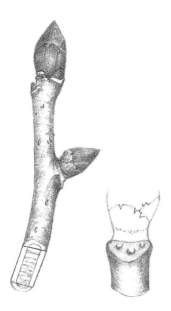

Davidia involucrata
Dove-tree

Nyssa sylvatica
Tupelo

rectangular plates. Small tree. ❸, occ ❹. PL 19......   *Medlar* **Mespilus germanica**
Terminal bud 2-3mm, dome-shaped, acute to obtuse; scales 3(4). Twigs mod (3-4mm diam);
pith solid but <u>diaphragmed with firm green partitions</u> (10-20 per cm). Usu by water. PL 20
....(scc **Al**) *Water Tupelo* **Nyssa aquatica**
Terminal bud absent. Lateral buds c1mm, ± globose, encased in hard greenish resin, soon
bursting into minute green leaves. Twigs slender (1-3mm diam), green at least nr tip, 5-8-
ridged, scurfy. ❸. PL 5...............................(see **AJ**) *Tree Groundsel* **Baccharis halimifolia**
Bundle scars not usu sunken nor with white rings (*Gleditsia triacanthos* var *inermis* keys out
here if superposed buds hidden under bark or lf scar)
Buds with at least some white hairs (or woolly-ciliate) nr base or tip. Twigs hairless to ±
woolly nr tip. Tree (occ small). Branchlets with woody spurs
Lf scars raised on a persistent late-deciduous green or red petiole base (look carefully, usu
absent late winter exposing true lf scar)
Terminal bud acute, (5)8-15(20)mm, ovoid, often sticky nr tip; scales (5)7, <u>green to
reddish</u> (*S. aria* influence) or <u>purplish</u> (*S. aucuparia* influence), with broad purplish-
brown margins, at least obscurely keeled, 3-toothed or apiculate (lowest scales are
modified petiole bases and have small scar at tip), hairless to woolly, often woolly-ciliate;
inner scales sticky, resin secreted from orange glands nr base. Lateral buds often ill-
developed, ± spreading to adpressed. Twigs usu mod (2.5-6mm diam), shiny <u>purplish-
to orange-brown</u>, rarely olive- to reddish-brown, occ grey skin, occ wool nr tip; lenticels ±
flat, oval, pale orange to white; pith occ turning brown. Lf scars on persistent <u>green (occ
red)</u> petiole base, crescent-shaped to triangular, weakly decurrent. Bark smooth, grey.
Crown round; branches ascending with ends of twigs curving up. Many taxa derived
from hybridisation of *S. aria, aucuparia* and *torminalis*. (*S.* x *hybrida* and *S.* x *thuringiaca*
(**AQ**) key out here if bundle scars 3). PL 32....................*Whitebeam* **Sorbus** subgen **Aria**
Terminal bud (±) obtuse, 5-9mm, ovoid to globose, often 'pea-like', not sticky; scales 5-7
(lowest scales are modified petiole bases and have small scar at tip), v obtuse, shiny
bright green (occ orange tinge) with brown margins, <u>minutely brown gland-fringed</u> (often
worn off), hairless, ciliate (occ long or ± woolly); inner scales not sticky. Lateral buds
often ill-developed, spreading. Lf scars on persistent <u>green</u> petiole base, semi-circular to
triangular, weakly decurrent. Twigs mod (3-4mm diam), dark purplish-brown (occ
orange-brown), adpressed-hairy to hairless, occ ± woolly nr tip, round; lenticels raised,
small, round, pale; pith ½ diam, occ turning brown, round. Bark later flaking in squarish
plates. Crown round; lower branches ± drooping with twigs upswept. ❺. PL 33
....*Wild Service-tree* **Sorbus torminalis**
Lf scars not on a persistent green or red petiole base (lf scars raised or not)
Lateral buds adpressed. Lf scars raised, equal to bud width.................(*Malus*) <u>Go to</u> **MAL**
Lateral buds spreading (*Populus alba* keys out here if stipule scars overlooked)
Lf scars not raised, ≥ bud width................(*Ribes odoratum,* rarely *R. rubrum*) <u>Go to</u> **RIB**
Lf scars raised, equal to bud width. Terminal bud 3-12mm, ovoid to globose. Often ❺
...(*Malus tschonoskii, Pyrus calleryana, P. elaeagnifolia, P. salicifolia*) <u>Go to</u> **MAL, PYR**
Lf scars raised, often > bud width. Terminal bud (2)3-6mm, ovoid, ± obtuse to sharply
acute; scales reddish-brown, short- to long-apiculate, at least lowest white-hairy. ❸,
occ ❹. PL 19...(see above) *Medlar* **Mespilus germanica**
Buds with golden hairs at tip (look carefully or break off scales to check). Twigs hairless to
hairy or woolly to white-felted. Tree (occ small). Branchlets with woody spurs. Occ ❹.
(*Nyssa sylvatica* may key out here if hairs buff)...(*Pyrus*) <u>Go to</u> **PYR**
Buds hairless even at tips, not ciliate (occ minutely ciliate or v rarely hairy in *Davidia*). Twigs
hairless (*Prunus cerasifera* (**PRU**) keys out here if stipule scars overlooked)
Twigs (±) stout (8-14mm diam), not zig-zagging, reddish to brown, ± round; lenticels usu
absent; inner bark with antiseptic odour; pith >¾ diam, (off-) white, round. Branchlets

81

AP

Mespilus germanica
Medlar

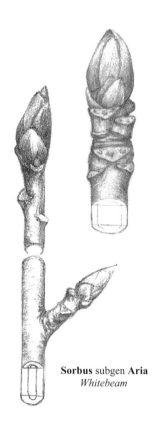

Sorbus subgen **Aria**
Whitebeam

Sorbus torminalis
Wild Service-tree

without woody spurs. Terminal bud (15)20-40mm, ovoid; scales c6, outer dark reddish-black and inner pinkish, acute, often c3-keeled, apiculate (occ long), loose. Lateral buds c5mm, often at least partly covered by lf scar. Lf scars not raised, triangular or semi-circular, large; bundle scars 3(5), often obscure. Shrub to 3m; branches few, irreg. PL 20

....*Tree Peony* **Paeonia** sect **Moutan**

Twigs mod (4-5mm diam), ± zig-zagging, round. Terminal bud shiny dark purple, (±) hairless. ❸. PL 11...(see above) *Dove-tree* **Davidia involucrata**

Twigs mod (4-5mm diam), not zig-zagging, finely lined. Terminal bud shiny purplish- or reddish-brown, (±) hairless to densely white-hairy....(*Malus* esp *M. tschonoskii*) Go to **MAL**

Twigs slender (1-3mm diam), often zig-zagging, shiny dark reddish-brown, round. Terminal bud shiny dark red, hairless.........................(unarmed) (see **AC**) *Hawthorn* **Crataegus** spp

Group AQ – *Stipule scars absent. Bundle scars 5 (rarely a mixture of 3, 4 and 5)*

■Pith orange-brown. Branchlets without woody spurs. (*Gymnocladus dioicus* rarely keys out here)

Twigs round. (Keys out here if terminal bud single and bundle scars multiplied). Shrub or small tree. PL 10.....................................(see **AE**) *Smoke-tree* **Cotinus coggygria**

Twigs 3-5-ridged. (Keys out here if stipule scars overlooked). Shrub. PL 21

....(see **AK**) *Atlantic Ninebark* **Physocarpus opulifolius**

■Pith white (occ brownish flecks in *Sorbus*). Twigs round

Twig (±) stout (≥7mm diam). Branchlets without woody spurs. Lf scars not raised

Shrub. Twigs stout (8-14mm diam); inner bark with antiseptic odour. PL 20

....(see **AP**) *Tree Peony* **Paeonia** sect **Moutan**

Tree. Twigs mod stout (7-10mm diam), brown, minutely hairy to hairless; lenticels small; inner bark with unpleasant sickly onion odour; pith ½-⅔ diam, round. Lf scars ± circular or heart-shaped, large, pale; bundle scars 5, in U shape. Terminal bud 5-10mm, >> lateral buds, broadly ovoid, often winter-killed or falling leaving scar, bursting later in spring than lateral buds; scales (modified petiole bases) c5, (reddish-) brown, triangular, buff-hairy at least nr tip. Lateral buds v small, flattened-globose; scales 3-5. Bark with long uninterrupted fissures. PL 36

....*Chinese Mahogany* **Toona sinensis**

Twigs mod (3-5mm diam). Branchlets with woody spurs. Lf scars raised. Terminal bud with scales at least obscurely keeled and 3-toothed or apiculate (lowest scales are modified petiole bases and have small scar at tip). Tree

Lf scars raised on a persistent late-deciduous green petiole base (usu absent late winter exposing true lf scar). Twigs hairless or v sparsely woolly nr tip

Terminal bud 10-15mm, conic-ovoid, acute, slightly curved, sticky; scales 4-6, shiny green, usu slightly reddish, v narrow brown margins, minutely reddish gland-fringed at 3-toothed tip (often obscure), obscurely keeled. Lateral buds to 10mm, ± spreading. Twigs shiny olive-brown, occ with grey skin; lenticels ± longitudinal, buff; inner bark odourless; pith ½ diam, white, round. Lf scars crescent-shaped. Bark smooth, grey-brown, later furrowed into flat scaly rectangular ridges. PL 32...*Service-tree* **Sorbus domestica**

Lf scars raised on a persistent late-deciduous red to purplish-black petiole base (usu absent late winter exposing true lf scar) contrasting with paler twig. Twigs hairless

Bundle scars usu a mixture of 3, 4 and 5. Twigs shiny purplish- to orange-brown or olive-brown, occ with grey skin; lenticels ± flat, oval, buff to white; inner bark usu with odour of bitter almonds or cherries. Terminal bud to 15mm, ovoid-conical, slightly curved, acute, resembling *S. aucuparia*; scales green to reddish-purple, woolly-ciliate. Lateral buds adpressed to spreading. Lf scars crescent-shaped to triangular

Lvs usu with 1 pr of free lfts. Crown usu ovate. *S. aucuparia* x *intermedia*. PL 32

....*Swedish Service-tree* **Sorbus x hybrida**

Lvs usu with (1)2-5 prs of free lfts. Crown usu fastigiate. *S. aucuparia* x *aria*. PL 33

....*Bastard Service-tree* **Sorbus x thuringiaca**

Toona sinensis
Chinese Mahogany

Paeonia sect **Moutan**
Tree Peony

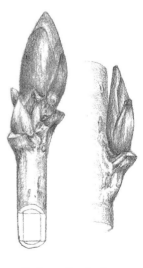

Sorbus domestica
Service-tree

Sorbus x **hybrida**
Swedish Service-tree

Sorbus x **thuringiaca**
Bastard Service-tree

Bundle scars 5. Twigs dark reddish-brown, usu with grey skin; lenticels low, oval, small, buff; inner bark with odour of bitter almonds or cherries; pith ½ diam, occ with brownish flecks. Terminal bud acute, slightly curved; scales (3)4-5, thick, the lower at least weakly 1(3)-keeled. Lateral buds adpressed to spreading. Lf scars crescent-shaped to triangular. Bark smooth, silvery-grey, with horizontal lenticels same colour as bark. Trunk often short, dividing at 1-2m into several erect limbs; crown ovate (*Sorbus* subgen *Sorbus*)

Common, native and widely planted

Terminal bud (6)8-16mm, conical-ovoid, shiny dark purplish-brown to -black (usu same colour as petiole base), densely white- or buff-hairy or woolly (esp inner scales or nr tip) to hairless, ciliate. Lateral buds adpressed, ± flattened, 2-10mm; scales weakly keeled. Lf scars raised on a purplish-black petiole base. Frs red. PL 32......*Rowan* **Sorbus aucuparia**

Occasional, planted

Terminal bud 15-22mm, narrowly conical, dark red (purple-black in 'Ravensbill'), occ with green scale bases, buff-hairy esp nr tip, rarely sticky (not in most UK planted cultivars); scales buff-ciliate. Lateral buds with scales not or weakly keeled. Lf scars raised on a dark red-black petiole base. Frs orange to red. PL 32..........*Japanese Rowan* **Sorbus commixta**

Terminal bud 10-16(22)mm, conical-ovoid, reddish; scales white-ciliate, may be buff-hairy at tip. Lf scars raised on a red petiole base

Frs white, bruising brownish, large, marble-like. Terminal bud occ dark red, ± hairless but with a tuft of buff hairs at tip. Lateral buds with lower scales often strongly keeled. PL 32 ....*Kashmir Rowan* **Sorbus cashmiriana**

Frs white to pinkish, small. Terminal bud reddish, occ greenish or orange, ± hairless but with a tuft of white or buff hairs at tip. Lateral buds with lower scales weakly keeled. PL 32..*Chinese Rowan* **Sorbus glabriuscula**

Frs yellow, small. Terminal bud often curved, ± hairless but usu with a tuft of buff hairs at tip. Lateral buds with lower scales weakly keeled. *S. commixta* x *?monbeigii*. PL 32 ....*Yellow-berried Rowan* **Sorbus 'Joseph Rock'**

Sorbus aucuparia
Rowan

Sorbus commixta
Japanese Rowan

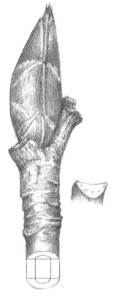

Sorbus cashmiriana
Kashmir Rowan

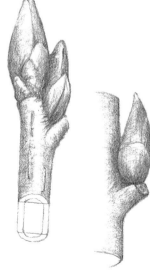

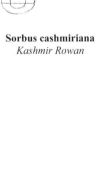

Sorbus glabriuscula
Chinese Rowan

Sorbus 'Joseph Rock'
Yellow-berried Rowan

Group AR – *Stipule scars absent. Bundle scars 7-30*

■Tree to 20m

Terminal bud absent, the end bud falling leaving large oval bud scar. Lateral buds in notch at upper margin of lf scar, 2-4(6)mm but flattened or partly sunken in bark (so ≤2mm high), globose-ovoid, << lf scars; scales 2(4), ± valvate, red-brown, hairy; inner pr occ visible. Twigs stout (8-15mm diam), reddish-brown, occ olive-green or grey, minutely hairy to hairless, ± round, tips dying back to bud scar by uppermost lateral bud; lenticels many, ± flat, elongated, orange; inner bark fetid (smelling of mice or rancid peanut butter); pith ≥¾ diam, orange-brown, ± round. Lf scars spiralling, not or weakly raised, heart- or shield-shaped, large, pale; bundle scars 7-9(14), occ divided, in a V-shaped row nr outer margin. Bark smooth, grey to greyish-brown, with pale wavy vertical stripes (flame-like pattern), eventually shallowly furrowed. Trunk ± forked, often repeatedly. Crown round, open; branches stout, with few branchlets. Suckering. Sap can be an irritant to some people. PL 4.....................*Tree-of-heaven* **Ailanthus altissima**

Terminal bud 6-10mm, >> laterals, conical, acute; scales 2 prs but may appear naked, densely pale buff-hairy. Lateral buds minute or absent. Lf scars spiralling, crowded, not raised, ± circular to flattened-elliptical, pale; bundle scars 15-30, ± scattered. Twigs mod stout (6-10mm diam), minutely adpressed brown-hairy nr tip, round; lenticels orange; pith ⅔ diam, white, round; latex white, drying black. Bark ± smooth, grey, with buff diamond-shaped lenticels. Not suckering. Late bursting. Caution! Sap is a caustic contact-poison. PL 36
....*Chinese Lacquer-tree* **Toxicodendron vernicifluum**

Terminal bud 10-20mm, ovoid, wider than twig, ± acute; scales (3)4-7, brown, triangular, silky-hairy, the outer 2-5 darker, apiculate, keeled, loose. Lateral buds 3-10mm, occ set well above lf scar. Twigs mod stout (4-6mm diam), brown, shaggy-hairy with stellate hairs to hairless, occ sessile yellow disc-like glands nr tip; lenticels many, raised, oval to longitudinal, buff; pith ½ diam, white to brown, 5-angled. Lf scars spiralling, not raised, heart-shaped or 3-lobed, ± large, white; bundle scars 7-20, ± scattered, occ in 3(4) groups. Bark smooth, grey-brown, eventually shaggy. Not suckering. Late bursting. PL 7.....................*Shagbark Hickory* **Carya ovata**

■Shrub to 3m. Twigs stout (8-14mm diam). PL 20.........(see **AP**) *Tree Peony* **Paeonia** sect **Moutan**

■Low shrub to 1m

Twigs mod (4mm diam), grey, hairless, round; lenticels ± absent; inner bark yellow, fetid; pith ½-⅔ diam, yellow, round. Terminal bud 8-16mm, cigar-shaped, acute; scales c5, green-purple, large (lowest scales >½ bud length), retuse, v long-apiculate (often broken off), keeled, hairless, minutely ciliate, occ white-dotted with stomata. Lateral buds adpressed, 1-4mm, flattened-ovoid; scales 1-3, obtuse. Lf scars not raised, broadly linear, almost meeting around twig; bundle scars 9-15, in a single line. Little-branched. Suckering. PL 37.....*Yellowroot* **Xanthorhiza simplicissima**

Ailanthus altissima
Tree-of-heaven

Toxicodendron vernicifluum
Chinese Lacquer-tree

Carya ovata
Shagbark Hickory

Xanthorhiza simplicissima
Yellowroot

89

B

Key to Groups in Division B
(Buds and If scars opp or subopp, occ 3-6-whorled)

Bud scales in decussate pairs (4-ranked) unless 1 pr (usu valvate) or otherwise stated (when counting bud scales remember to count in opposite prs). Twigs mostly unarmed, not zig-zagging. Lf scars 4-ranked unless otherwise stated

■Twigs without interpetiolar ridge (If scars without horizontal connecting line and not meeting around twig). Buds often subopp
Twigs green (occ turning purplish), usu with stomata (visible as minute white dots)...................**BA**
Twigs not green, without stomata (but may have lenticels)...**BB**
■Twigs with interpetiolar ridge (If scars with horizontal connecting line or If scars meeting around twig, occ weak). Buds always exactly opp
Climber or scrambler...**BC**
Tree or shrub
Buds not visible (hidden beneath If scar in *Philadelphus*) or scales obscure (*Fuchsia*)...........**BD**
Buds naked OR with 1 pr scales (occ fused, or split at tip)..**BE**
Buds with ≥2 prs scales
Twigs green, v hollow (*Leycesteria formosa*)..**BF**
Twigs not green or, if green, without large hollow (usu solid or with small hollow)
Buds mostly >12mm. Twigs mod stout. Lf scars large, usu shield-shaped. Usu a tree
(*Aesculus*)..**BG**
Buds ≤12mm. Twigs rarely mod stout. Lf scars rarely large or shield-shaped
Tree (occ small) (*Acer*)...**BH**
Shrub (occ a tree in *Sambucus nigra*)...**BI**

Group BA – *Twigs without interpetiolar ridge, green to purplish, with stomata visible (exc* Forsythia, Salix *and* Staphylea*)*

■Scrambler or climber. Twigs green, without lenticels; pith ⅔ diam, white, round. Terminal bud absent. Lf scars covered by shrivelled reddish-brown petiole base, small, decurrent; bundle scar 1, visible if petiole base fallen or removed. Stipule scars absent

Twigs 4-ridged (square); pith solid, occ diaphragmed

Twigs slender to mod (2-4mm wide), hairless. Buds single, adpressed, 4-10mm, ovoid-conical; scales (2)3-4(5) prs, green, usu brown-tipped, keeled, hairless, not ciliate; outermost pr reddish-brown and warty at base. Lf scars ± raised, not clasping. Not twining. PL 15 ....*Winter Jasmine* **Jasminum nudiflorum**

Twigs 6-8(12)-ridged; pith chambered (chambers v crowded, 18-50 per cm)

Twigs slender (2-3mm diam), usu hairless. Buds superposed, occ 3-whorled or hidden behind petiole base, (±) spreading, 1-2(4)mm (lower bud <1mm), flattened-ovoid, acute; scales 1(2) prs, green to brown or brown-tipped, usu acuminate, hairy to hairless, shortly ciliate. Lf scars v raised, clasping at base with small cartilaginous auricles. Often anticlockwise-twining. PL 15 ....*Summer Jasmine* **Jasminum officinale**

■Shrub (or small tree in *Euonymus europaeus*)

All buds <2mm; scales obscure. Twigs rush-like. PL 33 ....(see **AJ**) *Spanish Broom* **Spartium junceum**

At least some buds >2mm

Bud scale 1 (single). Twigs round...(*Salix purpurea*) Go to **SAL B**

Bud scales 1 pr (fused). Twigs round

Twigs mod (3-5mm diam), green to purplish, occ pruinose, hairless, occ developing interpetiolar ridge; lenticels ± raised, oval, white, often only in 2nd yr; inner bark odorous; pith ⅔ diam, white, round. Terminal bud absent. End bud(s) single or paired, 6-12mm, broadly ovoid, ± flattened, ± acute, slightly curved, with lateral keel; scale apparently 1 (2 fused scales), occ 2 or 4 fused inner scales exposed, green to reddish, hairless. Lateral buds spreading, often weakly oblique to lf scar. Lf scars not raised, semi-circular to broadly crescent-shaped; bundle scars 3, 5 or 7 in U shape. Stipule scars triangular, equal. Bark smooth, grey-green, striped with white vertical 'snake bark' pattern. Related spp occur in gardens. PL 34..*Bladdernut* **Staphylea pinnata**

Bud scales ≥2 prs

Twigs with stomata obscure or absent, 4-angled; lenticels raised. PL 13 ....(see **BB**) *Forsythia* **Forsythia x intermedia**

Twigs with stomata visible, round to 4-ridged, mod slender (2-4mm diam), ± dull green to purplish, hairless; lenticels usu absent; pith ½ diam, green, soon fragmenting. Terminal bud (±) 4-angled; scales (2)3-5(6) prs, hairless. Lateral buds similar but smaller. Lf scars occ subopp, weakly raised, usu semi-circular, occ crescent-shaped, whitish; bundle scar 1, short arc, occ protruding or split into 2. Stipule scars minute, round, often obscure

Terminal bud (10)15-30 x 3-6mm, spindle-shaped, occ curved at tip, v acute; scales 4-5 prs, green to purple (esp on sunlit side), obtuse, not keeled, obscurely toothed on thin brown margins. Lateral buds adpressed, incurved, 10-18mm. Twigs 3-4mm diam, often purplish on sunlit side, ± round to ± 4-angled; inner bark odourless; pith round. Branchlets round. Lf scars ≤ terminal bud width but ± equal to lateral bud width. Bark smooth. PL 12 ....*Large-leaved Spindle* **Euonymus latifolius**

Terminal bud 2-6mm, ovoid, acute. Lateral buds ± spreading, 1-5mm, ovoid; scales (2)3-5(6) prs, green, with acute to long-acuminate red-brown tips (breaking off), keeled, minutely orange gland-fringed (± minutely toothed). Twigs 2-3(4)mm diam, often 4-ridged at least nr base; inner bark weakly fetid, bitter-tasting (mildly toxic); pith round to 4-angled. Branchlets green, round to 4-ridged, often with buff corky wings along angles, branching ± 90° to twig. Lf scars small, ≤ bud width. Bark smooth to shallowly fissured, green to orange-grey. Occ small tree. PL 12..*Spindle* **Euonymus europaeus**

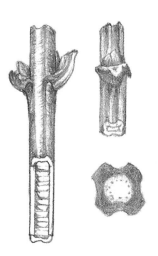

Jasminum officinale
Summer Jasmine

Jasminum nudiflorum
Winter Jasmine

Staphylea pinnata
Bladdernut

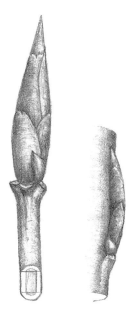

Euonymus europaeus
Spindle

Euonymus latifolius
Large-leaved Spindle

Group BB – *Twigs without interpetiolar ridge, not green.* ❶ *At least some buds 3(4)-whorled (3 entries).* ❷ *Branchlets with splitting bark (2 taxa).* ❸ *Stipules or stipule scars scars present (4 entries).* ❹ *Twigs thorny with odorous inner bark*

■Buds naked or scales obscure. Shrub (the tree *Paulownia tomentosa* may rarely key out here) Terminal bud absent. Lateral buds usu 3(4)-whorled, rarely opp, occ superposed, 1mm, globose, soon elongating revealing young reddish toothed lvs; scales and structure obscure. Twigs mod slender (1.5-3mm diam), red- to grey-brown, minutely crisped-hairy to (±) hairless, round; lenticels absent; bark soon <u>splitting esp in 2nd yr</u>, flaking revealing paler underbark; pith c½ diam, <u>green</u>, round, soon fragmenting. Lf scars v raised, half-elliptical; bundle scar 1, short arc, often obscure. Interpetiolar stipules often present, occ resembling an interpetiolar ridge. Arching or not. Early bursting. ❶❷❸. PL 13...*Fuchsia* **Fuchsia magellanica**
Terminal bud (if present) <1mm. Lateral buds superposed but the lower hidden by lf scar, 1mm, globose-ovoid, naked (occ appearing like 1(2) prs obscure scales), <u>dark purple</u>, brown-hairy. Twigs mod slender (2-3mm diam), pale grey, minutely white or buff septate-hairy to ± hairless, round to weakly 4-angled; lenticels raised, same colour as twig, raised; inner bark <u>fetid</u>; pith ⅔-¾ diam, white. Lf scars rarely 3-whorled, weakly raised, ± circular, notched at top; bundle scars 7-9 fused in 1 U-shape, occ 2 rib-bundles. Stipule scars absent. PL 9
..............................*Farges' Harlequin Glorybower* **Clerodendrum trichotomum** var **fargesii**
Terminal bud 3-5mm, naked (young lvs like two hands clasped in prayer), densely (buff-) grey-hairy, with 1 pr collateral buds. Lateral buds spreading, 3mm. Twigs mod (3-6mm diam), grey to brown, white- or buff-hairy to ± hairless, round to obscurely 4-angled; lenticels low, oval, white; pith ½ diam, white, round. Lf scar not raised, heart-to crescent-shaped, large, ≥ bud width, pale; bundle scars 3, usu multiplied into 3 groups, lowest v protruding. Stipule scars absent. Bark smooth, grey, occ v shallow fissures. Tree, often small; trunk short; crown broad. Also known as the 'Bee-bee Tree'. PL 35...*Korean Evodia* **Tetradium daniellii**
Terminal bud 5-15mm, naked, stellate-hairy, <u>short-stalked to 2(6)mm</u>. Lateral buds similar, with (0)1-2 <u>superposed</u> buds. Twigs slender (2-3mm diam), grey; pith ¾ diam, white, round. Lf scars not raised, ± circular; bundle scar 1. PL 7..(see **BE**) *Beautyberry* **Callicarpa bodinieri** var **giraldii**
■Bud scale 1 (single). Shrub..*(Salix purpurea)* <u>Go to</u> **SAL B**
■Bud scales 1 pr (1 scale split into 2 in *Cercidiphyllum*)
Twigs mod stout (4-7mm diam), shiny reddish- or orange-brown, hairless, round; lenticels paler; inner bark yellow-green; pith ⅔ diam, white, round. Buds all lateral, 2-3mm, broadly conical; scales overlapping, reddish-brown, rusty-hairy esp nr tip. Lf scars occ subopp, not raised, U-shaped, almost encircling bud, narrowed between bundle scars, pale; bundle scars 3, often divided. Stipule scars absent. Bark corky. Tree. Late bursting. PL 21
....*Amur Corktree* **Phellodendron amurense**
Twigs mod (3-5mm diam); inner bark odorous. Buds green to reddish. Stipule scars present. Bark striped. Shrub. ❸. PL 34...............................(see **BA**) *Bladdernut* **Staphylea pinnata**
Twigs mod slender (2-3mm diam); inner bark fetid. Buds dark purple. Stipules scars absent. PL 9
...................(see above) *Farges' Harlequin Glorybower* **Clerodendrum trichotomum** var **fargesii**
Twigs slender (1.5mm diam), red- to grey-brown or blackish, hairless, round; lenticels low, oval, small, pale; pith ⅓ diam, white or green, ± round. Branchlets slender, forked, with adpressed woody spurs. End bud pr have 'crab claw' appearance. Buds all lateral, on twig 'shoulders' (often developing into woody spurs), adpressed, 3-6mm, oblong, curved, acute; scale 1, red or brown, split revealing reddish sticky inner scales, appearing like 1 pr valvate scales, hairless, not ciliate. Lf scars raised, crescent-shaped, ± facing upwards on woody spurs, <u>deciduous</u> (easily removed or falling); bundle scars 3. Stipule scars absent. Bark smooth and brown with pale lenticels when young, becoming ± shaggy with long rectangular strips. Tree, usu small, occ multi-trunked at or nr base; trunk(s) often twisted; crown broadly pyramidal. Also known as the 'Caramel Tree' due to the scent of its decaying leaves. PL 8..............................*Katsura* **Cercidiphyllum japonicum**
■Bud scales >1 pr
Buds >5mm
Tree, often tall or medium-sized. Twigs round

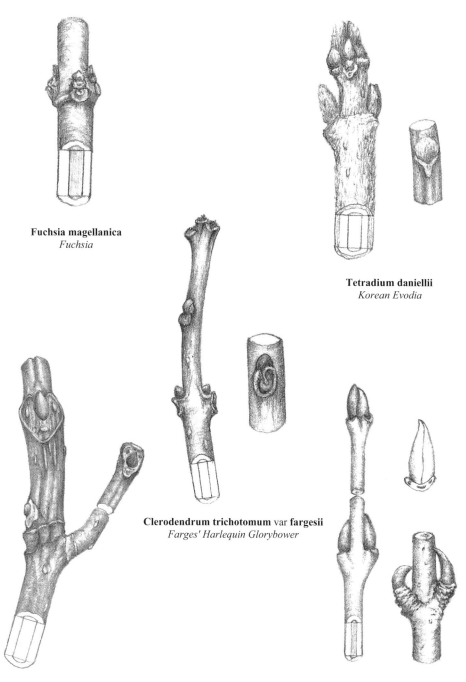

Fuchsia magellanica
Fuchsia

Tetradium daniellii
Korean Evodia

Clerodendrum trichotomum var **fargesii**
Farges' Harlequin Glorybower

Phellodendron amurense
Amur Corktree

Cercidiphyllum japonicum
Katsura

Twigs usu mod stout (3-8mm diam), usu grey, rarely olive, hairless, rigid; lenticels flat, oval, pale; pith c½ diam, white, ± round or lemon-shaped. Terminal bud 5-13mm, dome-shaped (like a 'bishops mitre'); scales 2-3 prs (modified petiole bases), usu with undeveloped lfts at tip, scurfy with minute granules. Lateral buds smaller, occ superposed, 1st pr usu at base of terminal bud, spreading; scales 1 pr. Lf scars broadly crescent-shaped to ± semi-circular, covered by a brown corky layer, equal to bud width, upper margin touching bud; bundle scars 7-15 in shallow arc or involute U-shape, often fused or obscured by cork. Stipule scars absent. Crown round; branches with end of twigs curving up

Buds opp, 5-10(13)mm, obtuse to ± acute; scales black (occ brown in deep shade), hairless. Twigs 4-8mm diam, grey but yellowish in 'Aurea'. Lf scars raised or not. Bark smooth and grey when young, later furrowed with intersecting ridges forming small diamond-shaped pattern. Late bursting. PL 13...*Ash* **Fraxinus excelsior**

Buds opp, 5-13mm, usu obtuse; scales grey, minutely hairy. Twigs (3)4-6mm diam. Lf scars raised or not. Bark remaining smooth pale grey. PL 13...............*Manna Ash* **Fraxinus ornus**

Buds 3(4)-whorled, 5-8mm, obtuse; scales brown, hairless. Twigs 4-5mm diam. Lf scars raised. Bark smooth grey when young. ❶

Bark becoming furrowed with intersecting ridges. Frequent. PL 13
....*Claret Ash* **Fraxinus angustifolia** ssp **oxycarpa**

Bark becoming blocky like 'crocodile-hide'. VR
.........................(not illustrated) *Narrow-leaved Ash* **Fraxinus angustifolia** ssp **angustifolia**

Shrub or small tree. Twigs round to 4-angled (at least nr tip)

Terminal bud usu absent, replaced by pr of end lateral buds. End buds spreading, 5-10mm, broadly ovoid, ± 4-angled, ± acute, slightly sunken behind raised lf scar; scales 3-5 prs, green or turning purplish, obtuse, apiculate, keeled, thick, hairless, glandular-ciliate when young; inner scales with sessile glands. Lateral buds smaller; scales 1-4 prs. Twigs usu mod (2-5mm diam), olive- or grey-brown, hairless; lenticels usu indistinct; pith ½ diam, white, round. Branchlets forked. Lf scars raised, crescent-shaped to semi-circular, ± small, ≤ end bud width, upper margin touching bud, dark, decurrent; bundle scars c7, ± fused into shallow arc or line, occ obscured by corky layer. Bark becoming scaly. PL 34.....................*Lilac* **Syringa vulgaris**

Terminal bud absent, usu replaced by short thorn. Twigs round. ❸❹. PL 26
....(see below) *Buckthorn* **Rhamnus cathartica**

Terminal bud single (but lateral buds often clustered), 2-5mm, often smaller than lateral buds (5-10mm). Twigs 4-angled. *F. suspensa* x *viridissima*. PL 13
....(see below) *Forsythia* **Forsythia** x **intermedia**

Buds usu <5mm

Tree

Twigs slender (1-1.5mm diam). Branchlets with splitting and peeling bark. Bundle scar 1

Twigs reddish-brown, hairless, round, often held in horizontal plane (plagiotropic); bark peeling; pith ≤⅓ diam, green. Branchlet scar above or to side of bud, circular, pale, ± flat, with several vb scars forming ring (often obscure). Terminal bud present. Lateral buds (±) opp, developing below or adjacent to branchlet scar, spreading at 90°, 3-4mm, ovoid, narrowed to base and appearing short-stalked to 1mm; scales 4-8 prs, yellow-brown, keeled, hairless, not ciliate. Lf scars obscure (below bud), not raised, elliptical, pale, weakly decurrent. Stipule scars absent. Bark reddish-brown, fibrous, stringy, peeling in longitudinal strips. Trunk continuous to tree tip, wider and grooved nr base; crown pyramidal. Conifer. ❷.
PL 19...*Dawn Redwood* **Metasequoia glyptostroboides**

Twigs mod to stout (4-10mm diam). Branchlets with bark not splitting. Bundle scars 10-20

Lf scars opp (rarely 3-whorled but not unequal size), not raised, occ slightly sunken, ± circular, ± notched at (hairy) tip, dark; bundle scars in a nearly closed ring (occ obscure or fused), not protruding. Twigs stout (5-8mm diam), dark brown or olive- to grey-brown, minutely (stellate-) hairy at least nr tip, round, ± flat at nodes, brittle, rarely with weak interpetiolar ridge; lenticels low, oval or elongated, pale; inner bark odorous (peanuts); pith

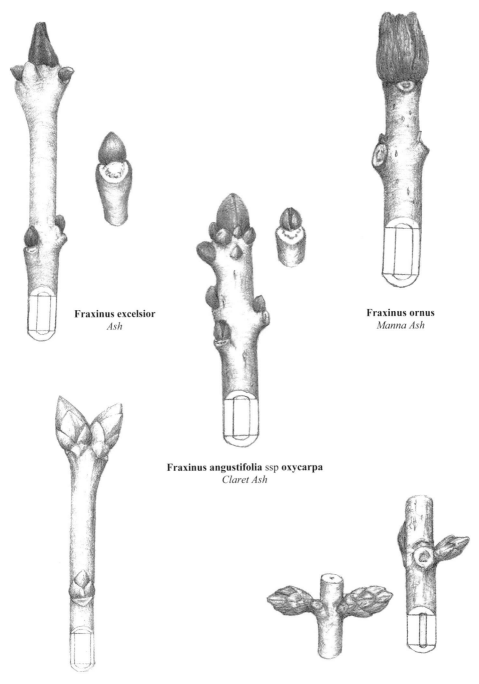

Fraxinus excelsior
Ash

Fraxinus ornus
Manna Ash

Fraxinus angustifolia ssp **oxycarpa**
Claret Ash

Syringa vulgaris
Lilac

Metasequoia glyptostroboides
Dawn Redwood

BB

c½ diam, white, round, weakly chambered (c10 chambers per cm), soon hollow. Buds all lateral, partly sunken in bark, (1)2mm, usu superposed (lower occ obscure), spreading, globose, obtuse; scales 2(3) prs, brown, obtuse, loose, occ hairy, not ciliate. Fl buds c1cm, in erect terminal clusters. Stipule scars absent. Bark smooth, grey-brown, with paler shallow wavy fissures (flame-like pattern), flaky with age. Crown round. Often suckering. Late bursting. PL 21...*Foxglove-tree* **Paulownia tomentosa**
Lf scars (±) 3-whorled, unequal size (2 large and 1 small, and vice-versa at next node), weakly raised, ± circular, sunken with raised rim (crater-like), pale; bundle scars 12-20 in a closed ellipse, lowest scar often projecting. Twigs mod to mod stout (4-9mm diam), orange-brown to brownish-grey, (±) hairless, round, ± flat at nodes, brittle, tips usu winter-killed; lenticels raised, ± round, orange-buff; inner bark odorous (stale coffee); pith ¾ diam, white, round, dense. Buds all lateral, partly sunken in bark, 1-2 x 2-3mm, single, spreading, globose or flattened, obtuse; scales 2-4 prs, (orange-) brown, keeled, often jagged, hairless, occ ciliate, loose. Stipule scars absent. Frs long cylindrical pods, often persisting; seeds long-rectangular, flat, long-ciliate at each end. Late bursting. ❶
  Bark scaly. Fr pods 10mm diam; seeds tapered at each end, c25mm exc cilia. Twigs mod stout (5-9mm diam). Buds usu with (±) adpressed scales. Crown round, wider than other *Catalpa* taxa. Widely planted. PL 7........................*Indian Bean-tree* **Catalpa bignonioides**
  Bark furrowed. R to VR
    Fr pods 7-10mm diam; seeds truncate at each end, c25mm exc cilia. Twigs mod stout (5-8mm diam). Buds usu with (±) adpressed scales. Crown ± narrow. PL 8
    ....*Northern Catalpa* **Catalpa speciosa**
    Fr pods (4)6-7mm diam; seeds ± acute at each end, c14mm exc cilia. Twigs usu mod (4-6mm diam). Crown ± narrow to round. Buds usu with (±) adpressed scales. *C. bignonioides* x *ovata*. PL 7..............................*Hybrid Catalpa* **Catalpa x erubescens**
    Fr pods 3-5mm diam; seeds ± rounded at each end, c6mm exc cilia. Twigs usu mod (4-6mm diam). Buds usu with spreading acuminate scales. Crown ± narrow. PL 8
    ....*Chinese Catalpa* **Catalpa ovata**
Low shrub to 0.5(1)m. Twigs ± slender (2-3mm diam). PL 11
....(see **AN**) *Mezereon* **Daphne mezereum**
Shrub 1-3(6)m (or small tree in *Rhamnus cathartica*). Twigs ± slender (1.5-4mm diam)
  Twigs 4-angled (occ weakly so)
    Twigs roughly hairy with minute raised hair bases, mod slender (2-4mm diam), grey-brown, occ ± round; lenticels raised, brown, oval; pith ½ diam, round or angled, white. Buds all lateral, spreading, rarely superposed, 3-5mm, ovoid; scales 3-5 prs, reddish-brown, hairy esp nr tip, occ notched. Fl buds 5-10mm, club-shaped, swollen; scales 10-12 prs. Lf scars raised, semi-circular to broadly crescent-shaped; bundle scar 1, usu 2 minute scars in upper corners (rib-bundles). Stipule scars absent. Fls during winter. PL 8
    ....*Wintersweet* **Chimonanthus praecox**
    Twigs hairless, mod slender (2-3mm diam), yellow- to olive-brown, occ green or purplish, brittle; lenticels raised, small, oval pith c½ diam, chambered (c30 chambers per cm), later hollow. Branchlets round. Terminal bud single, 2-5mm, often smaller than lateral buds, ovoid to spindle-shaped. Lateral buds single or with 1-3 collateral buds, occ 1 superposed bud, spreading, 5-10mm (fl buds nr max size), ovoid to spindle-shaped, ± 4-angled, acute; scales 3-6(10) prs, yellow-brown (inner parts green), papery, acute to obtuse, keeled, hairless, ciliate. Lf scars raised, triangular to semi-circular, equal to bud width, whitish, decurrent; bundle scar a short protruding horizontal line nr top of lf scar, occ 2 minute scars in upper corners (rib-bundles). Stipule scars absent. Bark pale brown, with raised round lenticels developing into shallow splits. Arching shrub, usu suckering. Fls late winter. *F. suspensa* x *viridissima*. PL 13..............................*Forsythia* **Forsythia x intermedia**

Paulownia tomentosa
Foxglove-tree

Catalpa bignonioides
Indian Bean-tree

Catalpa speciosa
Northern Catalpa

Catalpa x erubescens
Hybrid Catalpa

Catalpa ovata
Chinese Catalpa

Chimonanthus praecox
Wintersweet

Forsythia x intermedia
Forsythia

Twigs round (*Hippophae rhamnoides* and *Lonicera tatarica* rarely key out here)

Twigs pale olive-brown, slender (1.5-3mm diam); bark finely fissured; lenticels low, round, pale; pith <½ diam, white, round. Terminal bud to 5mm. Lateral buds occ superposed, 1-3mm, obtuse; scales 2-4 prs, green to dark purple-brown, weakly keeled, hairless, ciliate. Lf scars v raised, semi-circular to oval, small, upper margin touching bud. Bundle scar 1, flat arc. Semi-evergreen (lvs falling late winter). ❶

Bud scales obtuse (tips visibly unbroken), often dark purple-brown. Buds adpressed to spreading. Twigs usu with <u>minute hairs <0.1mm</u>, often becoming hairless, often 3-4-whorled at lower nodes; internodes often >5cm; lenticels often abundant. Lf scars often < bud width. PL 16...*Wild Privet* **Ligustrum vulgare**

Bud scales (±) acute or tips broken off, often green with brown tips. Buds spreading. Twigs <u>hairless</u>, rarely 3-whorled at lower nodes; internodes often ≤5cm; lenticels few or absent. Lf scars ± equal to bud width. PL 16.........................*Garden Privet* **Ligustrum ovalifolium**

Twigs dark brown, often with grey skin, mod slender (2-3mm diam), minutely hairy to hairless, rigid, (±) unlined; lenticels same colour as twig (more obvious on branchlets) or absent; inner bark odorous; pith ⅓-½ diam, white, ± round. Branchlets often at 90°, often subopp, with woody spurs. Thorns 3-8mm. Terminal bud usu absent, replaced by thorn, if present occ with narrow acute scales. Lateral buds often subopp, adpressed, (2)4-6mm, ovoid-conical, acute, talon-like; scales 5-7, <u>alt</u>, dark or blackish-brown, often with paler brown margins, obtuse, weakly keeled, hairless, ciliate, occ erose. Lf scars raised, oval, small, < bud width; bundle scars 3, minute, occ obscure or ± fused. Stipule scars oval, <u>small</u>, adjacent to top of lf scar; stipules rarely persisting, linear. Bark smooth, shiny purplish-brown, with horizontal lenticels, later dark grey-black, scaly. Late bursting. ❸❹. PL 26 ....*Buckthorn* **Rhamnus cathartica**

Ligustrum vulgare
Wild Privet

Ligustrum ovalifolium
Garden Privet

Rhamnus cathartica
Buckthorn

BC

Group BC – *Climber. Twigs with interpetiolar ridge; lenticels absent. Stipule scars absent. (Parthenocissus spp may key out here in error if tendril scar mistaken for opp lf scars, as will Jasminum spp if presence of interpetiolar ridge assumed)*

■Twigs (or branchlets) climbing using adventitious aerial roots. Lf scars distinct
  Bundle scar 1 (many ± fused in ring or U-shape)
    Twig mod stout (6-7mm diam), pale brown, hairless, with long septate-hairy interpetiolar ridge (hairs soon withering), round; aerial roots in 2 lines below nodes; pith c½ diam, white, round. Lf scars usu circular, occ shield-shaped to semi-circular, sunken. Buds 2-3mm; scales 2-3 prs, pale brown, hairless. Bark pale brown, eventually scaly. PL 7.. *Trumpet-vine* **Campsis radicans**
  Bundle scars 5
    Twigs mod (3-5mm diam), reddish- to orange-brown, round; aerial roots in 1-9 lines along internodes; pith ½ diam, green, round. Branchlets with bark splitting and peeling, occ with woody spurs. Terminal bud 8-15(20)mm, ± on ≤1mm purple stalk, occ with minute lateral bud at base, conical-ovoid, acute; scales 1 pr, usu overlapping, green to reddish, toothed nr apiculate tip, hairless, occ ciliate, with stomata. Lateral buds adpressed to spreading, short-stalked to 2mm, 2-8mm, ovoid, obtuse; scales 1 pr, often parted, apiculate. Lf scars crescent-shaped, >> lateral bud width (but ± equal to terminal bud width), ± meeting around twig. PL 15 ....*Climbing Hydrangea* **Hydrangea petiolaris**
■Twigs clockwise-twining around support. Lf scars mostly hidden by dried petiole base; bundle scars 3, often obscure
  Twigs slender (2mm diam), ± round, with persistent bud scale remnants at join with branchlet; pith ½-⅔ diam, white to brown, soon hollow. Older branchlets usu with bark finely peeling into fibres. Terminal bud often absent. Lateral buds often superposed, spreading at c60°; scales 2-5 prs, loose. Lf scars raised with lower margin projecting out, crescent-shaped. Early bursting
    Twigs without lf remnants encircling twig, pale grey or whitish- or yellowish-brown, occ with long (glandular-) hairs. Buds 1-15mm, ovoid, 4-angled, rapidly elongating late winter to spindle-shape revealing young (purple-) green lvs; outer scales 2-4 prs, brown, papery, narrowly triangular, acute, keeled, hairless, ciliate or not; inner scales (young lvs) 2-5 prs, (purple-) green. PL 17..*Honeysuckle* **Lonicera periclymenum**
    Twigs with uppermost pr(s) of lf remnants encircling twig, yellow-brown, long-hairy to hairless. Buds 3-4mm, same colour as twig or green-purple when bursting; scales 3-4(5) prs. *L. caprifolium* x *etrusca*. PL 17..*Garden Honeysuckle* **Lonicera x italica**
■Twigs anticlockwise-twining around support. Lf scars distinct; bundle scar 1
  Twigs mod (3-4mm diam), brown, hairless, round; pith soon hollow; latex white. Buds solitary, small, nearly concealed by lf scars. Lf scars v raised (peg-like), circular; bundle scar crescent-shaped. Stipule scars absent......................................(not illustrated) *Silk-vine* **Periploca graeca**
■Twigs twining using prehensile spiralling petiolules (lft stalks). Lf scars not formed (petioles not abscising, removed only by weathering or tearing); bundle scars not visible
  Twigs slender to mod (2-4mm diam), dark reddish-brown, hairless to sparsely silky-hairy nr tip, brittle, swollen at nodes; pith ½-¾ diam, white, round, occ developing small hollow. Branchlets pale grey; bark often peeling in longitudinal strips. Buds all lateral, spreading at 45-90°; scales dark purplish-brown to grey-brown, ± silky-hairy (esp nr tip). Petioles persistent, at 90° to twig
    Twigs round, not ridged (but striate). Buds 4-12mm, ovoid-conical, acute; scales 3-4 prs, v acute. PL 9..*Himalayan Clematis* **Clematis montana**
    Twigs 6-ridged. Buds 3-4mm, ovoid, obtuse; scales 4-8 prs, obtuse to acute, revealing silky-hairy young green lvs when bursting. PL 9................................*Traveller's-joy* **Clematis vitalba**
    Twigs 6-10-ridged...................(not illustrated) *Oriental Clematis* **Clematis tibetana** ssp **vernayi**
    Twigs (10)12-ridged............................(not illustrated) *Orange-peel Clematis* **Clematis tangutica**
    Twigs 14-ridged..(not illustrated) *Virgin's Clematis* **Clematis flammula**

Campsis radicans
Trumpet-vine

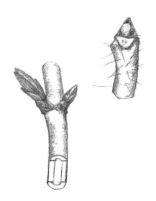

Lonicera periclymenum
Honeysuckle

Lonicera x **italica**
Garden Honeysuckle

Hydrangea petiolaris
Climbing Hydrangea

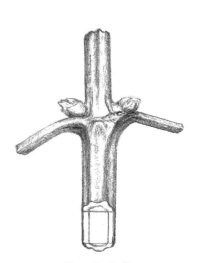

Clematis vitalba
Traveller's-joy

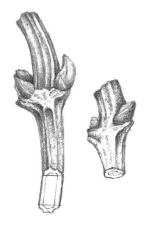

Clematis montana
Himalayan Clematis

Group BD – *Buds not visible, all lateral. Twigs with interpetiolar ridge. Stipule scars absent. Shrub.*
(Catalpa and Paulownia may key out here if all buds ill-developed)

■Buds usu 3-whorled, rarely opp. Bundle scar 1, often obscure

Bud scales and structure obscure. Twigs mod slender (1.5-3mm diam), red- to grey-brown, minutely crisped-hairy to (±) hairless; lenticels absent; bark soon <u>splitting esp in 2nd yr</u>, flaking; pith c½ diam, <u>green</u>, round. Lf scars v raised. Interpetiolar stipules often present, occ resembling an interpetiolar ridge. PL 13..(see **BB**) *Fuchsia* **Fuchsia magellanica**

■Buds opp, v rarely 3-whorled. Bundle scars 3

Buds all lateral, partly or completely concealed below whitish membrane covering lf scars, later rupturing revealing 1(2) prs of green ± valvate scales. Twigs reddish- or purplish-brown, ± lined to weakly 6-angled, brittle, with persistent bud scale remnants at join with branchlet; lenticels absent; bark <u>flaking</u>, revealing white underbark; pith ⅔ diam, white, ± round. Lf scars raised, broadly crescent-shaped to semi-circular, covered by a whitish membrane ruptured by the underlying bud (forming a triangular peak in centre of scar). Arching. Several closely related spp (and hybrids) commonly grown

Twigs hairless, mod slender (1.5-3mm diam). PL 21......*Mock-orange* **Philadelphus coronarius**

Twigs minutely hairy, v slender (0.8-2mm diam). PL 21
....*Littleleaf Mock-orange* **Philadelphus microphyllus**

Philadelphus coronarius
Mock-orange

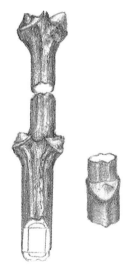

Philadelphus microphyllus
Littleleaf Mock-orange

Group BE – *Buds naked or with 1 pr scales.* ❶ *Twigs pruinose with odorous inner bark (2 spp).*
❷ *Buds with long-ciliate papery sheath ('hula skirt').* ❸ *Stipule scars present*

■Twigs with hairs simple or absent

Tree. Twigs round; pith ≥½ diam. Lf scars not raised, narrowly crescent- (or V-) shaped, ± narrowed between bundle scars; bundle scars 3, often multiplied to 5, 7 or 9 (in 3 groups)

Buds sessile or on short stalk 0-1mm. Pith white. Bark without distinct 'snake bark' pattern

Terminal bud white-hairy (at least tuft at tip). Lf scars (±) meeting around twig and extending upwards into an acute point (^)

Twigs mod (3-5mm diam), <u>green</u> to reddish-brown, <u>v pruinose</u>, minutely hairy to hairless, brittle; lenticels low, round to oval, buff; inner bark <u>odorous</u>. Terminal bud 3-8mm, single but flanked by uppermost pr(s) of lateral buds, short-stalked to 1mm, narrowly ovoid to ± globose, ± acute to obtuse; scales 1-2 prs, green to (reddish-) purple, silky-hairy, apiculate or with small scar at tip. Lateral buds short-stalked to 1mm, adpressed, 1-5mm, ovoid-globose, obtuse; scales 1(2) prs. Lf scars narrowly V-shaped, upper margin fringed with short orange-red papillae, occ white hair-fringed. Bark smooth, pale grey-brown, later with intersecting ridges. Trunk short; crown wide; lower branches stout, spreading, with twigs upturned at tips. ❶. PL 1..*Ashleaf Maple* **Acer negundo**

Terminal bud hairless. Lf scars not meeting around twig

Twigs with fetid inner bark, mod (3-4mm diam). Terminal bud usu slightly kinked, 3-5mm; scales (1)2-4 prs, red, buff-ciliate. Lateral fl buds clustered, globose. PL 2
....(see **BH**) *Silver Maple* **Acer saccharinum**

Twigs with inner bark odourless. Terminal bud (if present) not kinked

Twigs mod (3-4mm diam). Terminal bud 3-5mm; scales (1)2-4 prs, red, buff-ciliate. Lateral fl buds clustered, globose. PL 2 ....(see **BH**) *Red Maple* **Acer rubrum**

Twigs slender (1-2mm diam), shiny red to green-brown (often green on lower side), occ <u>pruinose</u>, rarely with occ long hairs; lenticels few or absent, round. End buds 2-4mm, usu paired, like a 'deer-hoof', sessile, ovoid-conical, acute, with long-ciliate papery sheath ('hula skirt') at base (occ ± covering bud); scales 1-2 prs, purple-red, ± acute, usu ciliate. Lateral buds spreading. Bark smooth, greenish-grey to pale brown, *Carpinus*-like. Small tree. ❷. PL 1..*Japanese Maple* **Acer palmatum**

Buds on 2-7mm stalk (terminal bud single or paired), acute; scales 1 pr, green when young or on shaded side, hairless, not ciliate. Pith usu brown (esp in branchlets). Bark smooth, green, striped with white vertical 'snake bark' pattern. Twigs slender to mod (2-4mm diam), hairless, round, often flexible; lenticels often absent. Lf scars not meeting around twig, usu sparsely red-brown hair-fringed. Branchlets occ with short shoots

Buds usu >10mm (exc stalk), pruinose, oblong-ovoid. Twigs pruinose

Buds (7)10-13mm on 2-3mm stalk, purple-red (beneath pruinose bloom). Twigs green or red on upper side. Branchlets greenish. Lvs distinctly 3-lobed. Frs with wings at obtuse angle.
PL 2..*Grey-budded Snakebark Maple* **Acer rufinerve**

Buds 5-10mm (exc stalk), pruinose or not, oblong. Twigs pruinose or not

Buds soon shiny <u>bright</u> red, not pruinose, on 2-5mm stalk. Twigs <u>reddish</u>, occ green below, not pruinose. Branchlets <u>orange to yellow</u>. Bark with <u>wart-like</u> lenticels. Lvs distinctly 3-lobed. Frs with curved wings. PL 2........*Moosewood* **Acer pensylvanicum 'Erythrocladum'**

Buds not shiny bright red, not or sparsely pruinose. Branchlets greenish

Buds shiny red, not pruinose (exc rarely on stalk), on 2-5mm stalk. Twigs dull green to red-purple, usu green below, <u>rarely</u> sparsely pruinose. Bark occ reddish-striped in some cultivars. Lvs <u>not or hardly lobed</u>. Frs with ± horizontal wings. Frequently planted. PL 1
....*Père David's Maple* **Acer davidii**

Buds dull purple (rarely reddish), <u>often</u> sparsely pruinose, on 2-7mm stalk. Twig shiny green to purplish, <u>often</u> sparsely pruinose. Lvs distinctly 3(5)-lobed. Frs with wings ± horizontal or at obtuse angle. PL 1............................*Red Snakebark Maple* **Acer capillipes**

Acer negundo
Ashleaf Maple

Acer palmatum
Japanese Maple

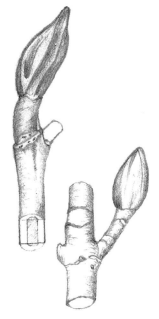

Acer rufinerve
Grey-budded Snakebark Maple

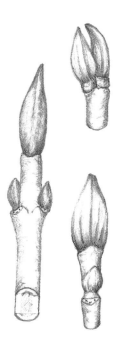

Acer capillipes
Red Snakebark Maple

Acer pensylvanicum
'Erythrocladum'
Moosewood

Acer davidii
Père David's Maple

BE

Shrub

Twigs mod stout (5-10mm diam)

Twigs hairless, reddish-brown, round; lenticels absent; bark occ flaking; pith ≥¾ diam, white, round. Terminal bud 1.5-2cm, naked (pr of young plicate lvs), conical, acute, (±) sessile, green to purple, hairless, often with minute globose lateral bud at base. Lateral buds sessile or v short-stalked, 3-10mm, ovoid, obtuse; scales 1 pr. Lf scars not raised, broadly triangular to shield-shaped or elliptical, large, >> lateral bud width (often ± equal to terminal bud width), rarely meeting around twig; bundle scars 3, nr lower margin, protruding. Bark pale brown, often flaking. Shrub to 1.2m. PL 14...................................Hydrangea **Hydrangea macrophylla**

Twigs densely roughly adpressed-hairy (strigose), reddish-brown, 4-angled; bark splitting; lenticels absent; pith ¾ diam, orange-brown, 4-5-angled. Terminal bud 0.5-1cm, naked (several prs of young lvs), dome-shaped, acute, sessile, pale yellow-grey to brown, densely brown-hairy. Lateral buds v small or absent, naked. Lf scars not raised, broadly triangular, large, on opp twig angles, >> lateral bud width, not meeting around twig; bundle scars 5(7), nr lower margin, protruding. Shrub to 1.5m. PL 14..Rough-leaved Hydrangea **Hydrangea aspera**

Twigs usu mod (3-6mm diam) (Lonicera involucrata keys out here if terminal bud overlooked)

Pith absent (v hollow). Twigs 3-6mm diam, green, hairless, round. Bundle scars 3. PL 16 ....(see **BF**) Himalayan Honeysuckle **Leycesteria formosa**

Pith ≥½ diam, round, white. Twigs 3-5mm diam, green to purplish, occ pruinose, hairless, round; inner bark odorous. Bundle scars 3, 5 or 7. Occ ❶, ❸. PL 34 ....(see **BA**) Bladdernut **Staphylea pinnata**

Pith ½ diam, 6-angled, white. Twigs 3-5mm diam, grey, occ purplish-brown, hairless, 6-angled, flexible; lenticels raised, round, small, same colour as twig; inner bark weakly odorous. Branchlets round, striped grey and reddish-brown. Terminal bud usu absent (replaced by pr of lateral buds), usu only present on vertical basal shoots, to 8mm, narrowly ellipsoid. Lateral buds ± adpressed, rarely spreading, 5-8(10)mm, short-stalked (≤1mm), lanceoloid to ovoid-globose, usu bluntly 4-angled, ± acute; scale apparently 1 (2 fused scales), shiny red-green, hairless, occ split at tip revealing green sticky fused inner scales with 3-lobed tip. Fl buds more globose than lf buds. Lf scars not raised, narrowly crescent- or V-shaped, narrowed between bundle scars, > bud width; bundle scars 3, nr upper margin, protruding. Bark smooth, grey. Arching shrub to 3(4)m, occ vertical shoots from horizontal branches nr ground, occ adventitious roots. PL 37...Guelder-rose **Viburnum opulus**

Twigs slender (<3mm diam)

Twigs with 2 opp lines, hairless; pith orange-brown. Bundle scar 1 (involute U-shaped), often obscure. PL 15.......................................(see **BI**) Tutsan **Hypericum androsaemum**

Twigs unlined, minutely hairy; pith green. Bundle scar 1, obscure (actually 3 but obscured by shrivelled lf scar or corky growth so only middle scar occ visible). S. microphyllus x orbiculatus. PL 34..(see **BI**) Hybrid Coralberry **Symphoricarpos x chenaultii**

Twigs unlined, minutely hairy; pith white. Bundle scars 3. PL 16 ....(see **BI**) Beautybush **Kolkwitzia amabilis**

Twigs unlined, hairless, pale brown; pith white. Bundle scars 3. Buds spreading, 3-5mm, conical; scales 2, same colour as twig, acuminate. Semi-evergreen. Early bursting ....Fragrant Honeysuckle **Lonicera fragrantissima**

■Twigs or buds with stellate hairs; inner bark odourless. Shrub

Twigs mod (3-5(6)mm diam), yellow- to orange-brown, scurfy-hairy with cream-coloured stellate hairs, weakly 6-angled, flexible; lenticels low, oval, brown, usu obscured by hairs; pith ⅔ diam, white, ± round. Branchlets pale grey-brown, round, fissured. Terminal bud present as ± globose fl bud or elongated lf buds; lf buds in prs, naked (young plicate lvs), with 2 minute scales at base soon falling, 10-20mm, narrowly oblong, often stalked to 15mm, pale yellow-green to grey, densely stellate-hairy with cream-coloured hairs; fl bud to 10mm diam, globose to crown-shaped, stalked to 15mm, woolly stellate-hairy, at least partly covered by bracts. Lateral buds similar to terminal lf buds, adpressed (occ spreading esp if long-stalked), 8-15mm, on 1-4(10)mm stalk. Lf scars not raised, V-shaped, weakly narrowed between bundle scars, > bud width; bundle scars 3, protruding. Bark scaly. Erect, to 3m, lower branches occ rooting. PL 37.......Wayfaring-tree **Viburnum lantana**

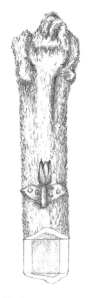

Hydrangea aspera
Rough-leaved Hydrangea

Hydrangea macrophylla
Hydrangea

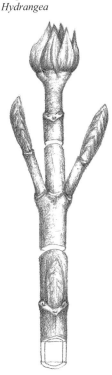

Viburnum opulus
Guelder-rose

Lonicera fragrantissima
Fragrant Honeysuckle

Viburnum lantana
Wayfaring-tree

Twigs slender (2-3mm diam), grey, stellate-hairy but soon hairless and rough with minute raised hair bases, often with minute sessile yellow glands, round or obscurely 4-angled, rigid; lenticels raised, elongate, pale; pith ¾ diam, white, round. Terminal bud stalked to 3(6)mm, naked, 5-15mm, oblong, stellate-hairy with cream-coloured hairs. Lateral buds similar, with (0)1-2 superposed buds, (±) spreading to adpressed, 4-10mm. Lf scars occ subopp or without interpetiolar ridge, not raised, ± circular, notched at top, pale; bundle scar 1, U-shaped. Frs small purple berries. Arching. PL 7....................................*Beautyberry* **Callicarpa bodinieri** var **giraldii**
∎Twigs or buds with medifixed hairs (hairs adpressed and attached in centre), occ sparse. Twigs mod slender (2-4mm diam), flexible; inner bark weakly odorous; pith white. Terminal bud usu present, often appearing naked; scales 1 pr, rarely more prs exposed. Lateral lf buds rarely superposed; scales 1 pr. Lf scars late-deciduous; initially v raised (persistent petiole base), small and < bud width; later falling (esp nr base of twig), low and >> bud width; bundle scars 3

Twigs square, 2-3mm diam, green or purplish, medifixed-hairy; lenticels v sparse or absent, low, oval, small, brown; pith ½ diam, ± round. Terminal bud either fl bud (globose) or lf bud (flattened-conical). Terminal fl bud stalked to 4mm, 4-7mm, globose, apiculate; scales 1 pr, green to purplish, medifixed-hairy. Lateral lf buds sessile, spreading at narrow angle, (3)4-8mm, flattened-conical, acute, greenish to dark brown, brown medifixed-hairy, keeled. Bark flaking in squarish curled scales, grey-brown. Shrub or small tree. PL 9.......................*Cornelian-cherry* **Cornus mas**

Twigs ± round to ± 6-angled, occ weakly ridged below lf scars, sparsely medifixed-hairy, interpetiolar ridge often weak to absent; pith ⅔ diam, obscurely 6-angled to ± round. All buds appearing naked; scales lf-like, faintly plicate, dark brown medifixed-hairy. Terminal bud stalked to 3mm, 5-8mm, ± onion-shaped to lanceoloid, flattened, surrounded by 1 pr narrow outer scales. Lateral lf buds ± stalked to 2mm, adpressed, (3)4-8mm, flattened-lanceoloid, acute. Bark smooth, later scaly. Shrub, suckering

Twigs dark red all around, 3-4mm diam; lenticels few, small, pale. Branchlets red. Widely planted. PL 9..*Red-osier Dogwood* **Cornus sericea**

Twigs red on sunlit side and usu green below, occ red all round, 2-3mm diam; lenticels usu absent until 2nd yr. Branchlets greyish. Often on calc soils. PL 9..*Dogwood* **Cornus sanguinea**

Twigs yellow-orange (brighter on sunlit side), minutely red-dotted, 2-3mm diam; lenticels usu absent. Branchlets yellow-orange, becoming greyish. Occ planted. PL 9

....*Orange-twig Dogwood* **Cornus sanguinea 'Midwinter Fire'**

Twigs yellow-green, 3-4mm diam; lenticels few, small, dark. Branchlets greyish. Often planted. PL 10..*Golden-twig Dogwood* **Cornus sericea 'Flaviramea'**

Group BF – *Twigs green, v hollow (>>¾ diam)*

∎Twigs mod to mod stout (3-6mm diam), occ pruinose, hairless, round, occ striate, with protruding narrow interpetiolar ridge (occ hair-fringed), with stomata, with persistent bud scale remnants at join with branchlet; lenticels absent; pith absent. Buds 2-6mm, ovoid-conical but soon elongating revealing young green lvs, occ slightly stalked; scales 1-2 prs, green (but smaller outermost pr brown), acuminate, fused at base, usu persistent as bud bursts. Lf scars v raised on persistent purplish petiole bases, crescent-shaped, shrivelled; bundle scars 3, indistinct. Stipule scars absent. Arching shrub. Early bursting. PL 16
....*Himalayan Honeysuckle* **Leycesteria formosa**

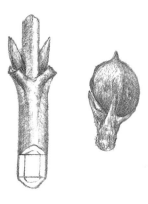

Cornus mas
Cornelian-cherry

Callicarpa bodinieri var **giraldii**
Beautyberry

Cornus sericea
Red-osier Dogwood

Cornus sanguinea
Dogwood

Leycesteria formosa
Himalayan Honeysuckle

Group BG – Aesculus. *End bud(s) mostly >12mm, single (terminal bud) or paired (lateral buds), ± ovoid, ± 4-angled; scales 2-8 prs, obtuse (acute in* A. parviflora*), usu apiculate, hairless; lowest pr scales small, usu keeled. Lateral buds usu spreading, small or absent nr twig base; scales fewer. Twigs mod stout, usu pale (grey-) brown, round, usu with interpetiolar ridge; lenticels low, ± round, orange; inner bark at least weakly fetid (strong in* A. glabra*), bitter-tasting; pith ½-⅔ diam, white, ± round. Branchlets occ with woody spurs. Lf scars not raised, usu semi-circular to shield-shaped, large, occ purplish when fresh, rarely meeting around twig; bundle scars (3)5-7(9), in a U- or V-shape, occ in 3 groups. Stipule scars absent. Bark smooth when young, later usu cracked into flaking scales or plates revealing orange underbark. Tree (shrub in* A. parviflora*); crown round*

■End bud(s) mostly >15mm. Twigs 7-9mm diam. Bundle scars 5-7

Terminal bud usu present, 15-30mm, occ curved, acute; scales 4-5(6) prs, <u>dark reddish-brown</u> (occ greenish), with broad thin margins, <u>often v sticky</u>, occ dry, not keeled (exc lowest 1-2 prs), not ciliate (occ sparsely so on lowest scales). Twigs occ minutely hairy. Trunk often divided into large branches; crown oblong or broadly conical; lower branches sharply curving up and down (like an elephant's trunk - imagination required!), with twigs upswept at tips. Capsule prickly. PL 3
....*Horse-chestnut* **Aesculus hippocastanum**

Terminal bud usu present, similar to *A. hippocastanum*; scales <u>(5)6-7 prs</u>. Twigs usu minutely hairy. Bark remaining <u>smooth</u>. Lower branches not sharply curving. Capsule warty. PL 4
....*Japanese Horse-chestnut* **Aesculus turbinata**

Terminal bud often absent. End buds in prs (at least on weaker shoots), similar to *A. hippocastanum*, 15-20(22)mm; scales 4-5 prs, greenish-brown, with broad thin margins, dry or slightly sticky. Twigs usu hairless. Bark similar to *A. hippocastanum*. Trunk often grafted; lower branches not curving. Capsule weakly prickly. Hybrid origin from A. *hippocastanum* x *pavia*. PL 3
....*Red Horse-chestnut* **Aesculus carnea**

■End bud(s) mostly <15mm

Buds sticky, shiny (reddish-) green, obtuse; scales 3-4(5) prs

End bud(s) occ paired, 8-15mm; scales minutely orange resin-dotted (x20), not or weakly keeled, not ciliate, the lower brown, occ apiculate. Twigs 6-10mm diam. Bundle scars (3)5(7). Branches drooping. Capsule smooth. PL 3...................*Indian Horse-chestnut* **Aesculus indica**

Buds not sticky

Buds whitish-grey, ± obtuse; scales 2 prs. Shrub, suckering, lower branches occ rooting

End bud(s) (6)10-15mm; scales covered in dry scurfy grey-white resin granules (centre of each granule red-black), greenish beneath scurf, not or weakly keeled, acute, outer pr apiculate, not ciliate. Lateral buds <u>adpressed</u>. Twigs <u>pale grey</u>, 6-9mm diam. Bundle scars 3(5). Bark smooth, grey. Capsule smooth. PL 3......*Bottlebrush Buckeye* **Aesculus parviflora**

Buds dull orange-brown (to greyish), acute; scales 4-8 prs

Large tree. Twigs 5-10mm diam. End bud(s) single or paired, 10-17mm; scales <u>(5)6 prs, not keeled</u> (exc small lowest 1-2 prs) but with <u>several obscure striations nr middle not forming keel but converging in apiculus</u>, occ grey patches, with darker margins, ciliate. Bundle scars in 3 groups of 1-2. Capsule smooth. PL 3...............................*Yellow Buckeye* **Aesculus flava**

Large tree. Twigs 5-10mm diam; inner bark <u>strongly</u> fetid. End bud(s) single or paired (often unequal), 10-15mm, with 'jagged' appearance; scales <u>8 prs</u>, striate with <u>middle striation raised forming a strong keel</u> (and occ long-apiculate, otherwise obtuse), rarely with horizontal wrinkles, tips spreading, with darker margins, ciliate or not. Bundle scars in 3 groups of 1-2. Bark later furrowed into long plates (unlike other *Aesculus*). Capsule weakly prickly. PL 3
....*Ohio Buckeye* **Aesculus glabra**

Small tree, occ multi-trunked. Twigs 5-7mm diam. End buds often paired, (6)10-15mm, dull orange-brown, occ greyish; scales <u>4-5 prs</u>, darker towards margins, <u>not keeled or striate</u>, obtuse, apiculate, minutely ciliate. Bundle scars (5)7. Capsule smooth. PL 3
....*Red Buckeye* **Aesculus pavia**

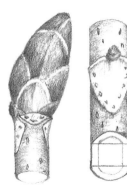

Aesculus hippocastanum
Horse-chestnut

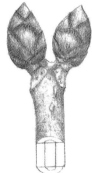

Aesculus carnea
Red Horse-chestnut

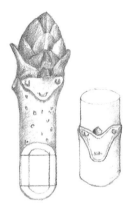

Aesculus indica
Indian Horse-chestnut

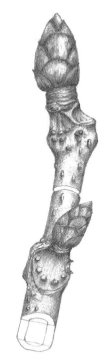

Aesculus turbinata
Japanese Horse-chestnut

Aesculus parviflora
Bottlebrush Buckeye

Aesculus flava
Yellow Buckeye

Aesculus glabra
Ohio Buckeye

Aesculus pavia
Red Buckeye

BH

Group BH – Acer. *End bud(s) ≤12mm, single (terminal bud) or paired (lateral buds), (+) ovoid, ±
4-angled; scales (1)2-8 prs, at least lower apiculate and usu weakly keeled. Lateral buds occ
short-stalked. Twigs usu round; lenticels flat or low, usu oval, pale; pith ≥½ diam, white (unless
stated), round. Lf scars not raised (or weakly so due to swollen nodes), usu narrowly crescent-
shaped, usu > bud width, ± narrowed between bundle scars, widely separated to almost meeting
around twig; bundle scars 3, often multiplied to 5, 7 or 9 (in 3 groups). Stipule scars absent. Tree;
crown ± round. (Aesculus pavia and A. parviflora rarely key out here if buds <12mm).* ❶ *Twigs
green, pruinose, with odorous inner bark.* ❷ *Suckering (2 entries).* ❸ *Twigs with white latex (3
spp; 5 entries).* ❹ *Buds with long-ciliate papery sheath ('hula skirt') and usu paired at tip (like a
deer's hoof) (2 spp).* ❺ *Branchlets with corky wings (2 entries)*

■Buds green with dark-margined scales, or green with reddish tints

    Buds hairy at least at tip (*A. campestre* with unseasoned buds keys out here)

        Twigs green to reddish-brown, often pruinose; inner bark odorous. ❶. PL 1

        ....(see **BE**) *Ashleaf Maple* **Acer negundo**

    Buds hairless (*A. platanoides* with unseasoned buds keys out here)

        Twigs green to reddish. ❷❸. PL 1...........(see below) *Cappadocian Maple* **Acer cappadocicum**

        Twigs grey (to olive-brown), mod stout (4-7mm diam). Branchlets with bark not fissured.
Terminal bud single or paired, usu flanked by two small adpressed lateral buds, 5-10mm, usu
acute; scales 3(4) prs, shiny green, occ reddish-green, white- or buff-ciliate; inner scales white-
woolly. Lateral buds usu spreading, smaller. Lf scars broadly crescent-shaped. Bark smooth,
grey, later flaking in square scales revealing pale or orange underbark. Late bursting (variable).
PL 2...*Sycamore* **Acer pseudoplatanus**

■Buds reddish or purple

    Buds with long-ciliate papery sheath ('hula skirt') at base

        Buds hairless, 2-4mm. ❹ PL 1.................................(see **BE**) *Japanese Maple* **Acer palmatum**

        Buds with silky-hairy inner scales visible, 4-8(10)mm, ovoid-conical, acute; scales 2(3) prs, the
outer pr(s) (exc sheaths) purple-red and hairless, not ciliate. Lateral buds spreading. Twigs
slender (1-2mm diam), shiny red to green-brown (often green on lower side); lenticels few or
absent, round. Bark smooth, later scaly. Small tree. ❹. PL 1

        ....*Downy Japanese Maple* **Acer japonicum**

    Buds without papery sheath, hairy at least nr tip

        Twigs (red-) brown, not pruinose. ❸❺. PL 1.................(see below) *Field Maple* **Acer campestre**

        Twigs green to reddish-brown, pruinose. ❶. PL 1............(see **BE**) *Ashleaf Maple* **Acer negundo**

    Buds without papery sheath, hairless (but scales ciliate)

        Twigs with white latex (around outer margin, occ sparse), usu mod stout (3-7mm diam), rigid

            Twigs olive-brown, rarely reddish, mod stout (4-7mm diam). Branchlets streaked with fine irreg
longitudinal diamond-shaped fissures. End bud usu single, flanked by 2 smaller adpressed
collateral buds, appearing turban-shaped, 6-10mm, ovoid, ± obtuse; scales (2)3 prs, shiny
dark red-purple (occ blackish), minutely white- or buff-ciliate; inner scales buff-hairy. Lateral
buds smaller (3-8mm), adpressed, flattened, occ short-stalked; scales 1(2) prs. Bark smooth
when young, grey-brown, occ with long fine ± intersecting fissures, later forming small
diamond-shaped furrows. ❸. PL 2...*Norway Maple* **Acer platanoides**

            Twigs green to shiny reddish or purplish (at least on sunlit side), often pruinose, usu mod
slender to mod (2-5(7)mm diam). Branchlets streaked with ± continuous fine pale longitudinal
lines (weak 'snake-bark' pattern). End bud(s) single or paired, often flanked by 1-2 smaller
collateral buds (but not turban-shaped), 3-7mm, ovoid, ± obtuse; scales (2)3(4) prs, green
turning purplish, minutely white- or buff-ciliate; inner scales buff-hairy. Lateral buds
adpressed or short-stalked and ± spreading, 3mm; scales c2 prs. Bark smooth greenish-grey
with weak 'snake-bark' pattern when young, finally shallowly furrowed. Often suckering. ❷❸.
PL 1...*Cappadocian Maple* **Acer cappadocicum**

        Twigs without latex, slender (3-4mm diam), ± flexible

113

Acer pseudoplatanus
Sycamore

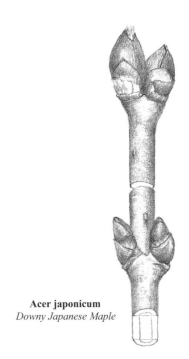

Acer japonicum
Downy Japanese Maple

Acer platanoides
Norway Maple

Acer cappadocicum
Cappadocian Maple

Terminal bud 3-5mm, often 1 pr small collateral buds, broadly ovoid to globose, obtuse; scales (1)2-4 prs, obtuse, red, buff-ciliate. Fl buds lateral, ± 3-6-whorled, spreading, sessile or short-stalked (<1mm), 3-5mm, ± globose; scales 1-2(3) prs, the smaller darker outermost pr v early deciduous. Twigs shiny reddish-brown, occ with grey skin, hairless; pith ⅔ diam, usu white. Bark smooth and pale grey when young. Trunk short. Late bursting. The hybrid of the following two spp, *A.* x *freemanii*, is occ planted and intermediate between its parents

   Terminal bud usu slightly kinked. Twigs occ olive below; inner bark weakly fetid; pith occ buff. Bark with orange fissures, eventually shaggy and flaking in long rectangular strips. Lower branches arching down with twigs upswept at tips ('droop and swoop'). Lvs with terminal lobe narrowed at the base. PL 2..*Silver Maple* **Acer saccharinum**

   Terminal bud rarely kinked. Twigs often redder; inner bark odourless; pith occ pink (esp in branchlets). Bark becoming darker, cracked into plates, occ shaggy but not flaking. Lower branches often horizontal, rarely declining but not drooping and twigs only slightly upturned at tips. Lvs with terminal lobe widest at the base. PL 2....................*Red Maple* **Acer rubrum**

■Buds brown to blackish (occ reddish-brown), usu hairy at least nr tip

   Buds >7mm. Lf scars white hair-fringed along upper margin (often visible on girdle scars on *A. velutinum*) and with additional obscure short buff gland-tipped hairs. Twigs with inner bark weakly odorous, shiny dark brown, hairless

      Bark smooth, grey, not flaking. Twigs mod (3-4(5)mm diam). End bud(s) occ paired, with 0-1 collateral buds, 7-12(15)mm, conical to broadly ovoid, acute; scales 6-8 prs, dark reddish-brown, silky-hairy (hairs occ buff nr scale tips), usu ciliate, often strongly keeled (at least lower prs), ± acute to obtuse. Lateral buds smaller, ± spreading. PL 3...*Velvet Maple* **Acer velutinum**

      Bark smooth, grey, flaking in square plates revealing pink underbark. Twigs mod (3-4mm diam). End bud(s) occ paired, 8-12mm, conical, acute; scales (4)5-6(7) prs, (dark reddish-) brown, (buff) silky-hairy at least nr tip, usu ciliate, striate nr centre and converging at apex (at least lower prs), ± acute to obtuse. Lateral buds smaller, ± adpressed. PL 1
....*Italian Maple* **Acer opalus**

   Buds <7mm. Twigs with inner bark odourless

      Lf scars short buff or white hair-fringed along upper margin

      Twigs slender (2-3mm diam), shiny dark or reddish-brown, hairless; pith white to buff. Terminal bud 4-7(8)mm, single, often with 2 smaller collateral buds, conical to ± broadly spindle-shaped, (±) acute; scales (3)5-7 prs, dark brown or blackish, white- or buff-hairy nr tip (or in centre of scales), usu ciliate, obtuse. Lateral buds adpressed. Lf scars with additional minute orange-red papillae along upper margin. Bark smooth, grey, later deeply furrowed into long thick irreg plates often curved back along 1 edge giving ploughed appearance. Trunk often ± continuous to tree tip; crown ovate; branches ascending

      Buds dark brown. PL 2.................................*Sugar Maple* **Acer saccharum** spp **saccharum**

      Buds blackish.............................(not illustrated) *Black Maple* **Acer saccharum** ssp **nigrum**

      Lf scars long white hair-fringed along lower (and occ upper) margin (occ short)

      End bud(s) dark reddish-brown to blackish, 4-5mm, single or paired, often with 1(2) prs smaller collateral buds, conical, acute; scales 3-6 prs, blackish, often hairy or ± tuft of white hairs at tip, long white-ciliate. Twigs slender (2mm diam), olive- to reddish-brown, hairless, round. Lf scars without minute papillae. Bark reddish, peeling in papery strips or sheets revealing paler underbark. Small tree. PL 1.............................*Paperbark Maple* **Acer griseum**

   Lf scars not hair-fringed

      Buds (mid-) brown, occ reddish/purplish-brown or green (esp lower parts). Twigs with latex

      Twigs slender (1.5-3mm diam), (red-) brown, often minutely hairy; bark often striate with fine pale longitudinal fissures. Branchlets occ with 4-5 corky wings. End bud(s) usu single (occ paired), 3-5mm, usu with 2 smaller collateral buds, ovoid, obtuse; scales 3-5 prs, hairy nr tips, ciliate. Lateral buds similar, ± adpressed to ± spreading. Bark furrowed, ± corky. Trunk short. Small to medium tree. ❸❺. PL 1.....................................*Field Maple* **Acer campestre**

      Buds dark reddish-brown to blackish. Twigs without latex

Acer saccharinum
Silver Maple

Acer rubrum
Red Maple

Acer opalus
Italian Maple

Acer velutinum
Velvet Maple

Acer saccharum ssp **saccharum**
Sugar Maple

Acer griseum
Paperbark Maple

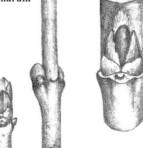

Acer campestre
Field Maple

End bud(s) 5-7mm, single or paired, often with 2(4) smaller collateral buds, conical, acute; scales 3-6 prs, tips often free, blackish, often hairy or ± tuft of white hairs at tip, long white-ciliate. Twigs mod slender (2-3mm diam), olive- to reddish-brown, hairless, round. Bark grey- to yellow-brown, <u>furrowed and flaking in vertical strips or scales</u> to reveal orange-brown inner bark (unlike the otherwise similar *A. griseum*). Small tree. Also known as the 'Roughbark Maple'. PL 2...*Three-flowered Maple* **Acer triflorum**

End bud(s) 2-3(4)mm, single or paired, occ with 2 smaller collateral buds, ovoid, ± obtuse to ± acute; scales (2)3(4) prs, dark reddish-brown to blackish, hairless to sparsely hairy nr tip, minutely white- or buff-ciliate. Twigs slender (1.5-2mm diam), dark reddish-brown, sparsely hairy to hairless. Branchlets with fissured bark. Bark smooth, greyish-brown, yellow-streaked, eventually fissured and scaly similar to *Crataegus*. Small tree. PL 2 ....*Tatarian Maple* **Acer tataricum**

Acer triflorum
Three-flowered Maple

Acer tataricum
Tatarian Maple

BI
118

Group BI – *Buds <12mm; scales ≥2 prs. Stipule scars absent. Shrub (occ tree in* Sambucus nigra*).*
❶ *Twigs or buds with stellate hairs (occ scale-like).* ❷ *Buds superposed (3 entries).* ❸ *Bundle scars 5(7).* ❹ *Bark spongy.* ❺ *Twigs with odorous inner bark*
■Twigs round, unlined, not ridged or angled (but occ angled nr tip)
Buds 1-3mm. Bundle scar 1, obscure (actually 3 but obscured by shrivelled lf scar or corky growth so only middle scar occ visible). Twigs slender (1-2mm diam)
Twigs often in horizontal plane (plagiotropic) or arching, dull, with persistent bud scale remnants at join with branchlet; lenticels absent; pith (or hollow) ½ diam. Buds usu all lateral, spreading, occ <u>collateral</u>; scales same colour as twig, triangular, acute, keeled (at least outer pr). Lf scars v raised, ± triangular, small, weakly decurrent forming short keel. Fr berry-like. Well-branched, usu suckering
Twigs hairless, usu grey-brown; bark often peeling into fibres esp on older growth; pith green, soon <u>hollow</u>. Buds 2-3mm, not hidden behind lf scar, ovoid; scales 2-4 prs, outer pr < bud length, hairless; inner scales green, visible as bud swells (from Feb). Frs 10-15(20)mm diam, white. Erect or arching, to 2m. PL 34...................*Snowberry* **Symphoricarpos albus**
Twigs minutely hairy (hairs crisped to ± patent), (purplish-) brown; bark soon splitting, later peeling into strips; pith green, <u>solid</u>. Buds 1(2)mm, partly hidden behind lf scar, ovoid-conical, ± flattened; scales 1-2(4) prs, outer pr equal to bud length, hairy; inner scales pink, visible as bud swells (from Feb). Frs 3-6mm diam, pink on upper side, white below. Arching, to (0.5)1m.
S. microphyllus x *orbiculatus.* PL 34.............*Hybrid Coralberry* **Symphoricarpos x chenaultii**
Buds (1.5)2-3mm. Bundle scars 3. Twigs slender (1.5-3mm diam)
Buds all lateral, spreading, ovoid; scales 1-3(4) prs, acuminate, reddish-brown (same colour as twig), hairy, outer pr fused at base, keeled. Twigs reddish- to grey-brown, minutely crisped-hairy, often <u>rough</u> due to occ short stiff hairs on raised hair bases (resembling lenticels); bark soon splitting; pith white, c½ diam. Lf scars raised, triangular crescent-shaped, white. Bark pale brown, splitting vertically and peeling revealing white underbark. Arching. PL 16
....*Beautybush* **Kolkwitzia amabilis**
Buds usu >3mm. Bundle scars 3 (occ obscure). Twigs slender to mod (1.5-5mm diam)
Twigs with medifixed hairs (occ sparse or confined to tip).........................(see **BE**) **Cornus** spp
Twigs with stellate scale-like hairs (occ sparse or confined to tip) (some garden *Viburnum* spp may key out here)
Twigs mod (2-4mm diam), reddish-brown, angled nr tip (usu with dead fl remnants or dying back); lenticels absent; bark splitting, peeling; pith <u>hollow</u> (⅓-¾ diam), occ loose, brown. Buds usu all lateral, occ collateral, v rarely 3-whorled, adpressed to spreading, 2-7mm, narrowly ovoid; scales (2)3-4(6) prs, same colour as twig, stellate-hairy, keeled; outer pr of scales >½ as long as bud and fused at base, acuminate. Lf scars not or weakly raised, triangular or 3-lobed to shield-shaped, rarely > bud width. Bark peeling, brown. Arching. Other spp occur in gardens. ❶. PL 12...............................*Deutzia* **Deutzia scabra**
Twigs without stellate or medifixed hairs
Twigs ashy-grey, slender to mod, round, brittle, with persistent bud scale remnants at join with branchlet; pith <½ diam, brown, soon <u>hollow</u>. Branchlets widely spaced; bark peeling. Lateral buds usu with 1-2 superposed buds (upper smallest), spreading at 60-90°; scales keeled. Lf scars raised, triangular, small, protruding at ends of persistent petiole bases, occ obscure or hidden by petiole base, with upper margin acutely projecting, occ without connecting interpetiolar ridge (esp *L. tatarica*). ❷
Twigs short-hairy at least nr tip, slender (1.5-2.5mm diam). Terminal bud single, 6-8mm, spindle-shaped; scales 4-5 prs, pale grey-brown, ± triangular, acute, hairy nr tips, long-ciliate. PL 17..*Fly Honeysuckle* **Lonicera xylosteum**
Twigs hairless, mod slender (2-3mm diam). Terminal bud single or with 2-4 clustered lateral buds, 4-5mm, ovoid; scales 5-6 prs, brown, ovate, ± obtuse, hairless, ciliate. PL 17
....*Tartarian Honeysuckle* **Lonicera tatarica**
Twigs shiny reddish-brown, mod (3-5mm diam), hairless, round, occ weakly angled; lenticels raised, round, small, brown; bark finely fissured esp in 2nd yr; pith c½ diam, green turning

Symphoricarpos x **chenaultii**
Hybrid Coralberry

Symphoricarpos albus
Snowberry

Kolkwitzia amabilis
Beautybush

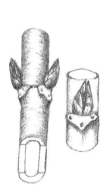

Lonicera xylosteum
Fly Honeysuckle

Deutzia scabra
Deutzia

Lonicera tatarica
Tartarian Honeysuckle

brown, soon fragmenting or hollow. Terminal bud 8-12mm, ovoid-conical, acute; scales 3(4) prs, shiny reddish, with scar at tip, keeled, occ sparse hairs, loose; inner scales green, white-hairy. Lateral buds occ v short-stalked (<1mm), adpressed to spreading, 5-8mm. Lf scars ≥ bud width, narrowed between protruding bundle scars. Bark weakly fissured to peeling, grey-brown. Early bursting, often fls during winter. Parent spp may occur in gardens. *V. farreri* x *grandiflorum*. PL 37..*Bodnant Viburnum* **Viburnum x bodnantense**

■Twigs round, 2-lined (raised lines occ weak or with stiff hairs), slender to mod. Branchlets with bark soon splitting

Bundle scar 1 (involute U-shaped), often obscure. Twigs slender (1-2(3)mm diam), reddish-brown, hairless, opp lines occ flared and wavy below nodes (lines running down from centre of interpetiolar ridge); lenticels absent; pith ½ diam, orange-brown, round. Buds all lateral, occ superposed, 2-4(10)mm (to 10mm when bursting), ovoid but soon elongated to long-conical revealing purple inner scales and young green lvs (occ with obscure translucent dots or veins); scales 1-3 prs, same colour as twig, triangular, acute, keeled, v loose. Lf scars not raised, triangular to semi-circular. Low to 0.8m. Early bursting. Occ ❷. PL 15 ....*Tutsan* **Hypericum androsaemum**

Bundle scars 3. Twigs slender to mod ((2)3-4(5)mm diam), reddish-brown, hairless but occ stiff hairs on opp lines running down from centre of interpetiolar ridge; lenticels flat, round to longitudinal, pale; pith ½-⅔ diam, white, round. Terminal bud present or replaced by dead fl remnants. Lateral buds v rarely 3-whorled, usu adpressed, 3-7mm, narrowly ovoid; scales 2-4(5) prs, reddish-brown (same colour as twig), acute, keeled, hairless (inner scales may be hairy), not ciliate, ± loose; outer scale pr fused at base and ½-1x as long as bud. Lf scars appearing sunken, triangular to broadly crescent-shaped, often > bud width, pale; bundle scars nr lower margin. Bark with shallow flaky ridges, grey-brown. Often arching to ground, to 3m. Other cultivars and hybrids occur in gardens. PL 37..*Weigela* **Weigela florida**

■Twigs 4-angled by 4 raised lines, mod slender (3-4mm diam). Branchlets with bark soon splitting

Bundle scars 3. Twigs pale orange- to reddish-brown, minutely hairy at least nr tip; lenticels absent; pith ⅔ diam, white, ± round. Terminal bud 6-10mm, 4-angled, ± acute; scales 3-4 prs, outer pr ± as long as bud, same colour as twig (inner occ purplish esp in lower ½), acute, keeled, hairless to hairy, occ dark red sessile glands, not fused at base, loose. Lateral buds usu spreading, 2-6mm; scales 1(2) prs. Lf scars raised with lower margin projecting, broadly V-shaped, equal to bud width, not meeting around twig, often covered by corky layer, decurrent from sides and centre. Erect, to 2.5m. PL 17.........*Californian Honeysuckle* **Lonicera involucrata**

■Twigs 8-angled (occ obscure), without raised lines, usu mod stout (4-8mm diam), grey, occ silvery sheen, with persistent bud scale remnants at join with branchlet; lenticels v raised, oval, buff; inner bark with fetid gravy odour; pith ⅔ diam, round. Branchlets rough with wart-like lenticels, round, later ridged. Lf scars not raised; bundle scars 5(7), nr lower margin, occ only 3 clearly visible. Bark blocky, like 'crocodile-hide', spongy. Occ ❷, ❸❹❺

Twigs with white pith. Terminal bud often present, 2-15mm, ovoid but soon elongated to long-conical revealing tips of young purple-green lvs; lowest scales (1)2 prs, brown, papery, apiculate, keeled, hairless, not or sparsely ciliate, loose; upper scales (when visible) 1-2(3) prs, green or purple. Lateral buds similar, sessile, often with 1(2) superposed buds, rarely 3-whorled, spreading. Lf scars crescent-shaped, >> bud width, often meeting around twig. Early bursting. PL 31...*Elder* **Sambucus nigra**

Twigs with orange-brown pith. Terminal bud absent. Lateral buds short-stalked to 3mm, occ 1-2 collateral or superposed, spreading, (5)8-15mm (fl buds nr max size), ellipsoid, acute, angled; scales 2-4 prs, broad, obtuse, apiculate, greenish-purple, hairless, usu ciliate, ± loose; lower pr of scales short, keeled. Lf scars shield-shaped, equal to (fl) bud width, rarely meeting around twig. PL 31...*Red-berried Elder* **Sambucus racemosa**

Hypericum androsaemum
Tutsan

Viburnum x bodnantense
Bodnant Viburnum

Weigela florida
Weigela

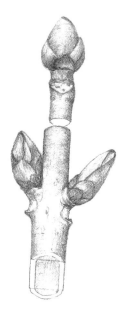

Lonicera involucrata
Californian Honeysuckle

Sambucus nigra
Elder

Sambucus racemosa
Red-berried Elder

C

Key to Groups in Division C
(Buds and lf scars 3(6)-whorled)

These spp key out with full descriptions in Division B but are repeated here to enable rapid identification

■Bundle scar 1 (obscure in *Jasminum* and *Fuchsia*)
Twigs green, 6-8(12)-ridged; bark not splitting. Scrambler. PL 15
....(see **BA**) *Summer Jasmine* **Jasminum officinale**
Twigs usu red-brown, round; bark splitting in 2nd yr. Shrub. PL 13
....(see **BB**) *Fuchsia* **Fuchsia magellanica**
Twigs pale grey, round to weakly 4-angled; bark not splitting but inner bark fetid. Bundle scars 7-9 fused into 1. Shrub. PL 9
......................(see **BB**) *Farges' Harlequin Glorybower* **Clerodendrum trichotomum** var **fargesii**
Twigs pale olive-brown, round; bark not splitting. Shrub
Bud scales obtuse. Twigs usu minutely hairy. PL 16.....(see **BB**) *Wild Privet* **Ligustrum vulgare**
Bud scales (±) acute. Twigs hairless. PL 16.......(see **BB**) *Garden Privet* **Ligustrum ovalifolium**
■Bundle scars 3 (occ multiplied in *Acer* but still in 3 groups)
Buds hidden below lf scar membrane. Shrub
Twigs hairless, mod slender (1.5-3mm diam). PL 21
....(see **BD**) *Mock-orange* **Philadelphus coronarius**
Twigs minutely hairy, v slender (1-2mm diam). PL 21
....(see **BD**) *Littleleaf Mock-orange* **Philadelphus microphyllus**
Buds visible
Twigs round, solid. Buds 3-6-whorled. Tree
Inner bark weakly fetid. PL 2.....................................(see **BH**) *Silver Maple* **Acer saccharinum**
Inner bark odourless. PL 2...(see **BH**) *Red Maple* **Acer rubrum**
Twigs round with 2 opp lines, solid. Shrub. PL 37.....................(see **BI**) *Weigela* **Weigela florida**
Twigs round, hollow, with peltate scales. Shrub. PL 12..............(see **BI**) *Deutzia* **Deutzia scabra**
■Bundle scars 4-7
Twigs with fetid inner bark; latex absent. Bundle scars 5(7). Small tree or shrub. PL 31
....(see **BI**) *Elder* **Sambucus nigra**
Twigs with odourless inner bark; latex present. Bundle scars 4-6. Small tree. PL 6
....(see **AI**) *Paper Mulberry* **Broussonetia papyrifera**
■Bundle scars usu >7. Tree
Bundle scars 7-10, in shallow arc, often ± fused
Bark becoming furrowed with intersecting ridges. Frequent. PL 13
....(see **BB**) *Claret Ash* **Fraxinus angustifolia** ssp **oxycarpa**
Bark becoming blocky like 'crocodile-hide'. VR
....(see **BB**) *Narrow-leaved Ash* **Fraxinus angustifolia** ssp **angustifolia**
Bundle scars 12-20, in an ellipse
Lf scars dark. Pith chambered to hollow. PL 21...(see **BB**) *Foxglove-tree* **Paulownia tomentosa**
Lf scars pale. Pith solid
Bark scaly. Fr pods stout (10mm diam). Twigs mod stout (5-9mm diam). Buds usu with (±) adpressed scales. PL 7..............................(see **BB**) *Indian Bean-tree* **Catalpa bignonioides**
Bark furrowed
Fr pods 7-10mm diam. Twigs mod stout (5-8mm diam). Buds usu with (±) adpressed scales. PL 8..(see **BB**) *Northern Catalpa* **Catalpa speciosa**
Fr pods (4)6-7mm diam. Twigs usu mod (4-6mm diam). Buds usu with (±) adpressed scales. *C. bignonioides* x *ovata*. PL 7......................(see **BB**) *Hybrid Catalpa* **Catalpa** x **erubescens**
Fr pods 3-5mm diam. Twigs usu mod (4-6mm diam). Buds usu with spreading acuminate scales. PL 8..(see **BB**) *Chinese Catalpa* **Catalpa ovata**

Keys to Selected Groups
(Typically representing genera or subgenera)

Group BET – Betula. *Twigs usu slender (1-2.5(3)mm diam), ± zig-zagging or not, flexible, dark (reddish-) brown, round, often with small reddish resin glands (occ swelling and turning whitish (or blackish in B. papyrifera); lenticels none to many, flat to raised, small, (±) dot-like, elongating transversely with age, white to pale orange; pith ⅓ diam, green, (±) 3-angled. Branchlets with woody spurs. Terminal bud only on woody spurs (absent in B. nigra), occ appearing stalked, (1)3-15mm, narrowly ovoid, acute, often sticky or coated in dry resin; scales (4)5-7(8), hairless, (sparsely) ciliate. Lateral buds occ oblique to lf scar, rarely collateral, adpressed to spreading, narrowly ovoid (ovoid-globose in B. nana), weakly 3-4-angled or flattened, often curved to side or incurved at tip, smaller; scales (2)3-4, spiralling but lowest 2 scales forming V-shape above lf scar, often green with brown margins (to dark purple-brown), at least obscurely striate with many faint parallel veins, with stomata (v obscure, best x60). Lf scars usu spiralling, occ 2-ranked, raised, crescent-shaped to ± (half-) elliptical, small, < bud width; bundle scars 3 (or groups of 3) nr upper margin. Stipule scars short-linear (to elliptical), ± equal. Bark shiny red-brown when young, often silver-white when mature, with horizontal linear lenticels, usu peeling in horizontal papery strips. Tree, rarely shrub; branches long, slender. Catkins usu present at end of twigs.* ❶ *Bud scales 2 (and terminal bud always absent).* ❷ *Bark v shreddy*

■Twigs with odorous inner bark (antiseptic 'germolene' odour)

Bark shiny reddish-brown, smooth, with horizontal lenticels, cherry-like (resembling *Prunus avium*), later grey-brown, fissured and scaly. Crown ovate; upper branches steeply ascending; lower branches horizontal or drooping. Twigs slender (1.5-2mm diam), shiny reddish-brown, occ with grey skin, hairless to densely hairy with minute (<0.1mm) and occ long (to 1mm) hairs, often with flat resin glands. Lateral buds spreading (lower buds occ adpressed), 5-7(8)mm, ovoid-conical, sharply acute; scales 3, 2-toned, green on lower part, reddish-brown on upper part, usu hairless. Lvs with 12-18 prs of close veins. PL 6......................................*Sweet Birch* **Betula lenta**

Bark shiny yellowish, usu ± shreddy and peeling in fine horizontal strips, with horizontal lenticels, eventually plate-like (but branches still ± shreddy). Twigs slender (1.5-2mm diam), dull to shiny reddish-brown, occ with grey skin, hairless to sparsely hairy with long (to 1mm) hairs nr tip (rarely with minute <0.1mm hairs), often with flat resin glands; inner bark odour usu weaker than *B. lenta*. Lateral buds spreading (lower buds occ adpressed), 5-7mm, ovoid-conical, sharply acute; scales 3(4), 2-toned, yellow-brown on lower part, reddish-brown on upper part, usu hairy nr tip. Crown irreg spreading. Lvs with 7-10 prs of widely spaced veins. PL 5
....*Yellow Birch* **Betula alleghaniensis**

■Twigs with odourless inner bark

All twigs hairless, often warty with swollen whitish resin glands. Trunk with black ∧-shaped mark above join with branches

Lateral buds 5-7mm, ± adpressed to spreading, acute, occ sticky or covered in dry resin; scales usu green in lower ½, reddish-brown in upper ½, hairless. Twigs slender (1-1.5mm diam), ± shiny dark reddish-brown, occ v warty, hairy on saplings and vigorous shoots. Bark becoming silver-white, with black diamond-shaped lenticels, peeling in horizontal strips. Trunk single, continuous to tree tip, slender (usu <40cm diam), developing black vertical fissures and knobbly ridges at base; crown narrowly pyramidal; branches ascending; branchlets strongly drooping. PL 6...*Silver Birch* **Betula pendula**

Lateral buds 9-15mm, usu ± spreading, (sharply) acute, sticky; scales green in lower ½, dark reddish- to blackish-brown in upper ½, occ with sparse hairs. Twigs usu mod slender ((1.5)2-2.5(3)mm diam), shiny reddish- or purplish-brown to ± black, occ warty with whitish and/or reddish to black resin glands. Bark chalky white, occ blackish and furrowed at base, peeling in horizontal strips or scroll-like sheets, revealing pinkish-orange underside. Trunk single or several, continuous to tree tip or not, mod (up to 75cm diam); crown pyramidal or irreg; branches ascending; branchlets slightly drooping to horizontal. PL 6
....*Paper Birch* **Betula papyrifera**

Betula lenta
Sweet Birch

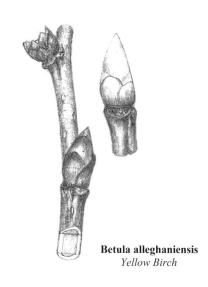

Betula alleghaniensis
Yellow Birch

Betula pendula
Silver Birch

Betula papyrifera
Paper Birch

BET

At least some twigs usu hairy (often minutely so), rarely warty (but often with flat resin glands)
Buds 1-2mm. Low shrub to 1m. Uplands, mostly Scot
Twigs slender (1-1.5mm diam), dull dark reddish-brown, densely minutely (0.2mm) patent-hairy, occ with resin glands. Lateral buds spreading, ovoid-globose; scales 3-4, lower parts green, upper reddish-brown, <u>long</u>-ciliate. Catkins in spring only. PL 6
....*Dwarf Birch* **Betula nana**
Buds (3)4-7mm. Twigs 1-1.5mm diam (to 2mm in *B. nigra*), usu <u>sparsely hairy</u>. Tree, occ shrub-like in *B. pubescens* ssp *tortuosa* (*B. pendula* keys out here if hairy saplings and vigorous shoots examined)
Bark v shreddy, reddish-brown, peeling irreg in thin strips which roll back and persist for several yrs, often revealing pinkish inner bark, eventually blackish and scaly. Branchlets drooping. Lateral buds usu adpressed, 4-7mm, <u>v acute</u>, not sticky; scales 2(3), overlapping, shiny reddish- to orange-brown, with some yellow-green, hairy to hairless, occ tuft of hairs at tip. Twigs reddish- to orange-brown, <u>crisped-hairy</u> (hairs 0.1-0.5mm) or ± short-woolly to hairless, often rough (due to swollen reddish-orange resin glands, lenticels and hair bases). Small to medium tree, occ multi-trunked; trunk(s) often short, with few ± spreading branches; crown ± narrowly oblong. ❶❷. PL 6..*River Birch* **Betula nigra**
Bark ± smooth, turning grey-white when mature, <u>weakly</u> peeling in horizontal strips, not furrowed at base (unlike *B. pendula*). Branchlets not or weakly drooping, rarely strictly erect. Lateral buds 5-7mm, sticky or not; scales 3-4, reddish-brown (often less green than *B. pendula*). Twigs dull dark reddish-brown, <u>densely to sparsely hairy</u> with long (0.5mm) spreading and/or minute (0.1mm) patent hairs
Buds 5-7mm, acute, not scented when bursting. Twigs usu without obvious resin glands. PL 6..*Downy Birch* **Betula pubescens** ssp **pubescens**
Buds 3-4mm, ± acute to obtuse, weakly scented when bursting. Twigs often with obvious resin glands. Often shrub-like. N Br. PL 6...*Mountain Birch* **Betula pubescens** ssp **tortuosa**
Buds (6)8-12mm. Twigs (1.5)2-2.5mm diam, <u>densely</u> hairy with <u>minute</u> (0.1mm) patent hairs and occ longer (to 0.5mm) spreading hairs. Branches held ± strictly erect
Lateral buds acute, rarely sticky; scales 3(4), dark purplish-brown (occ greenish nr base), hairy to hairless. Twigs dull dark reddish-brown but often grey due to hairs. Bark red-brown to bright silver-white, <u>peeling in horizontal strips or scroll-like sheets</u>. Intergrades with *B. jacquemontii* (West Himalayan Birch) (bright white bark) and *B. albosinensis* (Chinese Red-Barked Birch) (reddish bark) which are considered ssp of *B. utilis* by many authorities. PL 6
....*Himalayan Birch* **Betula utilis**

Betula nana
Dwarf Birch

Betula nigra
River Birch

Betula pubescens ssp **pubescens**
Downy Birch

Betula pubescens ssp **tortuosa**
Mountain Birch

Betula utilis
Himalayan Birch

COT

Group COT – Cotoneaster. *Buds all lateral, adpressed, naked but next season's stipules may be visible and resemble scales, usu densely yellowish-hairy. Twigs mod slender (2-3mm diam), usu (olive-) reddish-brown, occ with grey skin, usu with yellowish adpressed hairs, round, often angled nr tip; lenticels ± flat, oval, pale; pith ½ diam, white, round. Branchlets with fissured bark. Lf scars 2-ranked, raised, circular to crescent-shaped, small; bundle scars 3. Stipules (or remnants) often persistent, 2-8mm, narrowly triangular, red or green, usu breaking off above base (leaving broad bases at sides of lf scars); scars, if present, oval to linear. Tree or shrub. Only the most commonly encountered fully deciduous spp and a possible endemic are included.* ❶ *Twigs with inner bark with strong almond odour*

■Small tree; trunks 1(2), to 6m

Buds well-spaced along twig, 5mm, densely yellow-hairy. Twigs green nr tip. PL 10
....*Tree Cotoneaster* **Cotoneaster frigidus**

■Medium shrub; multi-stemmed, usu 1.5-3m. Buds well-spaced along twig

Frs red becoming bluish-black or purple, 7-9mm, globose. Shrub, rarely small tree
....(not illustrated) *Purpleberry Cotoneaster* **Cotoneaster affinis**
Frs red or orange

Frs cylindrical, 7-12mm, dark red; stones 2
....(not illustrated) *Spreading Cotoneaster* **Cotoneaster divaricatus**
Frs globose. Buds 5-8mm, densely yellow-hairy. Twigs yellow-hairy

Frs 8-11mm, shiny dark red; stones 4-5
....(not illustrated) *Bullate Cotoneaster* **Cotoneaster rehderi**
Frs 6-8mm, shiny bright red; stones (4)5. PL 10
....*Hollyberry Cotoneaster* **Cotoneaster bullatus**

■Low shrub, <1(1.5)m

Branches herringbone-like or fan-shaped (± in a flat plane); branchlets regular, spreading at 45-90° to main branch. Buds closely spaced along twig, occ overlapping, (1)2-3mm, densely yellow-hairy. Twigs densely yellowish-hairy; inner bark ± odourless

Branchlets spreading at 70-90° to main branch (herringbone-like). Frs 4-6mm, orange-red; stones 3. PL 10...*Wall Cotoneaster* **Cotoneaster horizontalis**
Branchlets spreading at 45-65° to main branch (fan-shaped). Frs 6-9mm, orange-red; stones 2-3............................(not illustrated) *Purple-flowered Cotoneaster* **Cotoneaster atropurpureus**
Branches not herringbone-like. Buds well-spaced along twig, c5mm, densely white-hairy. Twigs densely yellow-hairy nr tip; inner bark with strong almond odour. ?Native, Great Orme, occ propagated in collections. ❶. PL 10.............................*Wild Cotoneaster* **Cotoneaster cambricus**

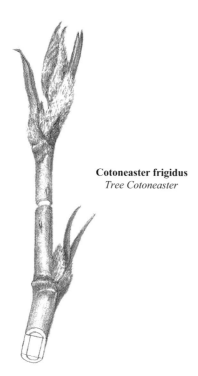

Cotoneaster frigidus
Tree Cotoneaster

Cotoneaster bullatus
Hollyberry Cotoneaster

Cotoneaster horizontalis
Wall Cotoneaster

Cotoneaster cambricus
Wild Cotoneaster

MAG

Group MAG – Magnolia. *Twigs not zig-zagging, often green (esp below) to olive- or orange-brown to dark purple-brown, round, with circular fl scars in branchlet axile (left hy fallen fl); lenticels ± flat, round, orange, fading to white; pith c½ diam, white, round; inner bark aromatic (perfumed soap, fruity-spicy or aniseed), bitter-tasting. Terminal bud usu a fl bud, 1-5cm, rarely appearing ± stalked (to 2mm); scale 1 (2 fused stipules forming hood), keeled with a small rudimentary lf scar on back nr base. Lateral buds smaller, adpressed to spreading, oblong to ovoid, usu less hairy. Lf scars spiralling, not raised, often wider than lateral buds; bundle scars (5)9-15, scattered or in 1-2 rows, ± protruding. Stipule scar a line encircling twig from top of lf scar, forming a shallow U-shape. Tree, often multi-trunked nr base, rarely a shrub. Only a selection of common or distinctive taxa are included; many more spp and cultivars occur which are ± indistinguishable using winter characters alone. ❶ Lf scars more crowded nr twig tip (2 spp). ❷ Inner bark with aniseed odour. ❸ Pith diaphragmed with firm green partitions (solid in other taxa). ❹ Bark furrowed (smooth in other taxa)*

■Buds purplish-black (under any hairs), hairless to densely hairy

Terminal bud 2-5cm, conical (equal to twig diam), curved, acute, pruinose, <u>hairless</u>, with minute yellowish dots, keel on back of bud with rusty or white hairs. Lateral buds often <u>sunken under bark</u>. Twigs mod stout (6-10mm diam), shiny reddish- to olive-brown, hairless, <u>swollen at base of each yrs growth</u>; inner bark aromatic. Lf scars <u>circular</u>, with scattered sessile yellow glands; bundle scars <u>9-15, scattered</u>. Bark grey. Small tree, often multi-trunked, erect or leaning; crown wide; branches spreading, with ends of twigs curving up. ❶. PL 18
....*Umbrella Magnolia* **Magnolia tripetala**

Terminal bud 1-2cm, flattened-cylindrical, curved, usu acute, occ obtuse or ± truncate, <u>densely hairy with white or rusty short adpressed hairs</u>. Lateral buds adpressed, c1cm, occ absent, not sunken. Twigs mod (c4mm diam), greyish (to greenish), occ hairy, not swollen at base; inner bark aromatic. Lf scars crescent-shaped; bundle scars <u>(7)9-11, in 1 row</u>. Bark pale orange-grey. Small tree, often multi-trunked, erect or leaning; crown round. PL 18
....*Chinese Magnolia* **Magnolia sieboldii** ssp **sinensis**

Terminal bud c1cm (usu a lf bud), cylindrical, obtuse, occ pruinose, <u>usu with a few adpressed hairs</u>, sparsely <u>yellow-dotted</u>; terminal fl bud 1-1.5cm, with 1-2mm white spreading hairs. Lateral buds small or absent, not sunken. Twigs mod slender (2-3mm diam), green to purplish-brown, hairless, not swollen at base; inner bark with <u>aniseed or fruity odour</u> (like *Sassafras*). Lf scars heart- or shield-shaped, occ broad crescent-shaped; bundle scars <u>5-9, usu ± scattered</u>. Bark grey. Small tree; trunk single, erect; crown round. ❷. PL 18
....*Willow-leaved Magnolia* **Magnolia salicifolia**

■Buds green and ± hairless in lower ½, densely silky-hairy at least in upper ½

Twigs mod slender (3-4mm diam), <u>green</u>, occ <u>pruinose</u>; inner bark aromatic (not soap); pith diaphragmed with firm green partitions (c15-20 per cm). Terminal bud 1-2cm, v narrowly conical to ± cylindrical (equal to twig diam), acute, green (occ purplish tinge), occ pruinose, (off-) white silky-hairy nr tip with short adpressed hairs. Lf scars elliptical to heart-shaped; bundle scars 10-15, scattered. Bark dark grey. Small tree, occ semi-evergreen; multi-trunked; crown narrow. ❸. PL 18...*Sweetbay Magnolia* **Magnolia virginiana**

■Buds densely white- or yellowish-hairy

Lf scars more crowded nr twig tip, heart-shaped; bundle scars 9-15, scattered. Terminal bud 2-5cm, cylindrical (equal to twig diam), <u>silvery-white</u>, with short silky hairs. Twigs mod stout (6-10mm diam), <u>blue-green</u> to yellowish-green, hairy. Bark pale grey. Tall tree; trunk single; crown conical to round. ❶...*Bigleaf Magnolia* **Magnolia macrophylla**

Lf scars ± equally spaced along twig

Terminal bud densely white silky-hairy with <u>short (<0.5mm) v adpressed</u> hairs, 1.5-2.5cm, oblong-conical (equal to twig diam), curved. Lateral buds adpressed, smaller, 3-10mm. Twigs mod (4-5mm diam), shiny olive- to purplish-brown, occ hairy; inner bark aromatic. Lf scars crescent-shaped; bundle scars 9-15, mostly in 1 row. Bark <u>furrowed</u>, pale grey-brown, flaky, revealing darker reddish-brown underbark. Tall tree; trunk single; crown conical, resembling *Pyrus* when young; branches ± slender, spreading below, ascending above. ❹. PL 18
....*Cucumber-tree* **Magnolia acuminata**

Magnolia salicifolia
Willow-leaved Magnolia

Magnolia tripetala
Umbrella Magnolia

Magnolia sieboldii ssp **sinensis**
Chinese Magnolia

Magnolia virginiana
Sweetbay Magnolia

Magnolia macrophylla
Bigleaf Magnolia

Magnolia acuminata
Cucumber-tree

Terminal bud densely white or yellowish furry-hairy with <u>long spreading to ± adpressed</u> hairs, ± ovoid-conical (> twig diam). Twigs slender to mod (2-5mm diam), ± hairless. Small tree, multi-trunked; crown wide

Terminal bud 2-3cm, with c1(2)mm white slightly spreading hairs. Lateral buds c15mm, ± equal to twig diam, short white silky-hairy. Lf scars broadly crescent-shaped to heart-shaped; bundle scars 9-15, ± scattered. *M. denudata* x *liliiflora*. PL 18
....*Saucer Magnolia* **Magnolia** x **soulangeana**

Terminal bud 1.5-2cm, with 2-4mm yellowish spreading hairs. Lf scars crescent-shaped; bundle scars 5-7, in 1 row. PL 18...*Star Magnolia* **Magnolia stellata**

Terminal bud 1-1.5cm, with 1-2mm white spreading hairs. Lf scars usu heart- or shield-shaped; bundle scars 5-9, usu ± scattered. ❷. PL 18
....(see above) *Willow-leaved Magnolia* **Magnolia salicifolia**

Magnolia x **soulangeana**
Saucer Magnolia

Magnolia stellata
Star Magnolia

MAL

Group MAL – Malus. *Twigs usu mod (2-5mm diam), dark reddish-brown, round but finely lined from decurrent lf scars; lenticels ± round; inner bark with ± sweet liquorice-like taste but outer bark bitter; pith ½ diam, white or green turning brown, ± round. Branchlets (and branches) with many stout curved woody spurs. Terminal bud present; scales apiculate (often broken) or 3-toothed, usu keeled (esp lower), v weakly striate; lower scales swollen (modified petiole bases). Lf scars spiralling, raised, crescent-shaped, equal to bud width; bundle scars 3, nr upper margin. Stipule scars absent. Bark smooth when young. Small tree. Frs usu remaining on tree or fallen below.*
❶ *Twigs with inner wood purple*

■Terminal bud broadly ovoid to globose, obtuse. Crown upright. Unarmed
 Terminal bud 6-8mm; scales 5-7, purplish, occ blackish, (±) hairless, occ hairy at tip, ciliate. Lateral buds adpressed to spreading, smaller. Twigs usu adpressed-hairy (to ± woolly) at least nr tip; lenticels raised, orange. Bark remaining ± smooth with lenticels. Frs 2-2.5cm diam, apple-like, green to reddish on sunlit side, covered in tiny lenticels. PL 19
 ....*Chonosuki Crab Apple* **Malus tschonoskii**
■Terminal bud ± ovoid, (±) acute to sharply so. Crown round
 Branchlets armed with thorns (look carefully)
  Terminal bud usu ± sharply acute, 3-8mm, usu white-woolly or hairy at least at base or tip, occ hairless; scales 4-5, obtuse, shiny purplish- or reddish-brown beneath any sparse to dense white hairs, ciliate. Lateral buds (1)2-5mm, flattened-ovoid, obtuse; scales (2)3-5, ovate, obtuse, ± woolly to hairless. Twigs usu hairless, occ ± woolly or adpressed-hairy nr tip; lenticels flat, white. Bark cracked into rectangular scales, dark brown. Frs 2-4cm diam, apple-like, usu green; sepals persisting. PL 19..*Crab Apple* **Malus sylvestris**
 Branchlets unarmed
  Frs >5cm diam, typical 'apples', green to red; sepals persisting
   Terminal bud 3-8mm, ovoid, (±) acute, usu white-woolly or hairy at least at base or tip; scales 4-5, obtuse, shiny purplish- or reddish-brown beneath sparse to dense white hairs, ciliate. Lateral buds (1)2-5mm, flattened-ovoid, obtuse; scales (2)3-5, ovate, obtuse, ± woolly to hairless. Twigs ± woolly or adpressed-hairy at least nr tip. Bark becoming cracked into rectangular scales, greyish-brown. Very common. PL 18........................*Apple* **Malus pumila**
  Frs 2cm diam, apple-like
   Frs red; sepals absent or reduced. Terminal bud 5-7mm, conical-ovoid, similar to *M. baccata* but more ovoid, acute; scales 5(6), dark reddish-brown, some woolly hairs esp nr tips. Twigs often woolly. *M. baccata x prunifolia*...................*Hybrid Siberian Crab Apple* **Malus x robusta**
   Frs yellow, occ with some orange-red; sepals absent. *M. baccata x sieboldii*
    ....(not illustrated) *Yellow Hornet Crab Apple* **Malus x zumi**
   Frs purple; sepals persisting. Twigs with inner wood purple ❶. *M. atrosanguinea x niedzwetzkyana*...................................(not illustrated) *Purple Crab Apple* **Malus x purpurea**
  Frs ≤1.5cm diam
   Frs 1-1.5cm diam, cherry-like, yellow to red; sepals absent. Terminal bud 5-7mm, conical-ovoid, acute; scales 5(6), dark reddish-brown, not woolly, sparsely hairy to hairless. Lateral buds similar, smaller (4-5mm), adpressed, (±) acute; scales 4. Twigs sparsely hairy to hairless; lenticels low, buff. Bark becoming fissured into rectangular scales. PL 18
    ....*Siberian Crab Apple* **Malus baccata**
   Frs <1cm diam, berry-like, yellow; sepals absent. Terminal bud like *M. baccata*; scales hairless, ciliate. Twigs hairless..............(not illustrated) *Cut-leaf Crab Apple* **Malus transitoria**

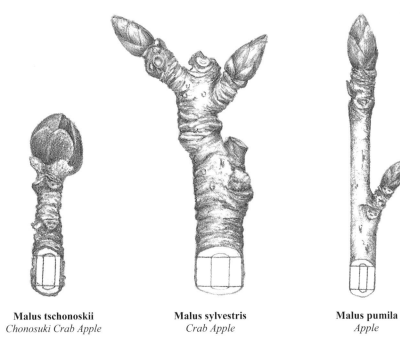

Malus tschonoskii
Chonosuki Crab Apple

Malus sylvestris
Crab Apple

Malus pumila
Apple

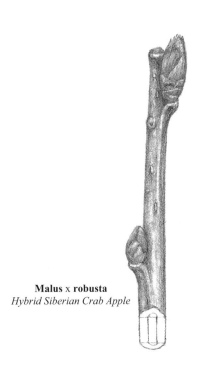

Malus x **robusta**
Hybrid Siberian Crab Apple

Malus baccata
Siberian Crab Apple

POP / POP A / POP B

Group POP – *Populus*. *Twigs round to angled or ridged; lenticels flat, round to longitudinal, orange, fading pale; inner bark with bitter astringent ('aspirin') taste; pith ½ diam, <u>5-angled</u>. Branchlets occ with woody spurs. Terminal bud (If bud) ± 3-angled, (sharply) acute, often sticky, usu balsam-scented. Lateral If buds smaller; lowermost scale <u>directly above If scar</u>, a 'thumb nail' as wide as bud, wrapping around bud so margin hidden behind bud, ± 2-keeled. Lateral fl buds (which can be dissected to determine sex of tree) often clustered nr twig base, usu swollen and larger than If buds, often curved outwards. Lf scars spiralling, (±) raised, triangular to oval or kidney-shaped to 3-lobed, equal to bud width, surface slightly convex with thin corky layer; bundle scars 3 or in 3 groups, often sunken. Stipule scars linear to narrowly triangular, equal. Tree, often suckering*

■Twigs white-felted at least nr tip and/or buds densely white-hairy. Terminal bud <1.2cm
....(White Poplar, Grey Poplar) **POP A**

■Twigs not white-felted, hairy to hairless. Buds not densely white-hairy

  Buds not sticky or strongly balsam-scented

    Twigs reddish-brown. Terminal bud usu <1.2cm..............................(Aspen, Grey Poplar) **POP B**

    Twigs shiny yellowish-brown. Terminal bud 0.8-2.5cm
....(Black-poplars, Hybrid Black-poplars) **POP C**

  Buds sticky and strongly balsam-scented, usu 1.2-2.5cm. Twigs usu reddish-brown
....(Balsam-poplars) **POP D**

Group POP A – *White Poplar, Grey Poplar (sect* Populus*). Twigs white-felted at least nr tip, round but weakly angled nr tip; pith white or green, <u>often turning brown</u>. Terminal bud <1.2cm. Lateral buds ± spreading; lowermost scale <½ bud length, (2)4-lobed. Bark smooth with diamond-shaped lenticels and grey-white when young, irreg fissured nr base, later shallowly furrowed. Trunk continuous to tree tip or not. Suckering; sucker shoots white-felted*

■Twigs ± slender (2-3mm diam), flexible, white-felted at least nr tip (often along entire length or occ v sparse), olive- to reddish-brown beneath felt. Terminal bud 2.5-8mm, ovoid, acute, not sticky, unscented; scales <u>3-5</u>, reddish-brown with dark margins (beneath any hairs), not resin-edged, usu white-felted (often sparse to absent), ciliate. Lateral buds similar; scales 3-5. Fl buds identical. Lf scars <u>dark brown</u>. Crown wide, asymmetric, open; branches curving up and down (like an elephant's trunk - imagination required!). PL 21.......................................*White Poplar* **Populus alba**

■Twigs ± mod (2-4(5)mm diam), rigid, white-felted or adpressed-hairy nr tip to hairless, olive- to reddish-brown beneath any hairs. Terminal bud 5-10mm, conical-ovoid, <u>swollen</u>, ± acute to sharply acute, not or slightly sticky, unscented; scales <u>(4)7-12</u>, reddish-brown (beneath any hairs), usu with dark margins, rarely pale resin-edged, often notched, (±) hairless to woolly or adpressed-hairy, ciliate. Lateral lf buds 3-6mm, narrower; scales 3-5, (±) hairless to woolly or adpressed-hairy, ciliate. Fl buds larger, c10mm, broadly ovoid, acute. Lf scars <u>pale brown</u>. Crown spreading; branchlets often drooping. *P. alba* x *tremula*. PL 22
........................(esp sucker shoots or backcrosses with *P. alba*) *Grey Poplar* **Populus** x **canescens**

Group POP B – *Aspen, Grey Poplar (sect* Populus*). Twigs shiny reddish-brown, round but weakly angled nr tip. Terminal bud usu <1.2cm; scales often notched. Lateral buds with 3-5 scales. Trunk pale grey to whitish, smooth but with diamond-shaped lenticels, irreg fissured nr base. Suckering*

■Lateral buds ± spreading. *P. alba* x *tremula*. PL 22
....(see **POP A**) *Grey Poplar* **Populus** x **canescens**

■Lateral buds adpressed, some ± spreading, tips often incurved, 5-8mm; scales hairless, occ sparsely hairy, occ ciliate; lowermost scale usu ≤¼ bud length, (2)4-lobed. Twigs ± slender (2-3mm diam), <u>shiny</u> olive- to <u>reddish-brown</u>, occ with grey skin, hairless (but sucker shoots often densely hairy); pith usu green, occ white, <u>not turning brown</u>. Terminal bud 6-12(14)mm, narrowly conical to ovoid, <u>sharply acute with fine point</u>; scales 7-12, shiny dark reddish-brown, pale resin-edged (occ fringed resembling cilia), obtuse, <u>hairless or occ adpressed-hairy nr base</u>, not ciliate, sticky and weakly balsam-scented when bursting only. Fl buds to 12mm, ± ovoid, swollen. Lf scars pale brown. Trunk continuous to tree tip; crown narrow to round. Late bursting. PL 22....*Aspen* **Populus tremula**

Populus alba
White Poplar

Populus x canescens
Grey Poplar

Populus tremula
Aspen

POP C / POP D

Group POP C – *Black-poplars, Hybrid Black-poplars (sect* Aigeiros*). Terminal bud 0.8-2.5cm, not sticky (unless squeezed) with yellow-orange resin usu dried, weakly balsam-scented (squeeze gently), narrowly ovoid-conical; scales (5)7-8(9), shiny yellowish-brown to dark brown or green, hairless, not ciliate. Lateral buds occ v small or absent; scales 2-3(4); lowest scale usu <½ bud length, ± entire. Twigs shiny yellowish-brown (straw-coloured), mod slender (2-3(4)mm diam), usu hairless, occ sparsely hairy; pith white or green, turning brown. Bark furrowed with ± sharp intersecting ridges. Many more cultivars exist*

■Terminal bud usu >12mm. Lateral lf buds adpressed to spreading and recurved, (7)10-15mm. Twigs round to strongly ridged (esp sucker shoots). Not resistant to mistletoe (*Viscum album*)

Terminal bud (1)1.2-2cm, slightly sticky (squeeze gently); scales greenish-yellow or orange to yellowish-brown or reddish, often yellow resin-edged. Fl buds spreading, swollen, to 2.5cm. Occ suckering. Many planted cultivars exist, derived from *P. deltoides* x *nigra*. PL 22
....*Hybrid Black-poplar* **Populus x canadensis**

■Terminal bud usu <12mm. Lateral buds usu adpressed, occ spreading. Twigs usu round, occ ridged nr tip (or on sucker growth). Resistant to mistletoe (*Viscum album*)

Crown ± round. Branches downcurved but twigs curved up at tips. Terminal bud 8-12mm. Lateral buds spreading to adpressed, ≤10mm. Trunk usu with burrs. Fls male (most trees) or female. PL 22...*Black-poplar* **Populus nigra** ssp **betulifolia**

Crown fastigiate. Terminal bud 5-10(12)mm. Lateral buds (3)5-7mm. Trunk without burrs but with abundant epicormic shoots, usu fluted nr base (Lombardy-poplars)

Crown narrowly fastigiate. Fls male or female. Common. *P. nigra* ssp *betulifolia* x *nigra* 'Italica'. PL 22...*Plantier's Poplar* **Populus nigra 'Plantierensis'**

Crown narrowly fastigiate. Fls male. VR. PL 22.............*Lombardy-poplar* **Populus nigra 'Italica'**

Crown narrowly fastigiate. Bark whitish. Fls female. VR
....*(not illustrated) Afghan Poplar* **Populus nigra 'Afghanica'**

Crown broadly fastigiate. Fls female. Frequent
....*(not illustrated) Female Lombardy-poplar* **Populus nigra 'Gigantea'**

Group POP D – *Balsam-poplars (sect* Tacamahaca*). Terminal bud usu 1.2-2.5cm, v sticky with yellow-orange resin, strongly balsam-scented, narrowly ovoid; scales (5)7-8(9), shiny green to reddish-brown or dark red, usu with sparse hairs or cilia esp on lower scales. Lateral buds 8-15mm, usu spreading and recurved; scales (2)3(4); lowest scale usu <½ bud length, ± entire. Twigs usu shiny reddish-brown (but yellowish-brown in* P. trichocarpa*); pith white or green, turning brown. Bark ± smooth*

■Twigs (green-) yellowish-brown, often green on shaded side. Bark whitish. Trunk continuous to tree tip; crown narrow

Twigs slender to mod stout (2-3(6)mm diam), usu curved up at tip, hairy to hairless, ridged to round. Branches usu long, (±) erect, with drooping twigs. Terminal bud (10)15-20mm; scales green to reddish-brown. Occ suckering. PL 22........*Western Balsam-poplar* **Populus trichocarpa**

■Twigs shiny dark olive- to reddish-brown. Bark usu not whitish

Twigs mod (3-4mm diam), usu hairless, occ minutely hairy esp at nodes, angled to round. Trunk not continuous to tree tip; crown spreading. Suckering

Terminal bud (10)15-20mm; scales 5-7, reddish-brown, occ greenish nr base. Lateral buds spreading to ± adpressed. *P. balsamifera* x *deltoides*. PL 22....*Balm-of-Gilead* **Populus x jackii**

Twigs mod slender (2-3mm diam), hairless, usu ridged. Not suckering

Trunk not continuous to tree tip; crown spreading. Terminal bud 10-16mm; scales green to brown. Lateral buds adpressed to spreading. *P. deltoides* x *trichocarpa*. PL 22
....*Generous Poplar* **Populus x generosa**

Trunk continuous to tree tip; crown narrow. Terminal bud c15mm; scales green with brown margins. Lateral buds spreading to ± adpressed. *P. balsamifera* x *trichocarpa*. PL 21
....*Hybrid Balsam-poplar* **Populus 'Balsam Spire'**

Populus x canadensis
Hybrid Black-poplar

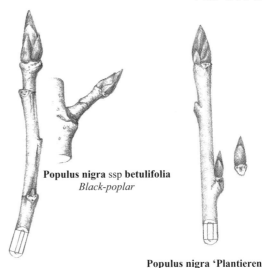

Populus nigra ssp **betulifolia**
Black-poplar

Populus nigra 'Plantierensis'
Plantier's Poplar

Populus nigra 'Italica'
Lombardy-poplar

Populus trichocarpa
Western Balsam-poplar

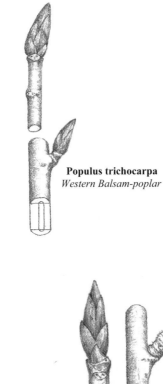

Populus x jackii
Balm-of-Gilead

Populus x generosa
Generous Poplar

Populus 'Balsam Spire'
Hybrid Balsam-poplar

Group PRU – Plunus. Twigs not zig zagging, occ with grey skin, usu round, occ weakly angled; inner bark usu weakly to strongly odorous, often with bitter almond taste; pith ½ diam, usu white, occ brown or green, usu round. Branchlets usu with woody spurs. Terminal bud absent in plums; present in cherries, peach, almond, apricot. Lateral buds often clustered around terminal bud (inc on woody spurs) and/or at base of twig (in cherries), spreading, usu ovoid; scales gland-fringed (often obscure or eroded), rarely ciliate, at least weakly 1(3)-keeled (esp lower), apiculate or with remnants of 3-toothed tip. Lf scars spiralling, raised, usu elliptical, occ ± circular to triangular, small, equal to bud width, usu weakly decurrent; bundle scars 3, usu nr upper margin. Stipule scars often joined to upper corners of lf scar, usu narrowly triangular, small, occ indistinct. Bark smooth when young, usu with elongated horizontal lenticels. Shrub or tree, all capable of suckering if roots damaged. ❶ Thorns present (4 entries). ❷ Twigs with strongly odorous inner bark (2 spp). ❸ Buds <2mm (2 spp). ❹ Twigs with hay-scented (coumarin) inner bark

■Twigs greenish (at least on underside, occ purplish above or rarely all round), often shiny, hairless, usu with stomata

Buds (2)3-5(6)mm, usu spreading. Twigs usu mod slender (2-4mm diam)

Tree or shrub, often suckering. Buds all lateral, 2-5(6)mm, conical, acute; scales 7-12. Occ ❶.
PL 23...(see below) *Wild Plum* **Prunus domestica**

Tree, not suckering

Terminal bud usu single, 3-4mm, acute; scales c12, dark reddish-brown (to blackish), hairless, ciliate. Lateral buds often with 1-2 collateral buds, 3-4mm. Twigs 3-4mm diam, shiny, soon purplish (where exposed to sunlight), stomata obscure or absent. Lf scars dark. PL 23
....*Apricot* **Prunus armeniaca**

Terminal bud with (1)2 collateral fl buds

Terminal bud hairless or hairy nr tip only, 4-5mm, ovoid, acute; scales 4-7 obtuse, dark reddish-brown, hairy, ciliate. Lateral buds similar, spreading. Fl buds ± globose, occ collateral to lf buds. Twigs c3mm diam, soon purplish (where exposed to sunlight), with stomata; pith white, often ± 5-angled. Lf scars dark. PL 23.................*Almond* **Prunus dulcis**

Terminal bud (densely) hairy, 3-5mm, ovoid, ± obtuse; scales 4-6, reddish-brown (occ obscured by hairs), occ green nr base, hairy, ciliate, often with ragged margin. Lateral buds spreading to ± adpressed, often with 1-2 collateral buds. Fl buds larger, often collateral to lf buds. Twigs 2-3mm diam, shiny green-yellow below and ± reddish-purple above, with stomata partly elongating; pith white to brown, often ± 5-angled. Lf scars dark. Bark smooth with horizontal lenticels, dark reddish-brown, scaly nr base. Trunk short; crown round; branches spreading with ascending branchlets. PL 23.......................*Peach* **Prunus persica**

Buds 1-2mm, usu adpressed. Twigs slender (1-2.5mm diam), with stomata

Twigs with lenticels usu absent; inner bark ± odourless, with weak bitter almond taste. Branchlets spreading at 60-90°, occ with grey skin; thorns usu on inner ones. Lf scars ± circular to semi-circular, v small, occ hair-fringed. Buds all lateral, usu adpressed, occ 1(2) minute collateral buds, ovoid, obtuse to ± acute; scales c4, pale brown, hairless, occ ciliate; inner scales purplish turning bud pink when bursting (in Feb). Stipule scars obscure, at top of (and ± behind) lf scar, oval to linear. Bark smooth, reddish-brown to dark grey, horizontal lenticels becoming vertical splits with age, eventually shallowly furrowed. Usu suckering; crown round or vase-shaped. ❸

Twigs green, occ purplish above. Fls white. PL 23....................*Cherry Plum* **Prunus cerasifera**

Twigs dark purple all around

Fls pale pink fading to white. Inner wood white in twigs. PL 23
...........................(not illustrated) *Purple-leaved Cherry Plum* **Prunus cerasifera 'Pissardii'**

Fls pink. Inner wood purple.....(not illustrated) *Black Cherry Plum* **Prunus cerasifera 'Nigra'**

■Twigs not greenish (or if green, then hairy or minutely so), hairy to hairless, usu without stomata

Twigs usu hairless

Twigs with strongly odorous inner bark (fetid bitter almonds or stale tobacco) ❷

Terminal bud 7-11mm, usu single, conical, ± sharply acute; scales 6-8, broad, obtuse but apiculate, 1(3)-keeled, shiny dark reddish-brown nr base with paler greyish margins, occ

Prunus dulcis
Almond

Prunus armeniaca
Apricot

Prunus cerasifera
Cherry Plum

Prunus persica
Peach

green nr base, usu hairless, occ hairs nr tip. Lateral buds 5-10mm, usu adpressed, rarely spreading, incurved at tip. Twigs mod slender (2-4mm diam), shiny <u>dark</u> olive- to dark reddish-brown or blackish, occ violet-brown or grey, ± hairless, occ minutely hairy at tip, <u>flexible</u>; lenticels low, oval, pale; pith white. Branchlets without woody spurs. Lf scars ± circular to triangular. Stipule scars ± equal or not. Bark dark brown, with horizontal lenticels, oozing yellow resin if damaged, Crown round; lower branches drooping. PL 24
....*Bird Cherry* **Prunus padus**

Terminal bud 3-4mm, occ with collateral bud, ovoid, occ ± flattened, acute; scales 4-5(6), shiny reddish-brown, with darker outer margin, occ greenish in lower ½, obtuse but apiculate, hairless. Lateral buds similar, usu spreading, rarely adpressed. Twigs slender (2-3mm diam), shiny reddish-brown, occ with grey skin, hairless; lenticels many, low, round, small, pale; pith white. Branchlets without woody spurs. Lf scars elliptic to triangular; bundle scars occ ± sunken. Stipule scars ± equal. Bark smooth with short horizontal lenticels when young; later v dark (nearly black), eventually breaking up into loose-looking curled rough scales, with reddish-brown underbark. Crown irreg oblong. PL 24.................*Rum Cherry* **Prunus serotina**

Twigs not fetid (may have weak almond or coumarin (hay) odour)

Terminal bud (6)7-12mm, with tuft of buff hairs at tip, narrowly ovoid, usu with (1)2(4) lateral buds clustered at twig tip, more spreading than *P. avium* or *P. serrula*, <u>acute</u>; scales 8-10, obtuse, shiny reddish-brown, without grey skin. Twigs mod (4-5mm diam), red-brown to grey, hairless; lenticels raised, oval; pith occ turning orange-brown. Bark hardly peeling (usu grafted on *P. avium* trunk). Not suckering. Many cultivars exist. PL 24
....*Japanese Cherry* **Prunus serrulata**

Terminal bud 2-7(8)mm, hairless (no tuft of hairs at tip), ovoid, occ with <u>grey skin</u>. Lateral buds spreading, often clustered around terminal bud (inc on woody spurs) and/or at base of twig. Twigs hairless; pith usu turning orange-brown. Suckering

Lateral buds 5-7(8)mm, ovoid, <u>± acute</u>; scales c10, shiny reddish-brown, margins often paler, ± smooth, obtuse. Terminal bud 5-7(8)mm, with 0-3 lateral buds clustered at twig tip. Twigs held more erect than *P. cerasus*, slender to mod (2-4mm diam), reddish-brown to grey; lenticels raised, round, buff. Bark smooth, reddish-brown to grey, with horizontal elongated buff lenticels ('tiger stripes'), weakly peeling into few horizontal strips exposing rough underbark, occ with lumps of reddish dried resin. Tree; trunk often ± continuous to tree tip; crown narrowly pyramidal, broader with age; branches ascending. PL 23
....*Wild Cherry* **Prunus avium**

Lateral buds 2-4mm, occ globose-ovoid, <u>± obtuse</u>; scales 4-7, <u>dark</u> reddish-brown, duller than *P. avium*, usu <u>minutely warty or pitted (sculptured)</u>, obtuse. Terminal bud to 5(8)mm, with 1-2 lateral buds clustered at twig tip. Twigs occ drooping, usu slender (1.5-2(4)mm diam). Shrub or small tree, without main trunk; crown spreading; branchlets drooping. Bark similar to *P. avium*. PL 23...*Dwarf Cherry* **Prunus cerasus**

Twigs usu hairy (occ sparsely so)

Twigs long-hairy (to 0.5mm); pith green. Buds 4-6mm, hairless or with tuft of white hairs at tip

Terminal bud with 0-2 lateral buds at twig tip, ovoid (fl buds swell to globose), (±) obtuse to ± acute; scales obtuse, reddish-brown. Twigs slender (2mm diam), usu orange-brown, occ with grey skin, with long wavy hairs on minute orange tubercules, weakly angled nr tip; lenticels <u>wart-like</u>; bark finely fissured. Bark shiny reddish-brown, with long horizontal lenticels, later slightly furrowed with scaly ridge tops, often peeling on grafted trees. Branches upright or (±) drooping. Fls in winter. Not suckering. PL 24........*Winter-flowering Cherry* **Prunus subhirtella**

Twigs minutely hairy (≤0.1mm); pith white

Buds (6)7-8(9)mm, occ with tuft of buff hairs at tip

Twigs slender (1.5-2mm diam), brown to grey, densely minutely hairy (<0.1mm), angled nr tip; lenticels round, buff. Terminal bud with 0-2 lateral buds at twig tip, ovoid-conical to spindle-shaped, v acute, curved, spreading to ± adpressed; scales 7-10, reddish-brown, v obtuse, sculptured, occ with sparse white hairs, not ciliate. Bark <u>strongly peeling</u> into horizontal strips, reddish-purple. Not suckering. PL 24..........*Tibetan Cherry* **Prunus serrula**

Prunus serotina
Rum Cherry

Prunus padus
Bird Cherry

Prunus serrulata
Japanese Cherry

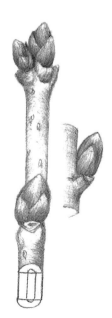

Prunus avium
Wild Cherry

Prunus cerasus
Dwarf Cherry

Prunus subhirtella
Winter-flowering Cherry

Prunus serrula
Tibetan Cherry

Buds 2-5(6)mm
Terminal bud absent. Lateral buds 2-5(6)mm, occ with 1-2 collateral buds, usu spreading, conical, acute; scales 7-12, dark brown, occ green nr base, obtuse, hairy to ± hairless, ciliate (or sparsely so). Twigs slender to mod (2-3.5mm diam), appearing swollen at nodes (due to raised lf scars), dull grey- to reddish-brown, occ greenish or purplish, occ with grey skin, densely minutely hairy to hairless, occ with stomata; lenticels obscure or absent. Branchlets with woody spurs. Thorns occ present. Bark usu smooth. Suckering. Hybrid origin from *P. cerasifera* x *spinosa* with variation ± continuous between spp. Occ ❶. PL 23
....*Wild Plum* **Prunus domestica**
Terminal bud usu with 2 lateral buds at twig tip. All buds 3-4mm, without collateral buds, spreading, ovoid-globose, ± obtuse, hairy nr tip; scales c7, v obtuse, reddish-brown, hairless (exc upper scales), not ciliate. Twigs slender (1.5-2mm diam), occ with grey skin, minutely hairy at least nr tip (occ sparse); lenticels same colour as twig; inner bark weakly hay-scented (coumarin). Branchlets with woody spurs, drooping. Bark usu fissured. Not suckering. ❹. PL 23...*St Lucie Cherry* **Prunus mahaleb**
Buds 1-1.5(2)mm (*P. domestica* rarely keys out here)
Terminal bud absent. Lateral buds usu with (1)2(4) small collateral buds (occ along, or collateral to, thorns), spreading, ± globose to ovoid, obtuse; scales 5-7, pale or dark reddish-brown, usu hairy, loose. Twigs slender (1-2(3)mm diam), dull blackish or dark brown, rarely greenish (in shade), occ with grey skin, usu minutely hairy, rarely hairless, rigid; lenticels sparse or absent; pith occ buff. Branchlets at 45-90°, often with woody spurs (often with crowded fl bud clusters). Thorns to 4cm (occ more), straight, often minutely hairy. Suckering, often strongly. ❶❸. PL 24...*Blackthorn* **Prunus spinosa**

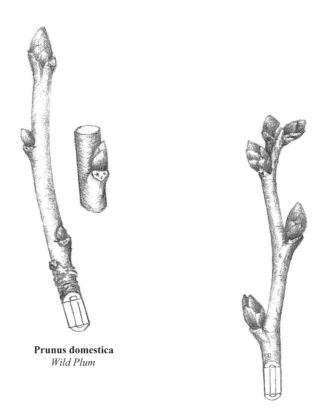

Prunus domestica
Wild Plum

Prunus mahaleb
St Lucie Cherry

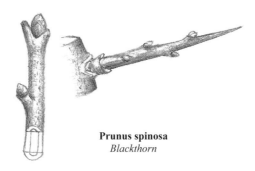

Prunus spinosa
Blackthorn

Group PYR – Pyrus. *Twigs not zig-zagging, angled to round, occ with grey skin; lenticels flat, small, oval, white or buff; pith ½ diam, (yellowish-) white to green, angled. Branchlets usu with woody spurs. Terminal bud present; scales ovate, obtuse, usu apiculate or 3-toothed, the lower ± keeled at least nr tip. Lateral buds similar. Lf scars spiralling, raised, ± broadly crescent-shaped, equal to bud width, weakly decurrent; bundle scars 3. Stipule scars absent. Bark cracked into square or rectangular scales. Tree, not suckering*

■Twigs white-felted or woolly at least nr tip, dark olive- (or purplish-) brown beneath hairs. Terminal bud white-hairy; scales (5)7-12

Terminal bud 3-8(10)mm, <u>ovoid</u>, <u>acute</u>, dark reddish-brown but often obscured by white hairs, <u>tuft of golden hairs at tip</u> or base (or scale margins). Lateral buds 3-5mm, acute, ovoid, ± adpressed to spreading. Twigs ± slender (2.5-3mm diam), white-silky (felted) to dark olive-brown beneath hairs, round to angled. Branchlets usu <u>drooping to strongly so (weeping)</u>. Lf scars <u>dark brown</u>. Unarmed. PL 25..*Willow-leaved Pear* **Pyrus salicifolia**

Terminal bud 6-12mm, <u>broadly ovoid to ± globose</u>, <u>obtuse</u>, reddish-brown but densely white-hairy esp nr tip, without golden hairs; scales <u>v obtuse</u>, <u>usu split</u>. Lateral buds spreading. Twigs mod (4-6mm diam), greyish- or whitish-woolly to sparsely so, dark olive- or purplish-brown beneath hairs, ± strongly ridged esp below nodes. Lf scars brown. Thorns rarely present. Rarely planted. PL 25..*Oleaster-leaved Pear* **Pyrus elaeagnifolia**

■Twigs (±) hairless, olive- to reddish-brown. Terminal bud white- or buff-hairy, without golden hairs

Terminal bud 6-10mm, broadly ovoid, obtuse; scales 7-11, reddish-brown (lower darker) but densely white- to buff-hairy. Twigs mod (3-4mm diam), olive- to reddish-brown. Branchlets with woody spurs occ thorny. Crown fastigiate to conical, with erect branches. Frs (0.5)10-15mm diam, globose, brown, with lenticels. PL 25..*Callery Pear* **Pyrus calleryana**

■Twigs usu hairless, occ hairy in some cultivars, reddish- or orange-brown. Terminal bud usu hairless but with <u>tuft of golden hairs at tip</u> (break scales to check), ovoid to conical, (sharply) acute; scales 4-6(7), usu dark reddish-brown, occ purplish-brown (or dark brown to red or black), often with grey skin (esp upper), distinctly 3-toothed, often buff- or white-ciliate. Lateral buds spreading. Fl buds often ovoid-globose and slightly narrowed at base. Thorns, if present, often with buds and/or lf scars along length. Trunk ± continuous to tree tip; crown ± pyramidal to rounded. Frs green

Thorns usu present. Twigs mod slender (3mm diam)

Buds 3-5mm; scales often with grey skin, hairless. Frs 2-4cm diam, ± globose. PL 25 ....*Wild Pear* **Pyrus pyraster**

Thorns often present. Twigs slender (1.5-2(3)mm diam), hairless

Frs 1.5-2cm diam, ± globose. Buds 4-6mm; scales reddish-brown, not or rarely with grey skin, hairless. PL 25...*Plymouth Pear* **Pyrus cordata**

Thorns absent. Twigs ± mod ((2)3-5mm diam)

Twigs hairless. Buds 4-8mm; scales often with grey skin, usu hairless. Frs 3-8cm diam, often typical 'pears'. PL 25...*Pear* **Pyrus communis**

Twigs with at least some hairs. Buds 3-8mm; scales often with grey skin, <u>hairy</u>. Frs 5-8cm diam, typical 'pears'..........(not illustrated) *Williams Pear* **Pyrus communis 'Williams' Bon Chrétien'**

Pyrus salicifolia
Willow-leaved Pear

Pyrus elaeagnifolia
Oleaster-leaved Pear

Pyrus calleryana
Callery Pear

Pyrus pyraster
Wild Pear

Pyrus cordata
Plymouth Pear

Pyrus communis
Pear

Group RIB – Ribes *subgenus* Ribesia. *Subgenus* Grossularia *(R.* uva-crispa*) keys out in* **AB***. Twigs usu mod slender ((1)2-4mm diam), not zig-zagging, round; lenticels absent (but minute warts in* R. sanguineum*); bark soon splitting, peeling in longitudinal strips (esp branchlets in 2nd yr); pith c½ diam, white or green, occ turning brown, round or obscurely 5-angled, soon fragmenting. Branchlets often with short twigs, occ with woody spurs. Terminal bud sessile, often surrounded by cluster of lateral buds at tip or base of twig; scales obtuse, weakly 3-keeled (3-veined; mid-vein strongest and usu ending in dark brown apiculus), loose. Lateral buds soon* short-stalked*; lowest large scale often directly above lf scar but often 2 smaller scales either side of lf scar forming V-shape. Lf scars up to ½ way around twig, spiralling, not or weakly raised, narrowly crescent-shaped, occ weakly narrowed between bundle scars, shortly decurrent; bundle scars 3, along upper margin. Bark peeling in longitudinal strips. Unarmed shrub to 2.5m, occ suckering.* ❶ *Buds 10-15mm.* ❷ *Buds >2.5 x as long as wide (2 spp).* ❸ *Twigs and/or buds aromatic with sessile glands (2 spp)*

■Buds green to reddish-purple, often multicoloured. Twigs usu minutely hairy

Buds 10-15mm

    Buds single, spindle-shaped, acute; scales 5-7, green to reddish-purple, often multicoloured, hairless, glandular-ciliate; inner scales with colourless to reddish sessile globose glands, with fruity odour. Lateral buds adpressed, short-stalked to 2mm, with lowest scale directly above lf scar. Twigs mod slender (2-3(4)mm diam), reddish-brown, minutely crisped-hairy, rough with minute warts; pith usu green. Lf scars >> lateral bud width. Bark reddish- to greyish-brown, peeling to reveal vertical rows of horizontal lenticels. Early bursting. ❶❷❸. PL 27
    ....*Flowering Currant* **Ribes sanguineum**

Buds <10mm

    Buds with strongly aromatic sessile disc-shaped yellow glands, single or 3-5-clustered at tip or base of twig, 3-8mm, ovoid, ± obtuse to ± acute; scales 3-6, yellow-green to purplish, occ brown, sparsely white-hairy, usu ciliate. Lateral buds ± spreading, short-stalked to 2mm, with lowest large scale directly above lf scar. Twigs mod (3-4mm diam), purplish-brown to pale brown or grey, minutely crisped-hairy, occ sessile disc-shaped yellow glands nr tip; inner bark odorous; pith white. Lf scars >> lateral bud width. Bark peeling to reveal vertical rows of horizontal lenticels. ❸. PL 26...*Black Currant* **Ribes nigrum**

    Buds without glands, single or 2-3-clustered at tip or base of twig (short twigs less frequent than in other *Ribes*), 5-7mm, narrowly ovoid, ± acute; scales 6-7, reddish-brown, occ purplish, sparsely white-hairy, ciliate. Lateral buds ± spreading, short-stalked to 2mm, with lowest large scale directly above lf scar. Twigs mod (3-4mm diam), reddish-brown, minutely white-hairy at least nr tip; inner bark not or weakly odorous; pith white or green. Lf scars ≥ lateral bud width. PL 26...*Buffalo Currant* **Ribes odoratum**

■Buds white, occ pinkish or pale brown, <10mm. Twigs hairless

    Buds single, 4-9mm, spindle-shaped, v acute; scales 5-9, hairless, minutely ciliate, often glandular-ciliate. Lateral buds adpressed, stalked to 1(2)mm, with lowest large scale directly above lf scar. Twigs slender (1-3mm diam), whitish to pale grey-brown; inner bark not or weakly odorous; pith green. Lf scars ≥ lateral bud width. Branches occ purplish-brown. ❷. PL 26
    ....*Mountain Currant* **Ribes alpinum**

■Buds dark (purplish-) brown, <10mm. Twigs hairless

    Buds usu 3-5-clustered at tip or nodes of each yrs growth, 3-7mm, ovoid to shortly spindle-shaped, ± acute; scales 6-7, minutely white-hairy to (±) hairless, ciliate or not. Lateral buds ± spreading, v short-stalked to 0.5mm, with lowest large scale usu not directly above lf scar. Twigs mod (3-4mm diam), usu pale grey-brown, occ dark purplish-brown; inner bark weakly odorous; pith white. Lf scars >> lateral bud width. Branchlets dark purplish-brown. Bark peeling to reveal many lenticels (not in vertical rows)

        Remnant lvs usu hairless or veins sparsely hairy below. PL 27..........*Red Currant* **Ribes rubrum**
        Remnant lvs softly hairy both sides. Gardens or limestone habs, R. Apparent hybrids with R. *rubrum* occ grown. PL 27..*Downy Currant* **Ribes spicatum**

Ribes nigrum
Black Currant

Ribes sanguineum
Flowering Currant

Ribes odoratum
Buffalo Currant

Ribes spicatum
Downy Currant

Ribes alpinum
Mountain Currant

Ribes rubrum
Red Currant

Group RUB – Rubus. *Twigs often prickly, with persistent bud scale remnants at join with branchlet; lenticels absent; pith ¾ diam, round. Buds all lateral, usu spreading, occ adpressed, usu superposed (but collateral in R. spectabilis) with lower bud often covered by petiole base; scales (3)4-5(7), herbaceous to papery, loose, at least the 2 outer scales keeled and 3-toothed. Lf scars spiralling, raised, appearing as a shrivelled stub on persistent petiole base (lvs deciduous above petiole base), crescent-shaped when petiole base removed or cut, ± decurrent; bundle scars 3, rarely visible, central scar long-protruding. Stipules occ persisting on petiole base, to 12mm, usu brown and papery, not falling. Shrub; stems biennial in some spp. In biennial spp, a new stem (primocane) grows from rootstock to its full length in 1st yr but does not produce any fls; in 2nd yr, the stem becomes a floricane producing lateral fl shoots which usu die after fr. Often patch-forming.* ❶ *Twigs reddish-purple with long reddish gland-tipped bristles.* ❷ *Twigs whitish-pruinose*

■Twigs erect, occ arching, with or without prickles; pith white or orange-brown....................**RUB A**
■Twigs sprawling over ground or vegetation, usu arching, with prickles; pith white................**RUB B**

RUB A – Twigs erect, occ arching, round, with or without prickles; pith white or orange-brown
■Twigs densely hairy
  Twigs greyish to yellowish-brown, minutely hairy (<0.1mm), mod (3-5mm diam), weakly or not zig-zagging; prickles to 1mm, slender, weak, straight, without broad bases, often reduced to warts; bark not or rarely weakly peeling; pith <u>orange-brown</u>. Buds 5-8mm, ovoid-conical, curved; scales (purplish-) brown, occ green nr base, often same colour as twig, hairy at least nr tip. Stipules (if present) linear. Stems biennial, erect to 1.5m. PL 28..........(primocane) *Raspberry* **Rubus idaeus**
  Twigs dull pale brown to orange-brown, minutely hairy (<0.1mm) to <u>± prickly with longer stiff hairs</u>, mod stout (5mm diam), not zig-zagging; bark not peeling; pith <u>white</u>. Buds 8-15mm, narrowly ovoid; scales brown, often green nr base, silky-hairy esp nr tip, the 2 outer scales darker. Stipules (if persistent) ovate-lanc. Stems usu biennial, erect, to 2m. PL 28
  ....*Thimbleberry* **Rubus parviflorus**
  Twigs reddish-purple, bristly hairy with long (5-7mm) reddish-brown gland-tipped bristles and shorter glandular hairs, mod (3-4mm diam), not zig-zagging; prickles to 5mm, ± broad-based; bark not peeling; pith <u>orange-brown</u>. Buds 4-6mm, densely white-hairy. Stipules (if present) linear. Stems biennial, erect to arching to 2m, occ scrambling, often rooting at tips. ❶. PL 28
  ....*Japanese Wineberry* **Rubus phoenicolasius**
■Twigs (±) hairless
  Twigs whitish-pruinose (purplish below pruinose covering); pith orange-brown
    Twigs mod slender (3-4mm diam), purplish, not zig-zagging; prickles 2-4mm, straight or often <u>upcurved</u>, broad-based (equalling height). Branchlets unarmed. Buds 5mm, reddish-green. Stipules (if persistent) linear. Stems biennial, arching. ❷. PL 28
    ....*White-stemmed Bramble* **Rubus cockburnianus**
  Twigs not whitish-pruinose or purplish
    Pith orange-brown (the hybrid of *R. odoratus* x *parviflorus* (*R.* x *fraseri*) has buff pith and keys out here)
      Bark not or rarely weakly peeling. Twigs mod (3-5mm diam), weakly or not zig-zagging, yellowish- to reddish-brown, occ sparsely hairy; prickles weak, often reduced to warts. Buds hairy to hairless. Stems biennial. PL 28.
      ....(see entry above for shared characters) (floricane) *Raspberry* **Rubus idaeus**
      Bark strongly peeling in broad longitudinal strips revealing orange-brown underbark. Twigs mod stout (4-8mm diam), ± zig-zagging, pale grey-brown, often minutely hairy nr tip and with sparse <u>long glandular hairs</u> (soon withering); prickles <u>absent</u>. Buds 6-8mm, ovoid; scales grey-brown, silky-hairy, the 2 outer scales darker. Stipules (if present) ovate-lanc. Stems perennial, erect to 2.5m. PL 28..........................*Purple-flowered Raspberry* **Rubus odoratus**
    Pith white. Bark weakly peeling longitudinally (esp nr base) revealing yellow underbark

151

RUB A

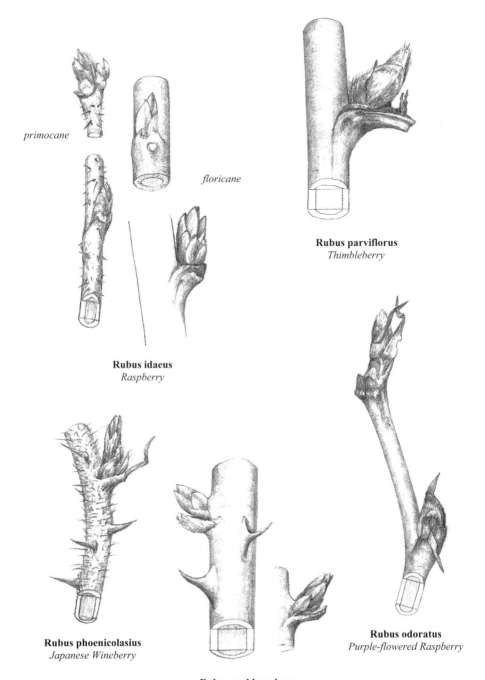

primocane

floricane

Rubus parviflorus
Thimbleberry

Rubus idaeus
Raspberry

Rubus phoenicolasius
Japanese Wineberry

Rubus cockburnianus
White-stemmed Bramble

Rubus odoratus
Purple-flowered Raspberry

Twigs mod (4-5mm diam), ± shiny orange-brown, (±) hairless, zig-zagging at least nr tip; prickles nr base, scattered, slender, weak, breaking easily. Buds ± adpressed to spreading, occ 1-2 <u>collateral</u> buds, (3)5-8(10)mm, ovoid; scales (4)5-7, same colour as twig, hairless or silky-hairy; Inner scales green and silvery-hairy when bursting. Stipules (if present) ovate-lanc. Stems perennial, erect to 2(3)m. PL 28..................................*Salmonberry* **Rubus spectabilis**

RUB B – Twigs sprawling over ground or vegetation, usu arching, not zig-zagging, with prickles; pith white. Stipules (if present) linear. Stems biennial

■Twigs 5-angled (occ weakly so), usu well-armed with prickles

Twigs slender to stout (usu 4-12mm diam), green to red-brown, rarely pruinose, hairy to hairless; prickles variable, often fierce, straight or curved. Buds 7-10mm, expanding early; scales green to brown or reddish, keeled, hairy; inner scales green. Often >3m long, forming large dense clumps, usu rooting at tips. Occ semi-evergreen. Early bursting (usu). Many microspecies. PL 28
....*Bramble* **Rubus fruticosus** agg

■Twigs round, weakly armed with prickles

Twigs v slender (2mm diam), purple-red, often sparsely pruinose, hairless; prickles 1-2mm, weak, curved, broad-based. Buds 2-3mm; scales reddish, hairy nr tip. Usu ± prostrate. PL 28
....*Dewberry* **Rubus caesius**

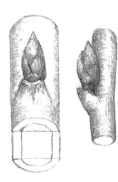

Rubus spectabilis
Salmonberry

Rubus fruticosus agg
Bramble

Rubus caesius
Dewberry

Group SAL – Salix. *Twigs not zig-zagging, flexible but occ brittle at base (i.e. easily snapped from branchlet above base of twig, often leaving spur); lenticels few, low, round, small, orange; inner bark with bitter astringent ('aspirin') taste (exc* S. triandra *which tastes of rosewater); pith ½ diam. Buds all lateral, often ± same colour as twig; scale 1 (actually 2 fused modified lvs), falling as a conical cap as the bud bursts. Branchlets occ with 2 collateral buds in 2nd yr. Lf scars spiralling, (±) raised, crescent-shaped, narrowed between bundle scars, usu equal to bud width; bundle scars 3. Stipule scars, if present, usu small (c0.5mm unless otherwise stated), ± oval, ± equal, often joined with lf scar. Often by water. Many spp (including those of mtns) may be planted in gardens away from their typical natural habitats. Hybrids frequently occur (intermediate between characters of parents)*

■Tree or tall shrub ≥1m, not rooting at nodes (may climb mtns)

Twigs and/or buds hairy to densely so (at least nr tip)..**SAL A**

Twigs and buds usu (±) hairless (occ v sparsely hairy)...**SAL B**

■Low shrub <1m, rooting at nodes. Often mtns (occ garden rockeries)..................................**SAL C**

SAL A

Group SAL A – *Twigs and/or buds hairy to densely so at least nr twig tip.* ❶ *Stipule scars absent*

■Buds adpressed, all similar in size and shape along twig (fl buds and lf buds ± identical)

Buds closely spaced along twig, some ± (or actually) overlapping. Pith usu round. Shrub

Buds reddish at least nr tip, yellow-green nr base, hairy to ± hairless, 4-6 x 1.5 2mm, (±) flattened-oblong, ± obtuse. Twigs slender (2-3mm diam), reddish on sunlit side, yellow-green below, whitish-woolly (esp nr tip) or sparsely so, later hairless, irreg 5(7)-ridged esp nr tip, ± brittle at base; pith white, round or 5-angled. Lf scars weakly decurrent. Stipule scars absent. Bark eventually fissured. ❶. PL 29..*Olive Willow* **Salix elaeagnos**

Buds pale grey or yellowish (occ reddish), densely short-silky-hairy (velvety) (but lower buds ± hairless), 5-9 x 3mm, ovoid, obtuse to ± acute, occ curved. Twigs mod slender (2-4mm diam), greenish-grey, minutely white-hairy (to velvety) at least nr tip, (±) round but angled at tip, later shiny olive to (reddish-) brown, ± brittle at base; pith white, 5-angled. Lf scars not decurrent. Bark furrowed. PL 31..*Osier* **Salix viminalis**

Buds spaced out along twig, not overlapping. Pith usu 5-angled

Tree

Branchlets strongly drooping (weeping)

Twigs branching at <90°, usu brittle at base, slender (1.5-2mm diam), shiny yellow, later hairless. PL 31.......(see **SAL B**) *Golden Weeping Willow* **Salix x sepulcralis 'Chrysocoma'**

Branchlets erect or drooping but not weeping (*Salix x pendulina* rarely keys out here)

Twigs branching at c90°, brittle at base, mod slender (2-3mm diam), usu (shiny) yellowish-orange to orange (obvious at a distance) or olive, sparsely hairy to hairless. Buds 6-12mm, often curved to 1-side, soon hairless. PL 29...........(see **SAL B**) *Crack-willow* **Salix x fragilis**

Twigs usu branching at c45-60°, rarely brittle at base, slender (1-3mm diam), olive- or reddish-brown (occ golden-yellow or red-orange in cultivars), silky-hairy at least nr tip (often densely so), ± angled nr tip; pith white, 5-angled. Buds 5-8mm, cylindric-lanceoloid, ± obtuse to ± acute, tips not curved, dark (reddish-) brown, or yellow to olive, often ± same colour as twig, silky-hairy. Bark furrowed with intersecting ridges, greyish-brown. Trunk usu short, often leaning, occ pollarded; crown wide; branches stout, ascending but outer twigs erect or drooping. PL 29..*White Willow* **Salix alba**

Shrub

Twigs mod slender (3mm diam), densely minutely adpressed-hairy at least nr tip, reddish, round, occ brittle at base. Buds 7-10mm, long-conical, v acuminate (occ recurved), coppery to reddish, hairless or silky at base. PL 29....................*Heart-leaved Willow* **Salix eriocephala**

Twigs mod slender (2-3mm diam), ± velvety (shortly hairy), olive- to reddish-brown, occ yellowish to orange, rarely purple-black; pith brown, ± 5-angled. Stipule scars relatively large to 1mm. Branches longer and less branched than *S. phylicifolia*, dull orange-brown or greenish to grey, ± hairless. Lf and fl buds similar (fl buds slightly larger but similar shape), 4-7mm, ovoid to ± lanceoloid, usu obtuse, rarely narrowed into 'beak', usu same colour as twig, silky-hairy (usu longer hairs nr base), occ hairless. Shrub, rarely small tree. Usu by gravelly rivers and lakes, rarely dune-slacks and rock ledges. Mostly N Br. PL 30 ....*Dark-leaved Willow* **Salix myrsinifolia**

■Buds spreading at least nr tip, spaced out along twig, of two kinds differing in size and shape (larger fl buds often intermixed with smaller lf buds) (exc *S. repens* which has ± identical fl and lf buds). Twigs never brittle at base

Twigs densely silky-hairy at least nr tip, v slender (1mm diam). Buds 2-4mm, minutely white-dotted with stomata (occ obscure). PL 31....................(see **SAL C**) *Creeping Willow* **Salix repens**

Twigs usu shortly ± patent-hairy

Twigs usu mod (3-5mm diam), usu greenish on lower side (for 2-several yrs), densely minutely hairy to hairless, not ridged nr tip

Twigs green to dark reddish-brown on upper side (rarely yellowish or red-black all round); pith ± 5-angled, white or buff. Branchlets hairless, without striae on wood. Lf buds 3-5 x 2-4mm, deltoid-ovoid, ± acute (but tips rounded), convex with lateral keels, (shiny) yellow-green to

157

Salix elaeagnos
Olive Willow

Salix viminalis
Osier

Salix alba
White Willow

Salix eriocephala
Heart-leaved Willow

Salix myrsinifolia
Dark-leaved Willow

orange or dark red, hairy to hairless. Fl buds (6)8-12(15) x 6-12mm, deltoid, swollen, with tips usu upturned. Stipule scars occ relatively large to 1mm. Trunk(s) pale grey with diamond-shaped orange lenticels, eventually furrowed with intersecting ridges and orange in furrows. Small tree, rarely shrub; crown round. PL 29.....................................*Goat Willow* **Salix caprea**

Twigs slender (1-2.5mm diam), dull brown-grey to reddish, rarely greenish (in 1st yr only), densely minutely hairy (occ persisting on 2nd yr branchlets), ridged nr tip. Branchlets and branches (c2-6 yrs) with striae (fine raised ridges) on wood visible when bark peeled off (corresponding to bark furrows on branches). Lf buds convex with lateral keels. Fl buds broadly ovoid, ± spreading nr tip with tip often ± upturned. Bark smooth, greyish-brown, later fissured. Crown round

Twigs (1)1.5-2.5mm diam, usu dull brown-grey to blackish-red, rarely greenish, often long and branched at <60°. Lf buds 3-5(6)mm, ovoid or ovoid-deltoid, usu ± acute, occ developing 'beak', brown or reddish-brown or orange, occ green or yellow, usu minutely hairy, occ hairless. Fl buds 5-10 x 4-6mm. Shrub or tree, 2-5(10)m. Lvs 2-8(16)cm, not rugose. PL 29 ....*Grey Willow* **Salix cinerea**

Twigs 1-1.5mm diam, <u>reddish</u>, rarely brownish, occ with grey skin, usu shorter and branched at 60-90°. Lf buds 1.5-2.5mm, ovoid to globose-deltoid, v obtuse, reddish, hairy to ± hairless. Fl buds (4)5-6(7)mm. Shrub, 0.5-2.5m. Lvs usu 1.5-3cm, rugose. Often bogs or acid habs. PL 29...*Eared Willow* **Salix aurita**

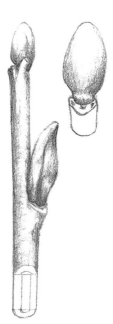

Salix caprea
Goat Willow

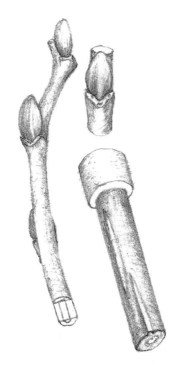

Salix cinerea
Grey Willow

Salix aurita
Eared Willow

Group SAL B – *Twigs and buds (±) hairless (occ v sparsely hairy). Pith white unless otherwise stated.* ❶ *Stipule scars absent (2 spp).* ❷ *Bark flaking.* ❸ *Branches weeping (2 entries; 4 taxa).* ❹ *Twigs and buds yellow (usu without other colour hues)*

■At least some buds (±) opp OR twigs pruinose

Twigs shiny greenish to red-brown (esp on sunlit side), occ purplish, v rarely pruinose, slender (1-2(3)mm diam), round, hairless; pith round. Branchlets often with side twigs ill-developed. Buds often of 2 sizes (fl and lf buds different sizes); lf buds 4-7mm, often nr twig tip or intermixed with larger fl buds; fl buds 10-15mm; all buds adpressed, flattened-cylindrical, obtuse, often narrowed to flat 'beak' at tip (but not curved upwards), with lateral keels, shiny yellow-orange to reddish, often turning purple-black, hairless; scale easily detached exposing young fls or lvs. Lf scars opp or subopp, without interpetiolar ridge. Stipule scars absent. Bark smooth, occ shallowly fissured, grey. Shrub. ❶. PL 30...*Purple Willow* **Salix purpurea**

Twigs pruinose (often patchy), dark reddish (occ greenish on underside), mod slender (2-3mm diam), hairless, round or angled nr tip; pith round to ± angled. Buds adpressed, 6-12mm (fl buds up to max), ovoid, (±) acute, shiny red to black or orange, usu hairless, rarely silky-hairy. Lf scars alt. Bark smooth. Shrub or small tree. PL 29.................................*Violet-willow* **Salix daphnoides**

■All buds alt. Twigs never pruinose

Twigs mod (usu 3-5mm diam). Buds spreading. PL 29........(see **SAL A**) *Goat Willow* **Salix caprea**

Twigs (±) slender (usu ≤3mm diam). Buds (±) adpressed (occ spreading in *S. pentandra*)

  Twigs ± strongly ridged (due to decurrent lf scars) at least above midpoint

    Twigs reddish on sunlit side, yellow-green below. ❶. PL 29

    ....(see **SAL A**) *Olive Willow* **Salix elaeagnos**

    Twigs ± shiny dark olive- to reddish-brown, occ yellowish, (1)2-3mm diam, occ hairy at tip, 7-ridged, often brittle at base; inner bark with odour (and taste) of rosewater perfume; pith obscurely 5-angled. Branchlets grey, mostly with long twigs, side twigs ill-developed. Buds 4-8mm, lanceoloid, often narrowed to flat 'beak' at tip (occ slightly recurved), ± obtuse, with lateral keels, ± same colour as twig, occ hairy at tip. Stipule scars relatively large to 1mm. Bark smooth, greenish-grey, flaking in large patches, revealing reddish-brown underbark. Shrub or small tree. ❷. PL 31...*Almond Willow* **Salix triandra**

  Twigs round to ± angled (occ weakly ridged nr tip)

    Twigs branching at c90°, brittle at base

      Twigs 2-3mm diam, usu (shiny) yellowish-orange to orange (obvious at a distance) or olive, usu hairless, occ sparsely silky-hairy nr tip, round to ± angled (esp nr tip); pith occ buff, 5-angled. Branchlets greenish-grey. Buds ± adpressed, with lateral keels, yellow to reddish, often ± same colour as twig, occ purplish to ± black (when bud scale dies), soon hairless; those of male trees 8-12 x 4mm, wider than twig, conical but curved to 1-side, acute; those of female trees c6 x 3mm, as wide as twig, lanceoloid, occ flattening to 'beak' at tip, ± acute. Bark furrowed with intersecting ridges. Tree; trunk often pollarded; crown wide, with twigs erect or drooping. *S. alba x euxina* (*S. euxina* was formerly named *S. fragilis* var *decipiens* and may refer to totally hairless specimens keying out here). PL 29

      ....*Crack-willow* **Salix** x **fragilis**

    Twigs branching at <90°, brittle at base or not (rarely snapping audibly)

      Branchlets strongly drooping (weeping). Twigs v long. Tree; trunk short, rarely pollarded. ❸

      Twigs usu brittle at base, shiny yellow, 1.5-2mm diam, occ adpressed-hairy nr tip; pith ± 5-angled. Buds 5-10mm, lanceoloid, ± obtuse, with lateral keels, yellow, hairless or sparsely adpressed-hairy esp nr tip. Bark furrowed. ❹. *S. alba x babylonica*. PL 31

      ....*Golden Weeping Willow* **Salix** x **sepulcralis 'Chrysocoma'**

      Twigs moderately (to strongly) brittle, shiny olive-brown, 1.5-2mm diam, hairless; pith ± 5-angled. Buds 5-7mm, lanceoloid, ± acute, with lateral keels, green- to reddish-brown, usu ± same colour as twig, hairless or sparsely adpressed-hairy esp nr tip. Bark furrowed. Often less strongly weeping than *S. x sepulcralis*. *S. babylonica x euxina* (or x *fragilis*). PL 30..*Weeping Crack-willow* **Salix** x **pendulina**

Salix daphnoides
Violet-willow

Salix purpurea
Purple Willow

Salix triandra
Almond Willow

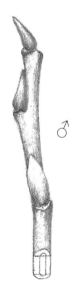

Salix x fragilis
Crack-willow

Salix x sepulcralis 'Chrysocoma'
Golden Weeping Willow

Salix x pendulina
Weeping Crack-willow

SAL B

Branchlets spiralling like a corkscrew, usu strongly drooping (weeping). Twigs long. Usu ❸
  Twigs shiny olive-brown, hairless
  ....(not illustrated) *Corkscrew Willow* **Salix babylonica** var **pekinensis 'Tortuosa'**
  Twigs shiny orange-yellow, occ adpressed-hairy nr tip. *S. alba* x *babylonica*
  ....(not illustrated) *Dragon's-claw Willow* **Salix** x **sepulcralis 'Erythroflexuosa'**
Branchlets not drooping or spiralling. Twigs long or short
  Buds v shiny, without obvious flattened 'beak' at tip
    Twigs slender to mod slender (1.5-3mm diam), <u>v shiny</u> olive-brown or yellow-green to
    dark red-brown, occ sparsely hairy and angled at tip; pith ± 5-angled, occ brown.
    Branchlets pale brown. Buds ± adpressed, often ± spreading and larger nr twig tip, 4-8 x
    2-3mm, oblong or lanceoloid, obtuse, occ with lateral keels (occ keels on upper and
    lower sides making buds ± 4-angled), <u>v shiny</u> yellow-green to dark red-brown (green or
    reddish at base), same colour as twig, hairless, slightly sticky and v weakly balsam-
    scented when bursting only. Stipule scars v small (<0.5mm). Bark mostly smooth,
    fissured on lower trunk. Shrub or small tree. PL 30...............*Bay Willow* **Salix pentandra**
  Buds dull, often with flattened 'beak' at tip
    Twigs mod slender (2-3mm diam), yellowish to orange or olive- to reddish-brown, rarely
    purple-black; pith <u>brown</u>. Branchlets dull orange-brown or greenish to grey, longer and
    less branched than *S. phylicifolia*. Lf buds and fl buds <u>similar size and shape</u>, 4-7mm,
    ovoid to ± lanceoloid, usu obtuse, rarely narrowed into 'beak', yellow or ± same colour
    as twig. Shrub, rarely small tree. PL 30
    ....(see **SAL A**) *Dark-leaved Willow* **Salix myrsinifolia**
    Twigs slender (2mm diam), short, well-branched, shiny <u>reddish-brown</u>, occ dark violet or
    olive. Branchlets usu more greyish-olive. Lf buds and fl buds <u>differing in size and shape</u>
    (one or mixture of both types on each twig). Lf buds occ in prs, adpressed, 5-9mm,
    narrowly ovoid to lanceoloid, acute, narrowed to ± flattened recurved 'beak', yellow to
    greenish-orange or same colour as twig, sparsely silky-hairy. Fl buds ± adpressed (but
    occ with upturned tips), 7-13 x 2-3mm, ovoid, ± swollen, occ turning black, hairless. Lf
    scars closely spaced (twigs appearing knobbly). Shrub, rarely small tree. By water or
    damp rocky places, often base-rich. N Br. PL 30......*Tea-leaved Willow* **Salix phylicifolia**

Salix pentandra
Bay Willow

Salix phylicifolia
Tea-leaved Willow

SAL C

Group SAL C – *Low shrub <1m, rooting at lower nodes. Often mtns (and rockeries).* ❶ *Stipule scars absent (2 spp).* ❷ *Buds with stomata (visible as minute white dots)*

■Twigs and buds (±) hairless. Buds ± equal in size and shape (lf and fl buds identical)
  Buds mostly >4mm
    Twigs mod slender (2-3mm diam), shiny green to dark purplish-brown, sparse hairs nr tip. Buds ± spreading, 3-9mm, ± obtuse, shiny bronze-brown. Mtns (usu), usu base-rich. PL 30
    ....*Whortle-leaved Willow* **Salix myrsinites**
  Buds mostly <4mm
    Twigs slender (1-2mm diam), shiny dark reddish-brown, occ greenish, hairless. Buds spreading, 2-4(6)mm, greenish- or reddish-brown, soon hairless. Mtns, base-rich. ❶. PL 31
    ....*Net-leaved Willow* **Salix reticulata**
■Twigs and/or buds hairy
  Buds 2mm, ± equal in size and shape (lf and fl buds identical)
    R, usu mtns. Twigs v slender (1mm diam), greenish-brown, silky-hairy. Branchlets v branched, shiny dark reddish-brown (almost blackish), hairless. Buds adpressed to spreading, oblong, obtuse, yellow-green, occ sparse hairs. Branches often underground. Prostrate dwarf shrub, often <5cm tall. ❶. PL 30..*Dwarf Willow* **Salix herbacea**
  Buds 2-4mm, ± equal in size and shape (lf and fl buds identical)
    Widespread, usu dunes-slacks, heathlands and moors, occ climbing mtns. Twigs v slender (1mm diam), yellowish- or reddish-brown, densely silky-hairy at least nr tip, round; pith ± 5-angled. Branchlets shiny red-brown or yellow, hairless. Buds spreading, ovoid-oblong, v obtuse, yellow to dark (blackish-) red, silky-hairy, minutely white-dotted with stomata (occ obscure). Prostrate to ascending, occ erect to 1.5m. ❷. PL 31.....................*Creeping Willow* **Salix repens**
    VR, mtns, often base-rich. Twigs slender (1-1.5mm diam), reddish-brown, minutely (±) adpressed-hairy. Branchlets reddish-brown, hairless. Buds usu spreading, ± obtuse, reddish-brown (same colour as twig), sparsely hairy. PL 29.................*Mountain Willow* **Salix arbuscula**
  Buds >4mm, often of two kinds differing in size and shape (larger fl buds and smaller lf buds)
    R, uplands or mtns. Lf buds mostly nr twig tip, adpressed, 4-5mm, ovoid-oblong, ± obtuse, dark brown, densely woolly or silky-hairy. Fl buds mostly towards twig base, 6-10mm, ovoid, rarely in prs or 3-whorled. Twigs slender (1-2mm diam), dark reddish-brown to purple-black, grey-woolly. Branchlets shiny purple-black. PL 30.............................*Downy Willow* **Salix lapponum**
    VR, mtns, base-rich. Lf buds mostly towards twig base, spreading, 4-5mm, ovoid-oblong, ± obtuse, orange-brown to dark reddish-brown, long-hairy. Fl buds nr twig tip, spreading, 6-10mm, broadly ovoid, orange (-brown) to dark reddish-brown, long-hairy to hairless. Twigs slender (1-2mm diam), usu greenish, sparsely woolly or long-hairy. PL 30
    ....*Woolly Willow* **Salix lanata**

Salix herbacea
Dwarf Willow

Salix myrsinites
Whortle-leaved Willow

Salix reticulata
Net-leaved Willow

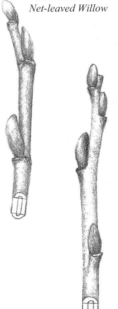

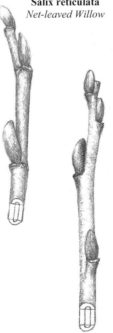

Salix arbuscula
Mountain Willow

Salix repens
Creeping Willow

Salix lapponum
Downy Willow

Salix lanata
Woolly Willow

Group SPI – Spiraea. *Twigs slender (0.5-3mm diam), ± zig-zagging or not, finely to strongly lined, often bearing terminal fl or fr clusters, brittle, with persistent bud scale remnants at join with branchlet; lenticels absent; bark eventually peeling in longitudinal strips; pith ½-⅔ diam, white, rarely brown, round. Buds usu all lateral, spreading to adpressed, single or with 1-2 collateral buds, 1-5mm, globose to ± spindle-shaped; scales usu same colour as twig, keeled, usu acute. Lf scars spiralling, raised or not, semi-circular or triangular to crescent-shaped, often shrivelled, small, ≤ bud width, decurrent; bundle scar 1, flat arc. Shrub. Other taxa occur in gardens. The key to* S. salicifolia *agg should be treated as tentative and often best to record them as the aggregate*

■Bud scales 2 (valvate). Twigs ridged, slender (1-2mm diam). To 2m

Twigs reddish-brown, hairless. Buds (±) spreading, 3-4mm, narrowly conical, often incurved; scales same colour as twigs, hairless, not ciliate. Erect, not or weakly suckering. PL 33
....*Nippon Spiraea* **Spiraea nipponica**

Twigs reddish-brown, soon hairless. Buds spreading, c2mm, ovoid. Arching, not or weakly suckering
....*Himalayan Spiraea* **Spiraea canescens**

Twigs pale grey, hairless. Arching, suckering
....(not illustrated) *Elm-leaved Spiraea* **Spiraea chamaedryfolia** ssp **ulmifolia**

■Bud scales 5-7. Shrub to 2m

Twigs ± round (but finely lined)

Twigs minutely hairy, dark reddish-brown to blackish, v slender (0.5-2mm diam). Buds 1-2mm, globose-ovoid; scales hairless to densely hairy, ciliate. Erect, not or weakly suckering
....*Bridal-wreath* **Spiraea 'Arguta'**

Twigs hairless, reddish-brown, v slender (1mm diam). Buds spreading, 2-3mm, narrowly conical, acute. Arching, not or weakly suckering. *S. cantoniensis* x *trilobata*
....*Van Houtte's Spiraea* **Spiraea** x **vanhouttei**

Twigs 5-7-ridged

Arching. Not or weakly suckering. Twigs reddish-brown, zig-zagging. PL 33
....*Russian Spiraea* **Spiraea media**

Erect. Strongly suckering, forming large patches (*S. salicifolia* agg)

Twigs and/or buds (buff-) woolly. Twigs reddish-brown, 2-3mm diam. Buds (1)2-3mm

Twigs (±) hairless or only hairy at tip. Buds buff-woolly
...................................(not illustrated) *Menzies' Steeple-bush* **Spiraea douglasii** ssp **menziesii**

Twigs usu densely hairy at least nr tip

Twigs short-hairy. Buds buff-woolly. Lvs toothed only towards tip. PL 33
....*Douglas' Steeple-bush* **Spiraea douglasii** ssp **douglasii**

Twigs ± woolly at least nr tip (rarely brown-hairy). Buds (buff-) white-woolly. Lvs toothed almost to base..(not illustrated) *Hardhack* **Spiraea tomentosa**

Twigs and/or buds not woolly (hairy to hairless)

Twigs usu yellowish-brown to orange, hairless or only hairy at tip

Common. Buds sparsely hairy at least nr tip. *S. douglasii* x *salicifolia*. PL 34
....(not illustrated) *Confused Bridewort* **Spiraea** x **pseudosalicifolia**

Uncommon. Buds hairless, (long-) ciliate. PL 33........................*Pale Bridewort* **Spiraea alba**

Rare. *S. alba* x *salicifolia*...............(not illustrated) *Intermediate Bridewort* **Spiraea** x **rosalba**

VR (much over-recorded)................................(not illustrated) *Bridewort* **Spiraea salicifolia**

Twigs reddish-brown

Twigs usu densely short-hairy at least nr tip, occ hairless. Buds hairy. *S. alba* x *douglasii*. PL
33...*Billard's Bridewort* **Spiraea** x **billardii**

Twigs (±) hairless or only hairy at tip

Common. Buds sparsely hairy at least nr tip. *S. douglasii* x *salicifolia*. PL 34
....................................(not illustrated) *Confused Bridewort* **Spiraea** x **pseudosalicifolia**

Uncommon. Buds hairless, (long-) ciliate. PL 33.....................*Pale Bridewort* **Spiraea alba**

■Bud scales (6)7-12. Low shrub, occ herb-like, usu 0.3-0.6m, not suckering

Twigs ± round (but finely lined), occ flattened or angled, 2-3mm diam, reddish-brown, hairy at least nr tip, not zig-zagging. Buds adpressed to (±) spreading, (1)2-5mm, conical, ± flattened; scales brown, occ hairy; inner occ purplish. Dead fls usu persisting in terminal umbel. Early bursting. PL 33
....*Japanese Spiraea* **Spiraea japonica**

Spiraea nipponica
Nippon Spiraea

Spiraea canescens
Himalayan Spiraea

Spiraea 'Arguta'
Bridal-wreath

Spiraea x **vanhouttei**
Van Houtte's Spiraea

Spiraea media
Russian Spiraea

Spiraea douglasii ssp **douglasii**
Douglas' Steeple-bush

Spiraea x **billardii**
Billard's Bridewort

Spiraea alba
Pale Bridewort

Spiraea japonica
Japanese Spiraea

Group TIL – Tilia. *Twigs slender (1-3mm diam), zig-zagging, greenish or reddish (esp sunlit side), round; lenticels few or absent, raised, oblong, small, usu dark; pith c½ diam, white, occ pink or yellow, round. Branchlets with some of the twigs arranged horizontally in 1-plane. Buds all lateral, spreading, oblique to lf scar, ovoid but lopsided (like 'boxing gloves') due to a smaller scale, obtuse to ± acute (unless otherwise stated), slimy and pleasant-tasting if chewed; scales 2-3, usu green or red (esp sunlit side), rarely ciliate; lowest scale ≥½ bud length. Lf scars 2-ranked, ± raised, semi-circular or ± elliptical; bundle scars 3 or multiplied, occ C-shaped, occ forming ellipse. Stipule scars triangular to linear, unequal, with 1-several vb scars occ visible. Bark shallowly furrowed with ridges ± parallel or long-intersecting, often cracked horizontally. ❶ Branches weeping. ❷ Trunk with burrs and dense epicormic shoots*

■Twigs with minute (0.2mm) spreading or adpressed stellate hairs (dense to v sparse and confined to nodes). Trunk without burrs or epicormic shoots

Branches drooping to weeping. Twigs 1-3mm diam, grey-green to purplish (esp on sunlit side), with adpressed stellate hairs often confined to nr nodes or on 1-side (occ v sparse); internodes usu short, 0.5-3(5)cm. Buds 4-7 x 3-4mm, obtuse; scales 2-3, reddish-green to red, ± stellate-hairy esp nr tip. ❶. PL 35..*Pendent Silver-lime* **Tilia 'Petiolaris'**

Branches spreading to ascending. Twigs 2-3mm diam, greyish due to dense minute (0.2mm) spreading or adpressed stellate hairs all along; internodes usu mod, (1.5)3-6cm. Buds 4-6 x 3-4mm, ± acute to ± obtuse; scales 2-3, reddish-brown, stellate-hairy. PL 35
....*Silver-lime* **Tilia tomentosa**

■Twigs hairless or with long (≥0.5mm) spreading simple or stellate hairs (esp on fruiting twigs)

Twig internodes usu long, 5-10cm, (±) hairless. Trunk often with burrs and abundant epicormic shoots

Buds 5-10 x 3-6mm, occ ciliate or (off-) white stellate-hairy at tip; scales (2)3, green to red. Twigs 2-3mm diam, usu reddish. Trunk straight, usu continuous to tree tip; crown narrowly pyramidal, becoming ovate or oblong; lower branches often drooping. ❷. *T. cordata* x *platyphyllos* (occ more strongly resembling *T. cordata* in winter characters). PL 35
....*Common Lime* **Tilia x europaea**

Twig internodes usu short, 0.5-4cm (but up to 8cm in *T.* x *euchlora*), hairy to hairless. Trunk without burrs, rarely with sparse epicormic shoots.

Twigs 1-2mm diam, greenish to reddish, hairless; internodes 0.5-3(4)cm. Buds 3-6 x 2-4mm, (±) obtuse; scales 2(3) but often the third visible at bud tip only and with a few buff hairs, green to orange-red. Crown broadly ovate to pyramidal; lower branches spreading to ± drooping. Late bursting. PL 35...*Small-leaved Lime* **Tilia cordata**

Twigs 2-3mm diam, usu reddish, hairless to densely long-hairy esp on fruiting twigs; internodes 1.5-3cm. Buds 4-10 x 5mm, obtuse to ± acute; scales 3, green to red, occ ciliate or hairy at tip. Crown pyramidal; lower branches more spreading than *T.* x *europaea*. PL 35
....*Large-leaved Lime* **Tilia platyphyllos**

Twigs (1.5)2-3mm diam, usu green, often orange-red on sunlit side, hairless or sparsely long-hairy (occ stellate-hairy); internodes 0.5-4(8)cm. Buds 5-10 x 5mm, usu narrowly ovoid, acute; scales (2)3, green to orange-red. Crown pyramidal when young, becoming rounded; lower branches arching up then strongly drooping. *T. dasystyla* x ?*cordata*. PL 35
....*Caucasian Lime* **Tilia x euchlora**

Tilia 'Petiolaris'
Pendent Silver-lime

Tilia tomentosa
Silver-lime

Tilia x europaea
Common Lime

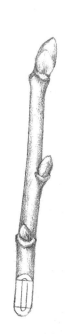

Tilia cordata
Small-leaved Lime

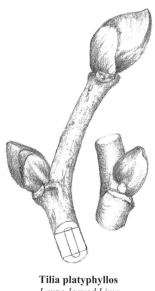

Tilia platyphyllos
Large-leaved Lime

Tilia x euchlora
Caucasian Lime

ULM

Group ULM – Ulmus. *Twigs slender to mod (1.5-3mm diam), zig-zagging or not, reddish-brown, round; lenticels flat, round to oblong, pale; bark peeling back when twig broken; inner bark ± slimy; pith ≤½ diam, white, ± round. Branchlets often with corky wings, occ herringbone-like in ± horizontal plane. Buds all lateral, spreading, usu of two kinds differing in size and shape (fl and lf buds separate); lf buds nr twig tips, usu narrowly ovoid; scales (4)5-6 (6-10 in U.* laevis*), 2-ranked, usu* notched*, often with some rusty hairs; fl buds towards twig base, ± globose (exc U.* laevis*). Lf scars 2-ranked, weakly raised, semi-circular to ± elliptical, with a corky layer; bundle scars 3 (rarely multiplied),* sunken*. Stipule scars semi-circular to narrowly oblong, small, unequal. Bark smooth when young. Tree, suckering (rarely so in U.* glabra*). Variation continuous within the U.* minor – U.* x hollandica *– U.* glabra *group as these and related taxa freely hybridise. U.* x hollandica *(and related taxa not described) key out between U.* glabra *and U.* procera *but may be closer to either parent. Numerous cultivars are known but many may be extinct due to Dutch Elm Disease or survive unrecognised in sucker form.* ❶ Bud scales >6*

■Twigs hairy and/or buds >3mm

Twigs with raised pale hair bases (lenticel-like, occ obscure), usu rough

Branchlets never corky-winged, with obscure fine pale fissures. Buds 5-8 x 4(5)mm, ± conical (almost 2x as long as wide), ± acute; scales purple-black, margins often paler reddish-brown, with rusty (occ whitish) hairs and/or cilia. Fl buds 3-6mm, globose. Twigs mod slender (2-3mm diam), dark reddish-brown (same colour as buds), hairy to hairless. Bark smooth, later furrowed with ridges ± parallel or long-intersecting. Trunk short, usu with burrs; crown round; branches ascending, with branchlets drooping but twigs upturned. Rarely suckering. PL 36
....*Wych Elm* **Ulmus glabra**

Branchlets occ corky-winged, with distinct (to obscure) fine pale fissures (forming thin 'blocky' bark). Buds 4-6mm, ovoid; scales purple-black, margins often paler reddish-brown, with rusty (occ whitish) hairs and/or cilia. Twigs mod slender (2-3mm diam), hairy to hairless, at least some pale raised hair bases, rough to smooth. Trunk short or continuing into crown; crown obovate; branches ascending, crooked. Bark fissured into squarish scales or ± parallel ridges (depending on cultivar). *U. glabra* x *minor*. Related taxa also usu key out here. PL 36
....*Dutch Elm* **Ulmus x hollandica**

Twigs without raised hair bases, rarely rough

Buds 5-8 x 3mm, ovoid to conical (usu ≥2x as long as wide), v acute; scales 6-8(10), purple-black to reddish-brown, margins darker, minutely white-hairy to hairless, occ with rusty cilia. Fl buds similar, swollen, 6-8 x 4mm. Twigs slender (2mm diam), minutely hairy with occ longer hairs, rarely hairless. Branchlets never corky-winged, without fissures. Bark furrowed, ridges scaly with reddish-brown underbark. Trunk usu with burrs, swollen with deep grooves at base; crown ± round. Occ suckering. ❶. R. PL 36.........................*European White-elm* **Ulmus laevis**

Buds (2)3-6 x 3mm, ovoid (usu <2x as long as wide), acute; scales 4-6, purple-black, margins often paler reddish-brown, sparsely white-hairy (often some rusty hairs), often with rusty cilia. Fl buds globose, larger. Twigs slender (1-2mm diam). Branchlets often corky-winged, with distinct fine pale fissures. Bark fissured into rectangular scales, often blocky like 'crocodile-hide', corky. Trunk without burrs. Crown obovate to oblong, with strong branches at all levels, rarely reaching maturity due to Dutch Elm Disease. Usu suckering. Commonest sp in hedges, now considered a cultivar of *U. minor*. PL 36....................................*English Elm* **Ulmus procera**

■Twigs (±) hairless. Buds 2-3mm. Branchlets often corky-winged. Usu suckering

Buds ovoid; scales purple-black, margins often paler reddish-brown, sparsely white-hairy (often some rusty hairs) to hairless, often with rusty cilia (occ whitish). Twigs slender (1-2mm diam), reddish- or yellowish-brown, soon olive-brown. Bark fissured into close parallel ridges or rectangular scales. Trunk with or without burrs; crown usu with some strong branches, only the lower drooping (if any). Late bursting

Crown ± spreading to narrow. Trunk not continuous to tree tip. PL 36
....*Field Elm* **Ulmus minor** agg

Crown pyramidal. Trunk continuous to tree tip
....(not illustrated) *Jersey Elm* **Ulmus minor 'Sarniensis'**

Ulmus x **hollandica**
Dutch Elm

Ulmus glabra
Wych Elm

Ulmus laevis
European White-elm

Ulmus procera
English Elm

Ulmus minor agg
Field Elm

LIST OF UNUSUAL CHARACTERS

These unusual characters (essentially 'spot characters') may be used as a shortcut to the identification of an unknown plant. The characters are not mutually exclusive and may not apply all the time. Not every species in a family or genus may share a particular character.

■Medifixed hairs (on twigs/buds)
Cornus spp Dogwoods **BE**

■Stellate hairs (on twigs/buds)
Buddleja alternifolia Alternate-leaved Butterfly-bush **AN**
Callicarpa bodinieri var *giraldii* Beautyberry **BE**
Carya ovata Shagbark Hickory **AR**
Deutzia scabra Deutzia **BI**
Fothergilla major Mountain Witch-alder **AF**
Hamamelis spp Witch-hazels **AF**
Hibiscus syriacus Hibiscus **AE**
Parrotia persica Persian Ironwood **AF**
Paulownia tomentosa Foxglove-tree **BB**
Quercus cerris Turkey Oak **AE**
Styrax japonicus Japanese Snowbell-tree **AF**
Tilia spp Limes **TIL**
Viburnum lantana Wayfaring-tree **BE**

■Peltate scales (on twigs/buds)
Deutzia scabra Deutzia **BI**
Elaeagnus spp **AN**
Hippophae rhamnoides Sea-buckthorn **AC**

■Twigs (±) stout, >8mm diam
Aesculus spp Horse-chestnuts & Buckeyes **BG**
Ailanthus altissima Tree-of-heaven **AR**
Aralia spp Angelica-trees **AA**
Catalpa bignonioides Indian Bean-tree **BB**
Catalpa speciosa Northern Catalpa **BB**
Ficus carica Fig **AG**
Fraxinus excelsior Ash **BB**
Hydrangea aspera Rough-leaved Hydrangea **BE**
Hydrangea macrophylla Hydrangea **BE**
Juglans regia Walnut **AF**
Magnolia spp Magnolias **MAG** (occ)
Paeonia sect *Moutan* Tree Peony **AP**
Paulownia tomentosa Foxglove-tree **BB**
Pterocarya fraxinifolia Caucasian Wingnut **AF**
Rhus typhina Stag's-horn Sumach **AG**
Robinia pseudoacacia False-acacia **AB**
Rosa spp Roses **AA**
Rubus fruticosus agg Bramble **RUB B**
Rubus odoratus Purple-flowered Raspberry **RUB A**
Sambucus spp Elders **BI**
Toona sinensis Chinese Mahogany **AQ**
Toxicodendron vernicifluum Chinese Lacquer-tree **AG**
Vitis coignetiae Crimson-glory-vine **AD**
Vitis vinifera Grape-vine **AD**

■Twigs green (occ becoming purplish on sunlit side)
Acer capillipes Red Snakebark Maple **BE**
Acer cappadocicum Cappadocian Maple **BH**
Acer davidii Père David's Maple **BE** (rarely)
Acer japonicum Downy Japanese Maple **BH**

Acer negundo Ashleaf Maple **BE**
Acer palmatum Japanese Maple **BE**
Acer rufinerve Grey-budded Snakebark Maple **BE**
Baccharis halimifolia Tree Groundsel **AJ**
Caragana arborescens Siberian Pea-shrub **AB**
Colutea arborescens Bladder-senna **AM**
Cornus spp Dogwoods **BE**
Cytisus spp Brooms **AJ**
Euonymus spp Spindles **BA**
Ficus carica Fig **AB**
Forsythia x *intermedia* Forsythia **BB**
Genista spp Brooms & allies **AJ**
Hippocrepis emerus Scorpion Senna **AJ**
Jasminum spp Jasmines **AJ**, **BA**
Juglans regia Walnut **AF**
Kerria japonica Kerria **AJ**
Laburnum spp Laburnums **AJ**
Leycesteria formosa Himalayan Honeysuckle **BF**
Liquidambar styraciflua American Sweetgum **AP**
Magnolia spp Magnolias **MAG** (occ)
Passiflora caerulea Passion-flower **AD**
Prunus armeniaca Apricot **PRU**
Prunus cerasifera Cherry Plum **PRU**
Prunus domestica Wild Plum **PRU** (occ)
Prunus dulcis Almond **PRU**
Prunus persica Peach **PRU**
Rosa spp Roses **AA**
Rubus fruticosus agg Brambles **RUB A**
Salix spp Willows **SAL** (occ)
Sassafras albidum Sassafras **AJ**
Spartium junceum Spanish Broom **AJ**
Staphylea pinnata Bladdernut **BA**
Styphnolobium japonicum Pagoda Tree **AJ**
Tilia spp esp *T.* x *euchlora* Limes **TIL**
Vaccinium corymbosum Blueberry **AN**
Vaccinium myrtillus Bilberry **AI**
Wisteria spp Wisterias **AD** (occ)

■Twigs (or buds) pruinose
Acer capillipes Red Snakebark Maple **BE**
Acer cappadocicum Cappadocian Maple **BH**
Acer davidii Père David's Maple **BE** (rarely)
Acer negundo Ashleaf Maple **BE**
Acer palmatum Japanese Maple **BE**
Acer rufinerve Grey-budded Snakebark Maple **BE**
Cotinus coggygria Smoke-tree **AE**
Genista lydia Lydian Broom **AJ** (occ)
Larix spp Larches **AN** (rarely)
Leycesteria formosa Himalayan Honeysuckle **BF**
Liriodendron spp Tulip-trees **AH**
Magnolia salicifolia Willow-leaved Magnolia **MAG**
Magnolia tripetala Umbrella Magnolia **MAG**
Magnolia virginiana Sweetbay Magnolia **MAG**
Pseudolarix amabilis Golden Larch **AN**
Rosa ferruginea Red-leaved Rose **AA**

Rubus caesius Dewberry **RUB B**
Rubus cockburnianus White-stemmed Bramble **RUB A**
Rubus fruticosus agg Bramble **RUB B** (rarely)
Salix daphnoldes Violet-willow **SAL B**
Salix purpurea Purple Willow **SAL B** (v rarely)
Sassafras albidum Sassafras **AJ**
Staphylea pinnata Bladdernut **BA**

■Twigs white-felted, silvery or white
Aronia spp Chokeberries **AP**
Elaeagnus spp esp *E. angustifolia* **AN**
Hibiscus syriacus Hibiscus **AE**
Malus spp Apples **MAL** (occ)
Mespilus germanica Medlar **AP** (occ)
Populus alba White Poplar **POP A**
Populus x *canescens* Grey Poplar **POP A**
Pyrus elaeagnifolia Oleaster-leaved Pear **PYR**
Pyrus salicifolia Willow-leaved Pear **PYR**

■Twigs developing grey skin
Acer rubrum Red Maple **BH**
Acer saccharinum Silver Maple **BH**
Alnus spp Alders **AH, AI**
Amelanchier lamarckii Juneberry **AP**
Arctostaphylos alpinus Arctic Bearberry **AN**
Aronia spp Chokeberries **AP**
Betula spp Birches **BET**
Caragana arborescens Siberian Pea-shrub **AB**
Cotoneaster spp Cotoneasters **COT**
Laburnum spp Laburnums **AJ**
Morus spp Mulberries **AL**
Populus tremula Aspen **POP**
Prunus spp Cherries & Plums **PRU**
Pyrus spp Pears **PYR**
Quercus spp Oaks **AE**
Rhamnus cathartica Buckthorn **BB**
Salix spp Willows **SAL**
Sorbus spp Whitebeams & Rowans **AP, AQ**
Stephanandra incisa Stephanandra **AF**
Stewartia pseudocamellia Deciduous Camellia **AI**
Tilia spp Limes **TIL**

■Twigs or buds with sessile glands
Callicarpa bodinieri var *giraldii* Beautyberry **BE**
Carya ovata Shagbark Hickory **AR**
Myrica gale Bog-myrtle **AP**
Myrica pensylvanica Bayberry **AP**
Ribes nigrum Black Currant **RIB**
Ribes sanguineum Flowering Currant **RIB**

■Twigs with aerial roots along internodes
Campsis radicans Trumpet-vine **BC**
Hydrangea petiolaris Climbing Hydrangea **BC**
Parthenocissus spp Virginia-creeper & Boston-ivy **AD**

■Twig or branchlet bark peeling, splitting, flaking or v fissured
Arctostaphylos alpinus Arctic Bearberry **AN**
Aronia spp Chokeberries **AP**
Berberis spp Barberries **AB**
Buddleja alternifolia Alternate-leaved Butterfly-bush **AN**
Clematis spp **BC**
Corylus avellana Hazel **AL** (bark netted between 3-5 yrs)
Corylus colurna Turkish Hazel **AL**
Cotoneaster spp Cotoneasters **COT**
Deutzia scabra Deutzia **BI**
Fuchsia magellanica Fuchsia **BB**
Genista anglica Petty Whin **AC**
Ginkgo biloba Ginkgo **AO**
Hydrangea aspera Rough-leaved Hydrangea **BE**
Hydrangea macrophylla Hydrangea **BE**
Hydrangea petiolaris Climbing Hydrangea **BC**
Hypericum androsaemum Tutsan **BI**
Kolkwitzia amabilis Beautybush **BI**
Lonicera spp Honeysuckles **BC, BE, BI** (esp older branchlets)
Metasequoia glyptostroboides Dawn Redwood **BB**
Philadelphus spp Mock-oranges **BD**
Physocarpus opulifolius Atlantic Ninebark **AK**
Potentilla fruticosa Shrubby Cinquefoil **AM**
Ribes spp Currants & Gooseberry **RIB**
Rubus idaeus Raspberry **RUB A** (v rarely)
Rubus odoratus Purple-flowered Raspberry **RUB A**
Rubus spectabilis Salmonberry **RUB A** (weakly)
Spiraea spp Spiraeas & Brideworts **SPI**
Stephanandra incisa Stephanandra **AF**
Symphoricarpos albus Snowberry **BI** (esp older branchlets)
Symphoricarpos x *chenaultii* Hybrid Coralberry **BI**
Vaccinium corymbosum Blueberry **AN**
Vaccinium uliginosum Bog Bilberry **AN**
Vitis coignetiae Crimson-glory-vine **AD**
Vitis vinifera Grape-vine **AD**
Weigela florida Weigela **BI**

■Twigs 2-lined
Hypericum androsaemum Tutsan **BI**
Weigela florida Weigela **BI**

■Twigs 3-angled
Alnus spp Alders **AH, AI**
Cydonia oblonga Quince **AI**
Fothergilla major Mountain Witch-alder **AF**
Hamamelis spp Witch-hazels **AF**
Parrotia persica Persian Ironwood **AF**
Physocarpus opulifolius Atlantic Ninebark **AK**
Solanum dulcamara Bittersweet **AD**

■Twigs 4-angled (occ weakly so)
Callicarpa bodinieri var *giraldii* Beautyberry **BE** (occ)
Caragana arborescens Siberian Pea-shrub **AB**
Clerodendrum trichotomum var *fargesii* Farges' Harlequin Glorybower **BB**
Daphne mezereum Mezereon **AN** (occ)

Euonymus opp Spindles **DA**
Forsythia x *intermedia* Forsythia **BB**
Hydrangea aspera Rough-leaved Hydrangea **BE**
Jasminum nudiflorum Winter Jasmine **BA**
Lonicera involucrata Californian Honeysuckle **BI**
Syringa vulgaris Lilac **BB**
Tetradium daniellii Korean Evodia **BB**

■Twigs 5-14-angled or -ridged or -lined
Baccharis halimifolia Tree Groundsel **AJ** (5-8-angled)
Berberis spp Barberries **AB** (5-9-ridged)
Buddleja alternifolia Alternate-leaved Butterfly-bush **AN** (5-ridged)
Castanea sativa Sweet Chestnut **AI** (5-angled)
Celastrus orbiculatus Staff-vine **AD** (5-lined)
Clematis spp (exc *C. montana*) **BC** (6-14-ridged)
Cytisus scoparius Broom **AJ** (4-5-ridged)
Genista Brooms & allies **AC**, **AJ** (various)
Hippocrepis emerus Scorpion Senna **AJ** (7-ridged)
Jasminum humile Yellow Jasmine **AJ** (5-ridged)
Jasminum officinale Summer Jasmine **BA** (6-12-ridged)
Kerria japonica Kerria **AJ** (5-lined)
Liquidambar styraciflua American Sweetgum **AP** (5-angled)
Passiflora caerulea Passion-flower **AD** (5-angled)
Philadelphus spp Mock-oranges **BD** (6-angled or -lined)
Physocarpus opulifolius Atlantic Ninebark **AK** (3-5-lined)
Quercus spp Oaks **AE** (weakly 5-angled)
Robinia pseudoacacia False-acacia **AB** (5-angled)
Rubus fruticosus agg Brambles **RUB B** (5-angled)
Salix elaeagnos Olive Willow **SAL A** (5-7-ridged)
Salix triandra Almond Willow **SAL B** (7-ridged)
Sambucus spp Elders **BI** (8-angled)
Solanum dulcamara Bittersweet **AD** (3-5-angled)
Spiraea spp Spiraeas & Brideworts **SPI** (5-7-ridged)
Vaccinium myrtillus Bilberry **AI** (3-5-ridged)
Viburnum lantana Wayfaring-tree **BE** (6-angled)
Viburnum opulus Guelder-rose **BE** (6-angled)

■Twigs (or branchlets) corky-winged
Acer campestre Field Maple **BH**
Liquidambar styraciflua American Sweetgum **AP**
Ulmus spp Elms **ULM** (some taxa)

■Twigs with inner bark (or buds) odorous (fetid or aromatic)
Acer negundo Ashleaf Maple **BE**
Acer opalus Italian Maple **BH** (weakly)
Acer saccharinum Silver Maple **BH**
Acer velutinum Velvet Maple **BH** (weakly)
Aesculus spp (esp *A. glabra*) Horse-chestnuts & Buckeyes **BG**
Ailanthus altissima Tree-of-heaven **AR**
Amelanchier lamarckii Juneberry **AP**
Aralia spp Angelica-trees **AA**
Aronia spp Chokeberries **AP** (weakly)
Baccharis halimifolia Tree Groundsel **AJ** (weakly)
Betula alleghaniensis Yellow Birch **BET**
Betula lenta Sweet Birch **BET**

Catalpa spp Bean-trees **BB**
Clerodendrum trichotomum var *fargesii* Farges' Harlequin Glorybower **BB**
Cornus spp Dogwoods **BE**
Cotinus coggygria Smoke-tree **AE**
Cotoneaster spp esp *C. cambricus* Cotoneasters **COT**
Cytisus scoparius Broom **AJ**
Daphne mezereum Mezereon **AN**
Euonymus europaeus Spindle **BA** (weakly)
Ficus carica Fig **AG** (weakly)
Frangula alnus Alder Buckthorn **AG**
Genista lydia Lydian Broom **AJ**
Juglans spp Walnuts **AF**
Larix spp Larches **AN** (weakly)
Liquidambar styraciflua American Sweetgum **AP**
Liriodendron spp Tulip-trees **AH**
Magnolia spp Magnolias **MAG**
Morus spp Mulberries **AL** (weakly)
Myrica gale Bog-myrtle **AP**
Myrica pensylvanica Bayberry **AP**
Paeonia sect *Moutan* Tree Peony **AP**
Paulownia tomentosa Foxglove-tree **BB**
Populus spp Poplars **POP**
Prunus spp Cherries & Plums **PRU** (weak in most spp)
Prunus mahaleb St Lucie Cherry **PRU**
Prunus padus Bird Cherry **PRU**
Prunus serotina Rum Cherry **PRU**
Pseudolarix amabilis Golden Larch **AN** (weakly)
Pterocarya fraxinifolia Caucasian Wingnut **AF**
Rhamnus cathartica Buckthorn **BB**
Rhododendron luteum Yellow Azalea **AN** (weakly)
Ribes nigrum Black Currant **RIB**
Ribes rubrum Red Currant **RIB** (weakly)
Ribes sanguineum Flowering Currant **RIB**
Ribes uva-crispa Gooseberry **AB** (weakly)
Robinia pseudoacacia False-acacia **AB**
Salix triandra Almond Willow **SAL B**
Sambucus nigra Elder **BI**
Sambucus racemosa Red-berried Elder **BI** (weakly)
Sassafras albidum Sassafras **AJ**
Solanum dulcamara Bittersweet **AD**
Sorbus subgen *Sorbus* Rowans **AQ**
Staphylea pinnata Bladdernut **BA**
Styphnolobium japonicum Pagoda Tree **AJ**
Taxodium distichum Swamp Cypress **AN**
Toona sinensis Chinese Mahogany **AQ**
Xanthorhiza simplicissima Yellowroot **AR**

■Twigs with white latex
Acer campestre Field Maple **BH**
Acer cappadocicum Cappadocian Maple **BH**
Acer platanoides Norway Maple **BH**
Broussonetia papyrifera Paper Mulberry **AI**
Ficus carica Fig **AG**
Maclura pomifera Osage-orange **AC**
Morus spp Mulberries **AL**

Periploca graeca Silk-vine **BC**
Rhus typhina Stag's-horn Sumach **AG**
Toxicodendron vernicifluum Chinese Lacquer-tree **AG**

■Twigs with persistent bud scale remnants at join with branchlet (usu brown and papery)
Colutea arborescens Bladder-senna **AM**
Jasminum spp Jasmines **AJ, BA**
Leycesteria formosa Himalayan Honeysuckle **BF**
Lonicera spp Honeysuckles **BC, BE, BI**
Philadelphus spp Mock-oranges **BD**
Ribes spp Currants & Gooseberry **RIB**
Rubus spp **RUB**
Symphoricarpos spp Snowberries & Coralberries **BI**
Vaccinium corymbosum Blueberry **AN**
Vaccinium myrtillus Bilberry **AI**
Vaccinium uliginosum Bog Bilberry **AN**

■Pith orange-brown (occ pink, brown or buff)
Ailanthus altissima Tree-of-heaven **AR**
Alnus spp Alders **AH, AI**
Carya ovata Shagbark Hickory **AR**
Cercis siliquastrum Judas Tree **AF**
Corylus spp Hazels **AL**
Cotinus coggygria Smoke-tree **AE**
Elaeagnus spp **AN**
Fallopia baldschuanica Russian-vine **AD** (occ)
Gymnocladus dioicus Kentucky Coffeetree **AF**
Hippophae rhamnoides Sea-buckthorn **AC**
Hydrangea aspera Rough-leaved Hydrangea **BE**
Hypericum androsaemum Tutsan **BI**
Lonicera periclymenum Honeysuckle **BC**
Lonicera tatarica Tartarian Honeysuckle **BI**
Lonicera x *italica* Garden Honeysuckle **BC**
Lonicera xylosteum Fly Honeysuckle **BI**
Malus spp Apples **MAL** (occ)
Physocarpus opulifolius Atlantic Ninebark **AK**
Populus spp (exc *P. tremula*) Poplars **POP**
Potentilla fruticosa Shrubby Cinquefoil **AM**
Prunus avium Wild Cherry **PRU**
Prunus cerasus Sour Cherry **PRU**
Prunus persica Peach **PRU**
Prunus serrulata Japanese Cherry **PRU** (occ)
Ribes spp Currants **RIB** (occ)
Rubus cockburnianus White-stemmed Bramble **RUB A**
Rubus idaeus Raspberry **RUB A**
Rubus odoratus Purple-flowered Raspberry **RUB A**
Rubus phoenicolasius Japanese Wineberry **RUB A**
Salix spp (esp *S. myrsinifolia*) Willows **SAL**
Sambucus racemosa Red-berried Elder **BI**
Sorbaria sorbifolia Sorbaria **AP**
Sorbus spp Whitebeams & Rowans **AP, AQ** (occ)
Stephanandra incisa Stephanandra **AF**
Viburnum x *bodnantense* Bodnant Viburnum **BI**
Vitis spp Vines **AD**
Wisteria spp Wisterias **AD** (occ)

■Pith (or inner wood) purple

Malus x *purpurea* Purple Crab Apple **MAL**
Prunus cerasifera 'Nigra' Black Cherry Plum **PRU**

■Pith green

Alnus spp Alders **AH, AI**
Amelanchier lamarckii Juneberry **AP**
Betula spp Birches **BET**
Carpinus betulus Hornbeam **AK**
Castanea sativa Sweet Chestnut **AI**
Cercidiphyllum japonicum Katsura **BB**
Colutea arborescens Bladder-senna **AM**
Diospyros lotus Date-plum **AI**
Euonymus spp Spindles **BA**
Fagus sylvatica Beech **AL**
Fothergilla major Mountain Witch-alder **AF**
Fuchsia magellanica Fuchsia **BB**
Genista anglica Petty Whin **AC**
Hamamelis spp Witch-hazels **AF**
Hydrangea petiolaris Climbing Hydrangea **BC**
Larix spp Larches **AN**
Lycium spp Teaplants **AC**
Malus spp Apples **MAL** (occ)
Metasequoia glyptostroboides Dawn Redwood **BB**
Myrica gale Bog-myrtle **AP**
Myrica pensylvanica Bayberry **AP**
Ostrya carpinifolia Hop-hornbeam **AL**
Parrotia persica Persian Ironwood **AF**
Parthenocissus spp Virginia-creeper & Boston-ivy **AD**
Passiflora caerulea Passion-flower **AD**
Populus alba White Poplar **POP A** (occ)
Populus x *canescens* Grey Poplar **POP A** (occ)
Populus tremula Aspen **POP B**
Prunus subhirtella Winter-flowering Cherry **PRU**
Pseudolarix amabilis Golden Larch **AN**
Pyrus spp Pears **PYR** (occ)
Rhododendron luteum Yellow Azalea **AN**
Ribes alpinum Mountain Currant **RIB**
Ribes odoratum Buffalo Current **RIB**
Ribes sanguineum Flowering Currant **RIB**
Ribes uva-crispa Gooseberry **AB** (occ)
Solanum dulcamara Bittersweet **AD**
Styrax japonicus Japanese Snowbell-tree **AF**
Styphnolobium japonicum Pagoda Tree **AJ**
Symphoricarpos spp Snowberry & Coralberry **BI**
Taxodium distichum Swamp Cypress **AN**
Vaccinium corymbosum Blueberry **AN**
Vaccinium myrtillus Bilberry **AI**
Vaccinium uliginosum Bog Bilberry **AN**
Viburnum x *bodnantense* Bodnant Viburnum **BI**

■Pith yellow

Berberis spp Barberries **AB** (pith actually white but surrounding wood yellow)
Frangula alnus Alder Buckthorn **AG** (pith actually white but surrounding wood yellow)
Ginkgo biloba Ginkgo **AO**

Populus spp Poplars **POP** (occ)
Pyrus spp Pears **PYR** (occ)
Xanthorhiza simplicissima Yellowroot **AR**

■Pith chambered or diaphragmed
Actinidia deliciosa Kiwifruit **AD**
Celtis australis European Nettle-tree **AK**
Corylus spp Hazels **AL**
Davidia involucrata Dove-tree **AP**
Diospyros lotus Date-plum **AI** (lace-like)
Forsythia x *intermedia* Forsythia **BB**
Jasminum nudiflorum Winter Jasmine **BA** (weakly)
Jasminum officinale Summer Jasmine **BA**
Juglans spp Walnuts **AF**
Liriodendron spp Tulip-trees **AH**
Magnolia virginiana Sweetbay Magnolia **MAG**
Nyssa spp Tupelos **AI**, **AP**
Parthenocissus spp Virginia-creeper & Boston-ivy **AD** (occ)
Paulownia tomentosa Foxglove-tree **BB**
Pterocarya fraxinifolia Caucasian Wingnut **AF**
Vitis spp Vines **AD** (occ adjacent to nodes)

■Pith absent (hollow) or soon fragmenting
Caragana arborescens Siberian Pea-shrub **AB**
Clematis spp **BC** (occ)
Deutzia scabra Deutzia **BI**
Euonymus spp Spindles **BA**
Fallopia baldschuanica Russian-vine **AD** (occ)
Forsythia x *intermedia* Forsythia **BB**
Fuchsia magellanica Fuchsia **BB**
Jasminum nudiflorum Winter Jasmine **BA**
Leycesteria formosa Himalayan Honeysuckle **BF**
Lonicera x *italica* Garden Honeysuckle **BC**
Lonicera periclymenum Honeysuckle **BC**
Lonicera tatarica Tartarian Honeysuckle **BI**
Lonicera xylosteum Fly Honeysuckle **BI**
Lycium spp Teaplants **AC** (occ)
Passiflora caerulea Passion-flower **AD**
Paulownia tomentosa Foxglove-tree **BB**
Periploca graeca Silk-vine **BC**
Ribes spp Currants & Gooseberry **RIB**
Solanum dulcamara Bittersweet **AD**
Symphoricarpos albus Snowberry **BI**
Viburnum x *bodnantense* Bodnant Viburnum **BI**

■Pith 3-5(8)-angled
Alnus spp Alders **AH**, **AI** (3-angled)
Arctostaphylos alpinus Arctic Bearberry **AN** (± 3-angled)
Baccharis halimifolia Tree Groundsel **AJ** (5-8-angled)
Betula spp Birches **BET** (3-angled)
Carpinus betulus Hornbeam **AK** (5-angled)
Carya ovata Shagbark Hickory **AR** (5-angled)
Castanea sativa Sweet Chestnut **AI** (5-angled)
Cercidiphyllum japonicum Katsura **BB** (3-angled)
Euonymus europaeus Spindle **BA** (4-angled)

Ginkgo biloba Ginkgo **AO** (3-angled)
Hippophae rhamnoides Sea-buckthorn **AC** (occ ± 3-angled)
Hydrangea aspera Rough-leaved Hydrangea **BE** (4-5-angled)
Liquidambar styraciflua American Sweetgum **AP** (5-angled)
Populus spp Poplars **POP** (5-angled)
Prunus persica Peach **PRU** (occ ± 5-angled)
Quercus spp Oaks **AE** (5-angled)
Robinia pseudoacacia False-acacia **AB** (5-angled)
Salix spp Willows **SAL** (occ 5-angled)

■Branchlets with woody spurs (brachyblasts)
Acer spp Maples **BH** (some taxa)
Aesculus spp Horse-chestnuts & Buckeyes **BG** (occ)
Alnus viridis Green Alder **AI**
Betula spp Birches **BET**
Caragana arborescens Siberian Pea-shrub **AB**
Cercidiphyllum japonicum Katsura **BB**
Crateagus spp Hawthorns **AC** (occ)
Davidia involucrata Dove-tree **AP**
Fagus sylvatica Beech **AL**
Ginkgo biloba Ginkgo **AO**
Hibiscus syriacus Hibiscus **AE**
Hydrangea petiolaris Climbing Hydrangea **BC**
Laburnum spp Laburnums **AJ**
Larix spp Larches **AN**
Liquidambar styraciflua American Sweetgum **AP**
Malus spp Apples **MAL** (weakly)
Mespilus germanica Medlar **AP**
Nyssa spp Tupelos **AI**, **AP**
Populus spp Poplars **POP** (occ)
Prunus spp esp *P. avium, cerasus* & *serrulata* Cherries **PRU**
Pseudolarix amabilis Golden Larch **AN**
Pyrus spp Pears **PYR**
Rhamnus cathartica Buckthorn **BB** (occ)
Ribes spp Currants and Gooseberry **RIB** (occ)
Sorbus spp Whitebeams & Rowans **AP**, **AQ**

■Branchlets with short twigs (morphologically between long shoots and woody spurs)
Berberis spp Barberries **AB** (occ)
Castanea sativa Sweet Chestnut **AI**
Cercis siliquastrum Judas Tree **AF**
Cotoneaster Cotoneasters **COT**
Cydonia oblonga Quince **AI**
Frangula alnus Alder Buckthorn **AG** (occ)
Hippophae rhamnoides Sea-buckthorn **AC** (occ)
Lycium spp Teaplants **AC** (occ)
Quercus spp Oaks **AE** (occ)
Ribes spp Currants & Gooseberry **RIB**
Ulmus spp Elms **ULM**
Vitis spp Grape-vines **AD**

■Buds with unusual shapes
Acer palmatum Japanese Maple **BE** (hula skirt; terminal bud resembles a tiny red deer-hoof)
Acer platanoides Norway Maple **BH** (turban-shaped)
Alnus glutinosa Alder **AH** (club-shaped)

Alnus incana Grey Alder **AH** (club-shaped)
Alnus rubra Red Alder **AH** (canoe-shaped)
Cercidiphyllum japonicum Katsura **BB** (crab claws)
Corylus avellana Hazel **AL** (boxing gloves)
Fagus sylvatica Beech **AL** (cigar-shaped)
Fothergilla major Mountain Witch-alder **AF** (scalpel-shaped)
Fraxinus spp Ashes **BB** (bishop's mitre)
Hamamelis spp Witch-hazels **AF** (scalpel-shaped)
Juglans regia Walnut **AF** (bishop's mitre)
Koelreuteria paniculata Pride-of-India **AI** (rugby ball wedged in twig axil, or like a 'hershey kiss'
   chocolate (more for our American readers))
Liriodendron spp Tulip-trees **AH** (duck's bill)
Nothofagus alpina Rauli **AL** (Phillips screwdriver head)
Populus spp Poplars **POP** (lateral buds with lowest scale resembling a thumbnail)
Rhamnus cathartica Buckthorn **BB** (talon-like)
Sorbus torminalis Wild Service-tree **AP** (pea-like)
Stewartia pseudocamellia Deciduous Camellia **AI** (knife-like)
Tetradium daniellii Korean Evodia **BB** (hands clasped in prayer)
Tilia spp Limes **TIL** (boxing gloves)
Viburnum lantana Wayfaring-tree **BE** (If buds like lamb's or fawn's ears; fl buds onion-shaped)

■Buds long, >2.5x as long as wide
Amelanchier lamarckii Juneberry **AP**
Aronia spp Chokeberries **AP**
Fagus sylvatica Beech **AL**
Myrica gale Bog-myrtle **AP**
Populus spp Poplars **POP**
Prunus padus Bird Cherry **PRU**
Ribes alpinum Mountain Currant **RIB**
Ribes sanguineum Flowering Currant **RIB**
Ribes uva-crispa Gooseberry **AB**
Sorbus subgen *Sorbus* Rowans **AQ** (occ)
Stewartia pseudocamellia Deciduous Camellia **AI**
Xanthorhiza simplicissima Yellowroot **AR**

■Buds sticky (or with dry resin or resin glands)
Aesculus carnea Red Horse-chestnut **BG**
Aesculus hippocastanum Horse-chestnut **BG**
Aesculus indica Indian Horse-chestnut **BG**
Aesculus parviflora Bottlebrush Buckeye **BG**
Aesculus turbinata Japanese Horse-chestnut **BG**
Alnus spp esp *A. viridis* Alders **AH**, **AI**
Betula spp Birches **BET** (occ resin glands in most spp)
Betula papyrifera Paper Birch **BET**
Betula pendula Silver Birch **BET** (esp inner scales)
Betula pubescens ssp *pubescens* Downy Birch **BET** (occ)
Betula pubescens ssp *tortuosa* Mountain Birch **BET**
Betula utilis Himalayan Birch **BET**
Cercidiphyllum japonicum Katsura **BB** (inner scales)
Larix spp Larches **AN**
Nothofagus alpina Rauli **AL** (esp inner scales)
Populus spp Poplars **POP** (not or weakly so in sect *Populus*)
Salix pentandra Bay Willow **SAL B** (when bursting)
Sorbus subgen *Aria* Whitebeams **AP**
Sorbus commixta Japanese Rowan **AQ**

Sorbus domestica Service-tree **AQ**
Taxodium distichum Swamp Cypress **AN** (occ)
Viburnum opulus Guelder-rose **BE** (inner scales)

■Buds stalked
Acer capillipes Red Snakebark Maple **BE**
Acer cappadocicum Cappadocian Maple **BH**
Acer davidii Père David's Maple **BE**
Acer negundo Ashleaf Maple **BE**
Acer pensylvanicum 'Erythrocladum' Moosewood **BE**
Acer rubrum Red Maple **BH** (fl buds)
Acer rufinerve Grey-budded Snakebark Maple **BE**
Alnus spp (exc *A. viridis*) Alders **AH**
Amelanchier lamarckii Juneberry **AP** (occ appearing stalked)
Betula spp Birches **BET** (occ appearing stalked)
Callicarpa bodinieri var *giraldii* Beautyberry **BE**
Cercis siliquastrum Judas Tree **AF** (fl buds)
Cornus spp Dogwoods **BE**
Fagus sylvatica Beech **AL** (occ appearing stalked)
Fothergilla major Mountain Witch-alder **AF**
Hamamelis spp Witch-hazels **AF**
Hydrangea macrophylla Hydrangea **BE** (v short)
Hydrangea petiolaris Climbing Hydrangea **BC**
Leycesteria formosa Himalayan Honeysuckle **BF**
Liquidambar styraciflua American Sweetgum **AP**
Liriodendron spp Tulip-trees **AH**
Magnolia spp Magnolias **MAG** (occ appearing stalked)
Metasequoia glyptostroboides Dawn Redwood **BB**
Parrotia persica Persian Ironwood **AF**
Pterocarya fraxinifolia Caucasian Wingnut **AF**
Ribes spp (exc *R. uva-crispa*) Currants **RIB**
Sambucus racemosa Red-berried Elder **BI**
Stephanandra incisa Stephanandra **AF**
Styrax japonicus Japanese Snowbell-tree **AF**
Viburnum x *bodnantense* Bodnant Viburnum **BI** (occ)
Viburnum lantana Wayfaring-tree **BE**
Viburnum opulus Guelder-rose **BE** (short)

■Buds oblique to lf scar
Alnus viridis Green Alder **AI**
Betula spp Birches **BET** (occ)
Castanea sativa Sweet Chestnut **AI**
Corylus avellana Hazel **AL** (occ)
Corylus colurna Turkish Hazel **AL**
Fagus sylvatica Beech **AL**
Fothergilla major Mountain Witch-alder **AF**
Hamamelis spp Witch-hazels **AF**
Morus spp Mulberries **AL** (occ)
Ostrya carpinifolia Hop-hornbeam **AL**
Parrotia persica Persian Ironwood **AF**
Quercus spp Oaks **AE** (occ)
Staphylea pinnata Bladdernut **BA**
Tilia spp Limes **TIL**
Ulmus spp Elms **ULM**
Vitis coignetiae Crimson-glory-vine **AD** (occ)

Vitis vinifera Grape-vine **AD** (occ)
Zelkova carpinifolia Caucasian Zelkova **AL**
Zelkova serrata Japanese Zelkova **AL**

■Buds superposed (or set well above lf scar)
Alnus glutinosa Alder **AH** (rarely)
Aralia spp Angelica-trees **AA** (set well above lf scar, not superposed)
Callicarpa bodinieri var *giraldii* Beautyberry **BE**
Carya ovata Shagbark Hickory **AR** (set well above lf scar, not superposed)
Celastrus orbiculatus Staff-vine **AD** (rarely)
Cercis siliquastrum Judas Tree **AF**
Chimonanthus praecox Wintersweet **BB** (rarely)
Cladrastis kentukea Kentucky Yellowwood **AF**
Clerodendrum trichotomum var *fargesii* Farges' Harlequin Glorybower **BB** (obscure)
Cornus spp Dogwoods **BE** (rarely)
Daphne mezereum Mezereon **AN**
Elaeagnus spp **AN**
Forsythia x *intermedia* Forsythia **BB** (occ)
Fothergilla major Mountain Witch-alder **AF**
Fraxinus spp Ashes **BB** (occ)
Fuchsia magellanica Fuchsia **BB**
Gleditsia triacanthos Honey-locust **AB**, **AF**
Gymnocladus dioicus Kentucky Coffeetree **AF**
Hamamelis spp Witch-hazels **AF**
Hydrangea macrophylla Hydrangea **BE**
Hypericum androsaemum Tutsan **BI** (occ)
Jasminum officinale Summer Jasmine **BA**
Juglans nigra Black Walnut **AF**
Juglans regia Walnut **AF**
Ligustrum ovalifolium Garden Privet **BB**
Ligustrum vulgare Wild Privet **BB**
Liriodendron spp Tulip-trees **AH** (occ)
Lonicera spp Honeysuckles **BC**, **BE**, esp **BI** (unusual as uppermost bud smallest)
Ostrya carpinifolia Hop-hornbeam **AL** (v rarely)
Parrotia persica Persian Ironwood **AF**
Paulownia tomentosa Foxglove-tree **BB**
Pterocarya fraxinifolia Caucasian Wingnut **AF**
Robinia pseudoacacia False-acacia **AB**
Rosa spp Roses **AA** (set well above lf scar, not superposed)
Rubus spp (exc *R. spectabilis*) **RUB**
Sambucus nigra Elder **BI**
Sambucus racemosa Red-berried Elder **BI**
Stephanandra incisa Stephanandra **AF**
Styrax japonicus Japanese Snowbell-tree **AF**

■Buds collateral
Acer spp Maples **BH**
Akebia quinata Chocolate-vine **AD**
Berberis spp Barberries **AB** (occ)
Caragana arborescens Siberian Pea-shrub **AB**
Cercis siliquastrum Judas Tree **AF**
Chaenomeles spp 'Flowering Quinces' **AC**
Corylus colurna Turkish Hazel **AL**
Crataegus spp Hawthorns **AC**
Daphne mezereum Mezereon **AN**

Deutzia scabra Deutzia **BI**
Elaeagnus spp **AN**
Fallopia baldschuanica Russian-vine **AD** (occ)
Ficus carica Fig **AG**
Forsythia x *intermedia* Forsythia **BB**
Hippocrepis emerus Scorpion Senna **AJ**
Hippophae rhamnoides Sea-buckthorn **AC**
Kerria japonica Kerria **AJ**
Liquidambar styraciflua American Sweetgum **AP** (rarely)
Lycium spp Teaplants **AC** (occ)
Maclura pomifera Osage-orange **AC**
Mespilus germanica Medlar **AP**
Morus spp Mulberries **AL**
Parthenocissus quinquefolia Virginia-creeper **AD**
Parthenocissus tricuspidata Boston-ivy **AD**
Prunus cerasifera Cherry Plum **PRU**
Prunus domestica Wild Plum **PRU**
Prunus spinosa Blackthorn **PRU**
Rubus spectabilis Salmonberry **RUB A**
Salix spp Willows **SAL** (on branchlets only)
Sambucus racemosa Red-berried Elder **BI**
Sorbaria sorbifolia Sorbaria **AP**
Symphoricarpos albus Snowberry **BI**
Symphoricarpos x *chenaultii* Hybrid Coralberry **BI**
Tamarix gallica Tamarisk **AN**
Tetradium daniellii Korean Evodia **BB**
Vitis coignetiae Crimson-glory-vine **AD**
Vitis vinifera Grape-vine **AD**
Zelkova carpinifolia Caucasian Zelkova **AL**
Zelkova serrata Japanese Zelkova **AL**

■Buds hidden
Actinidia deliciosa Kiwifruit **AD**
Gleditsia triacanthos Honey-locust **AB**, **AF**
Gymnocladus dioicus Kentucky Coffeetree **AF**
Hibiscus syriacus Hibiscus **AE**
Philadelphus spp Mock-oranges **BD**
Robinia pseudoacacia False-acacia **AB**
Taxodium distichum Swamp Cypress **AN**

■Buds naked (or scales and structure obscure)
Buddleja alternifolia Alternate-leaved Butterfly-bush **AN**
Callicarpa bodinieri var *giraldii* Beautyberry **BE**
Cladrastis kentukea Kentucky Yellowwood **AF**
Clerodendrum trichotomum var *fargesii* Farges' Harlequin Glorybower **BB** (scales obscure)
Cornus spp Dogwoods **BE** (appearing naked)
Cotoneaster spp Cotoneasters **COT**
Fothergilla major Mountain Witch-alder **AF** (occ)
Frangula alnus Alder Buckthorn **AG**
Fuchsia magellanica Fuchsia **BB** (scales obscure)
Genista anglica Petty Whin **AC**
Genista pilosa Hairy Greenweed **AJ**
Hamamelis spp Witch-hazels **AF** (occ)
Hydrangea aspera Rough-leaved Hydrangea **BE**
Hydrangea macrophylla Hydrangea **BE**

189

Juglans nigra Black Walnut **AF** (appearing naked)
Parrotia persica Persian Ironwood **AF** (occ appearing naked)
Pterocarya fraxinifolia Caucasian Wingnut **AF**
Rhus typhina Stag's-horn Sumach **AG**
Robinia pseudoacacia False-acacia **AB**
Styrax japonicus Japanese Snowbell-tree **AF**
Tetradium daniellii Korean Evodia **BB**
Toxicodendron vernicifluum Chinese Lacquer-tree **AG**
Viburnum lantana Wayfaring-tree **BE**

■Bud scale 1
Cercidiphyllum japonicum Katsura **BB**
Fothergilla major Mountain Witch-alder **AF** (occ)
Hamamelis spp Witch-hazels **AF** (occ)
Platanus spp Planes **AG**
Salix spp Willows **SAL**
Viburnum opulus Guelder-rose **BE**

■Bud scales 2 (or 1 pr)
Acer capillipes Red Snakebark Maple **BE**
Acer cappadocicum Cappadocian Maple **BH**
Acer davidii Père David's Maple **BE**
Acer negundo Ashleaf Maple **BE**
Acer palmatum Japanese Maple **BE**
Acer pensylvanicum 'Erythrocladum' Moosewood **BE**
Acer rubrum Red Maple **BH**
Acer rufinerve Grey-budded Snakebark Maple **BE**
Acer saccharinum Silver Maple **BH**
Ailanthus altissima Tree-of-heaven **AR**
Alnus spp Alders **AH, AI**
Arctostaphylos alpinus Arctic Bearberry **AN**
Baccharis halimifolia Tree Groundsel **AJ**
Betula nigra River Birch **BET**
Broussonetia papyrifera Paper Mulberry **AI**
Cercidiphyllum japonicum Katsura **BB**
Cercis siliquastrum Judas Tree **AF**
Clerodendrum trichotomum var *fargesii* Farges' Harlequin Glorybower **BB**
Colutea arborescens Bladder-senna **AM**
Cornus spp Dogwoods **BE** (appearing naked)
Cydonia oblonga Quince **AI**
Cytisus spp Brooms **AJ**
Diospyros lotus Date-plum **AI**
Ficus carica Fig **AG** (occ)
Fothergilla major Mountain Witch-alder **AF**
Genista spp Brooms & allies **AJ**
Hamamelis spp Witch-hazels **AF**
Hippophae rhamnoides Sea-buckthorn **AC**
Hydrangea petiolaris Climbing Hydrangea **BC**
Koelreuteria paniculata Pride-of-India **AI**
Leycesteria formosa Himalayan Honeysuckle **BF**
Liriodendron spp Tulip-trees **AH**
Parrotia persica Persian Ironwood **AF**
Parthenocissus quinquefolia Virginia-creeper **AD**
Parthenocissus tricuspidata Boston-ivy **AD**
Phellodendron amurense Amur Corktree **BB**

Potentilla fruticosa Shrubby Cinquefoil **AM**
Spiraea canescens Himalayan Spiraea **SPI**
Spiraea nipponica Nippon Spiraea **SPI**
Staphylea pinnata Bladdernut **BA**
Stewartia pseudocamellia Deciduous Camellia **AI**
Tamarix gallica Tamarisk **AN**
Tilia spp esp *T. cordata* Limes **TIL** (occ)
Vaccinium corymbosum Blueberry **AN**
Vaccinium myrtillus Bilberry **AI**
Vaccinium uliginosum Bog Bilberry **AN**
Vitis coignetiae Crimson-glory-vine **AD**
Vitis vinifera Grape-vine **AD**
Wisteria spp Wisterias **AD** (occ)

■Bud scales 3
Baccharis halimifolia Tree Groundsel **AJ**
Colutea arborescens Bladder-senna **AM**
Cytisus spp Brooms **AJ**
Genista spp Brooms & allies **AJ**
Potentilla fruticosa Shrubby Cinquefoil **AM**
Tamarix gallica Tamarisk **AN**
Tilia spp Limes **TIL**

■Bud scales 4 (mostly as 2 prs)
Acer cappadocicum Cappadocian Maple **BH**
Acer japonicum Downy Japanese Maple **BH**
Acer negundo Ashleaf Maple **BE**
Acer palmatum Japanese Maple **BE**
Acer platanoides Norway Maple **BH**
Acer rubrum Red Maple **BH**
Acer saccharinum Silver Maple **BH**
Aesculus parviflora Bottlebrush Buckeye **BG**
Baccharis halimifolia Tree Groundsel **AJ**
Catalpa spp Bean-trees **BB**
Celtis australis European Nettle-tree **AK**
Fraxinus spp Ashes **BB**
Juglans nigra Black Walnut **AF**
Juglans regia Walnut **AF**
Leycesteria formosa Himalayan Honeysuckle **BF**
Rubus spp **RUB**

■Bud scales >12 (or >6 prs)
Acer nigrum Black Maple **BH** (occ)
Acer saccharum Sugar Maple **BH** (occ)
Acer velutinum Velvet Maple **BH**
Aesculus glabra Ohio Buckeye **BG**
Aesculus turbinata Japanese Horse-chestnut **BG** (occ)
Carpinus betulus Hornbeam **AK** (occ)
Fagus sylvatica Beech **AL**
Metasequoia glyptostroboides Dawn Redwood **BB**
Myrica gale Bog-myrtle **AP**
Quercus spp Oaks **AE**
Taxodium distichum Swamp Cypress **AN** (occ)

■Bud scales 2-, 4- or 5-ranked

Amelanchier lamarckii Juneberry **AP** (2-ranked)
Aronia spp Chokeberries **AP** (2-ranked)
Carpinus betulus Hornbeam **AK** (4-ranked)
Celtis australis European Nettle-tree **AK** (2-ranked)
Fagus sylvatica Beech **AL** (4-ranked)
Morus spp Mulberries **AL** (2-ranked)
Myrica gale Bog-myrtle **AP** (5-ranked)
Nothofagus alpina Rauli **AL** (4-ranked)
Nothofagus obliqua Roble **AK** (2-ranked)
Ostrya carpinifolia Hop-hornbeam **AL** (2-ranked)
Quercus spp Oaks **AE** (5-ranked)
Ulmus spp Elms **ULM** (2-ranked)
Zelkova carpinifolia Caucasian Zelkova **AL** (4-ranked)
Zelkova serrata Japanese Zelkova **AL** (4-ranked)

■Bud scales 1(3)-keeled

Acer spp Maples **BH** (weakly)
Acer velutinum Velvet Maple **BH**
Aesculus spp Horse-chestnuts & Buckeyes **BG** (weakly or lowest pr only)
Aesculus glabra Ohio Buckeye **BG**
Amelanchier lamarckii Juneberry **AP**
Aronia spp Chokeberries **AP**
Carya ovata Shagbark Hickory **AR**
Catalpa spp Bean-trees **BB**
Celastrus orbiculatus Staff-vine **AD**
Cercis siliquastrum Judas Tree **AF**
Cornus mas Cornelian-cherry **BE**
Crataegus spp Hawthorns **AC** (occ)
Daphne mezereum Mezereon **AN**
Deutzia scabra Deutzia **BI**
Euonymus europaeus Spindle **BA**
Forsythia x *intermedia* Forsythia **BB**
Hypericum androsaemum Tutsan **BI**
Jasminum spp Jasmines **AJ**, **BA**
Kolkwitzia amabilis Beautybush **BI**
Larix spp Larches **AN**
Ligustrum ovalifolium Garden Privet **BB**
Ligustrum vulgare Wild Privet **BB**
Lonicera spp Honeysuckles **BC**, **BE**, **BI**
Magnolia spp Magnolias **MAG** (some taxa)
Malus spp Apples **MAL** (weakly)
Metasequoia glyptostroboides Dawn Redwood **BB**
Paeonia sect *Moutan* Tree Peony **AP**
Physocarpus opulifolius Atlantic Ninebark **AK**
Populus spp Poplars **POP** (2-keeled)
Pseudolarix amabilis Golden Larch **AN**
Pyrus spp Pears **PYR**
Rhamnus cathartica Buckthorn **BB** (weakly)
Rhododendron luteum Yellow Azalea **AN**
Ribes spp Currants & Gooseberry **RIB**
Rosa spp Roses **AA**
Rubus spp **RUB**
Sambucus nigra Elder **BI**
Sambucus racemosa Red-berried Elder **BI**

Sorbus spp Whitebeams & Rowans **AP, AQ**
Spiraea spp Spiraeas & Brideworts **SPI**
Stewartia pseudocamellia Deciduous Camellia **AI**
Symphoricarpos albus Snowberry **BI**
Symphoricarpos x *chenaultii* Hybrid Coralberry **BI**
Syringa vulgaris Lilac **BB**
Taxodium distichum Swamp Cypress **AN**
Vaccinium corymbosum Blueberry **AN** (weakly)
Vaccinium uliginosum Bog Bilberry **AN**
Viburnum x *bodnantense* Bodnant Viburnum **BI**
Weigela florida Weigela **BI**
Xanthorhiza simplicissima Yellowroot **AR**

■Bud scales striate
Acer opalus Italian Maple **BH**
Aesculus flava Yellow Buckeye **BG**
Aesculus glabra Ohio Buckeye **BG**
Betula spp Birches **BET**
Broussonetia papyrifera Paper Mulberry **AI**
Carpinus betulus Hornbeam **AK**
Ficus carica Fig **AG**
Malus spp Apples **MAL** (v rarely)
Nothofagus alpina Rauli **AL**
Ostrya carpinifolia Hop-hornbeam **AL**
Platanus spp Planes **AG**
Potentilla fruticosa Shrubby Cinquefoil **AM**

■Bud scales toothed at least at tip
Euonymus europaeus Spindle **BA**
Hydrangea petiolaris Climbing Hydrangea **BC**
Rosaceae (all genera) (3-toothed)

■Lf scars with unusual shapes
Juglans nigra Black Walnut **AF** (monkey face)
Juglans regia Walnut **AF** (monkey face)
Pterocarya fraxinifolia Caucasian Wingnut **AF** (monkey face)

■Lf scars 2-ranked
Alnus spp Alders **AH, AI**
Amelanchier lamarckii Juneberry **AP**
Aronia spp Chokeberries **AP**
Betula spp Birches **BET** (occ)
Carpinus betulus Hornbeam **AK**
Celtis australis European Nettle-tree **AK**
Cercis siliquastrum Judas Tree **AF**
Cladrastis kentukea Kentucky Yellowwood **AF**
Corylus spp Hazels **AL**
Cotoneaster spp Cotoneasters **COT**
Fagus sylvatica Beech **AL**
Fothergilla major Mountain Witch-alder **AF**
Ginkgo biloba Ginkgo **AO** (on long shoots)
Hamamelis spp Witch-hazels **AF**
Hippocrepis emerus Scorpion Senna **AJ**
Kerria japonica Kerria **AJ**

Liquidambar styraciflua American Sweetgum **AP** (rarely)
Lycium spp Teaplants **AC**
Maclura pomifera Osage-orange **AC**
Mespilus germanica Medlar **AP**
Nothofagus alpina Rauli **AL**
Nothofagus antarctica Antarctic Beech **AL**
Nothofagus obliqua Roble **AK**
Ostrya carpinifolia Hop-hornbeam **AL**
Parrotia persica Persian Ironwood **AF**
Parthenocissus spp Virginia-creeper & Boston-ivy **AD**
Platanus spp Planes **AG**
Stephanandra incisa Stephanandra **AF**
Styrax japonicus Japanese Snowbell-tree **AF**
Tilia spp Limes **TIL**
Ulmus spp Elms **ULM**
Vitis coignetiae Crimson-glory-vine **AD**
Vitis vinifera Grape-vine **AD**
Zelkova spp Zelkovas **AL**

■Lf scar or stipule scars (±) encircling twig or bud (ring- or collar-shaped)
Fagus sylvatica Beech **AL** (almost)
Ficus carica Fig **AG**
Magnolia spp Magnolias **MAG**
Platanus spp Planes **AG**
Rhus typhina Stag's-horn Sumach **AG** (almost)

■Lf scar > bud width
Aralia spp Angelica-trees **AA**
Aronia spp Chokeberries **AP**
Berberis spp Barberries **AB**
Deutzia scabra Deutzia **BI** (rarely)
Hydrangea petiolaris Climbing Hydrangea **BC**
Mespilus germanica Medlar **AP** (often)
Ribes spp Currants & Gooseberry **RIB**
Rosa spp Roses **AA**
Sambucus spp Elders **BI**
Viburnum spp Guelder-Rose, Viburnums & Wayfaring-tree **BE, BI**
Weigela florida Weigela **BI**

■Lf scar < bud width
Berberis spp Barberries **AB**
Betula spp Birches **BET**
Celtis australis European Nettle-tree **AK**
Cornus spp Dogwoods **BE** (early winter before deciduous base falling)
Cytisus spp Brooms **AJ**
Deutzia scabra Deutzia **BI** (usu)
Genista spp Brooms & allies **AJ**
Larix spp Larches **AN**
Ligustrum vulgare Wild Privet **BB** (often)
Nothofagus antarctica Antarctic Beech **AL**
Ostrya carpinifolia Hop-hornbeam **AL**
Parrotia persica Persian Ironwood **AF**
Pseudolarix amabilis Golden Larch **AN**
Rhamnus cathartica Buckthorn **BB**
Syringa vulgaris Lilac **BB** (on end buds)

■Bundle scar 1
Actinidia deliciosa Kiwifruit **AD**
Arctostaphylos alpinus Arctic Bearberry **AN**
Buddleja alternifolia Alternate-leaved Butterfly-bush **AN**
Callicarpa bodinieri var *giraldii* Beautyberry **BE**
Chimonanthus praecox Wintersweet **BB**
Clerodendrum trichotomum var *fargesii* Farges' Harlequin Glorybower **BB**
Colutea arborescens Bladder-senna **AM**
Cytisus spp Brooms **AJ**
Daphne mezereum Mezereon **AN**
Diospyros lotus Date-plum **AI**
Elaeagnus spp **AN**
Euonymus spp Spindles **BA**
Forsythia x *intermedia* Forsythia **BB**
Fuchsia magellanica Fuchsia **BB**
Genista spp Brooms & allies **AJ**
Hippocrepis emerus Scorpion Senna **AJ**
Hippophae rhamnoides Sea-buckthorn **AC**
Hypericum androsaemum Tutsan **BI**
Jasminum spp Jasmines **AJ**, **BA**
Larix spp Larches **AN**
Ligustrum spp Privets **BB**
Lycium spp Teaplants **AC**
Metasequoia glyptostroboides Dawn Redwood **BB**
Periploca graeca Silk-vine **BC**
Potentilla fruticosa Shrubby Cinquefoil **AM**
Pseudolarix amabilis Golden Larch **AN**
Rhododendron luteum Yellow Azalea **AN**
Solanum dulcamara Bittersweet **AD**
Spartium junceum Spanish Broom **AJ**
Spiraea spp Spiraeas & Brideworts **SPI**
Stewartia pseudocamellia Deciduous Camellia **AI**
Symphoricarpos spp Snowberry & Coralberry **BI**
Tamarix gallica Tamarisk **AN**
Taxodium distichum Swamp Cypress **AN**
Vaccinium corymbosum Blueberry **AN**
Vaccinium myrtillus Bilberry **AI**
Vaccinium uliginosum Bog Bilberry **AN**
Wisteria spp Wisterias **AD**

■Bundle scars 2
Ginkgo biloba Ginkgo **AO**

■Bundle scars 4
Hibiscus syriacus Hibiscus **AE**
Sorbus x *hybrida* Swedish Service-tree **AQ** (occ)
Sorbus x *thuringiaca* Bastard Service-tree **AQ** (occ)

■Bundle scars 5-7
Acer spp Maples **BE**, **BH** (3-9) (occ)
Aesculus spp Horse-chestnuts & Buckeyes **BG** (3-9)
Akebia quinata Chocolate-vine **AD**
Broussonetia papyrifera Paper Mulberry **AI**
Cotinus coggygria Smoke-tree **AE**
Hydrangea aspera Rough-leaved Hydrangea **BE**

Hydrangea petiolaris Climbing Hydrangea **BC**
Magnolia spp Magnolias **MAG** (some taxa)
Paeonia sect *Moutan* Tree Peony **AP**
Passiflora caerulea Passion-flower **AD**
Physocarpus opulifolius Atlantic Ninebark **AK**
Platanus spp Planes **AG**
Sambucus spp Elders **BI**
Sorbus subgen *Sorbus* Rowans **AQ**
Sorbus domestica Service-tree **AQ**
Sorbus x *hybrida* Swedish Service-tree **AQ**
Sorbus x *thuringiaca* Bastard Service-tree **AQ**
Staphylea pinnata Bladdernut **BA**
Toona sinensis Chinese Mahogany **AQ**

■Bundle scars >7
Acer spp **BE**, **BH** (rarely)
Aesculus spp Horse-chestnuts & Buckeyes **BG**
Ailanthus altissima Tree-of-heaven **AR**
Aralia spp Angelica-trees **AA**
Carya ovata Shagbark Hickory **AR**
Castanea sativa Sweet Chestnut **AI**
Catalpa spp Catalpas **BB**
Ficus carica Fig **AG**
Fraxinus spp Ashes **BB**
Liriodendron spp Tulip-trees **AH**
Magnolia spp Magnolias **MAG** (some taxa)
Morus spp Mulberries **AL**
Parthenocissus spp Virginia-creeper & Boston-ivy **AD**
Paulownia tomentosa Foxglove-tree **BB**
Platanus spp Planes **AG**
Quercus spp Oaks **AE**
Syringa vulgaris Lilac **BB**
Vitis spp Vines **AD**
Xanthorhiza simplicissima Yellowroot **AR**

■Bundle scars sunken
Baccharis halimifolia Tree Groundsel **AJ**
Chaenomeles spp 'Flowering Quinces' **AC**
Davidia involucrata Dove-tree **AP**
Mespilus germanica Medlar **AP**
Nyssa spp Tupelos **AI**, **AP**
Populus spp Poplars **POP**
Prunus serotina Rum Cherry **PRU** (occ)
Ulmus spp Elms **ULM**

■Stipules persistent
Colutea arborescens Bladder-senna **AM**
Cotoneaster spp Cotoneasters **COT**
Genista lydia Lydian Broom **AJ**
Hippocrepis emerus Scorpion Senna **AJ**
Laburnum spp Laburnums **AJ**
Nothofagus spp **AK**, **AL** (occ)
Potentilla fruticosa Shrubby Cinquefoil **AM**
Quercus cerris Turkey Oak **AE**
Rubus spp **RUB**

■Bark smooth, not green or striated (mature trees only)
Acer pseudoplatanus Sycamore **BH**
Acer velutinum Velvet Maple **BH**
Aesculus spp Horse-chestnuts & Buckeyes **BG** (early maturity)
Ailanthus altissima Tree-of-heaven **AR**
Carpinus betulus Hornbeam **AK**
Fagus sylvatica Beech **AL**
Fraxinus spp Ashes **BB** (at least in early maturity)
Paulownia tomentosa Foxglove-tree **BB**
Populus sect *Tacamahaca* Balsam-poplars **POP D**
Sorbus spp Whitebeams & Rowans **AP, AQ**

■Bark green, smooth with diamond-shaped lenticels
Laburnum spp Laburnums **AJ**

■Bark green, smooth but striated (vertically striped or lined with a contrasting colour, 'snake bark')
Acer capillipes Red Snakebark Maple **BE**
Acer davidii Père David's Maple **BE**
Acer pensylvanicum 'Erythrocladum' Moosewood **BE**
Acer rufinerve Grey-budded Snakebark Maple **BE**
Amelanchier lamarckii Juneberry **AP**

■Bark with diamond-shaped lenticels or pits
Laburnum spp Laburnums **AJ**
Populus sect *Populus* White & Grey Poplar, Aspen **POP A, POP B**
Salix caprea Goat Willow **SAL A**
Toxicodendron verniclfluum Chinese Lacquer-tree **AR**

■Bark peeling (paper-like)
Acer griseum Paperbark Maple **BH**
Betula spp esp *B. papyrifera* & *pendula* Birches **BET**
Prunus spp esp *P. serrula* Cherries **PRU**

■Bark flaking in scales or plates, or mottled (with differential colour patterns)
Acer opalus Italian Maple **BH**
Acer pseudoplatanus Sycamore **BH** (over maturity)
Acer triflorum Three-flowered Maple **BH**
Aesculus spp Horse-chestnuts & Buckeyes **BG** (late maturity)
Betula nigra River Birch **BET**
Catalpa bignonioides Indian Bean-tree **BB**
Cornus mas Cornelian-cherry **BE**
Crataegus spp Hawthorns **AC**
Davidia involucrata Dove-tree **AP**
Larix spp Larches **AN**
Malus spp Apples **MAL**
Mespilus germanica Medlar **AP**
Nothofagus obliqua Roble **AK**
Parrotia persica Persian Ironwood **AF**
Platanus spp Planes **AG**
Prunus serotina Rum Cherry **PRU**
Pseudolarix amabilis Golden Larch **AN**
Rhamnus cathartica Buckthorn **BB**
Salix triandra Almond Willow **SAL B**
Stewartia pseudocamellia Deciduous Camellia **AI**

Zelkova spp Zelkovas **AI**

■Bark shreddy or shaggy
Acer rubrum Red Maple **BH** (occ)
Acer saccharinum Silver Maple **BH**
Betula nigra River Birch **BET**
Carya ovata Shagbark Hickory **AR**
Cercidiphyllum japonicum Katsura **BB**
Ostrya carpinifolia Hop-hornbeam **AL**

■Bark blocky, deeply furrowed into small square or rectangular blocks resembling charcoal briquettes or crocodile-skin
Betula pendula Silver Birch **BET** (at base)
Cercis siliquastrum Judas Tree **AF**
Diospyros lotus Date-plum **AI**
Fraxinus angustifolia ssp *angustifolia* Narrow-leaved Ash **BB**
Nyssa sylvatica Tupelo **AP**
Pyrus spp Pears **PYR**
Sambucus nigra Elder **BI**
Ulmus spp Elms **ULM** (occ)

■Bark ridges intersecting
Acer negundo Ashleaf Maple **BE**
Acer platanoides Norway Maple **BH**
Broussonetia papyrifera Paper Mulberry **AI** (weakly)
Castanea sativa Sweet Chestnut **AI**
Fraxinus spp exc *F. ornus* Ashes **BB** (at least in late maturity)
Juglans spp esp *J. nigra* Walnuts **AF**
Liriodendron spp esp *L. tulipifera* Tulip-trees **AH**
Populus sect *Aigeiros* Black Poplars & Hybrid Black-poplars **POP C**
Pterocarya fraxinifolia Caucasian Wingnut **AF** (weakly)
Quercus spp esp *Q. cerris, petraea* & *robur* Oaks **AE**
Robinia pseudoacacia False-acacia **AB**
Salix alba White Willow **SAL A**
Salix caprea Goat Willow **SAL A**
Salix x *fragilis* Crack-willow **SAL B**

■Bark spongy/corky
Acer campestre Field Maple **BH**
Phellodendron amurense Amur Corktree **BB**
Sambucus nigra Elder **BI**
Ulmus spp Elms **ULM** (some taxa)

■Trunk with epicormic growth
Aesculus spp Horse-chestnuts & Buckeyes **BG**
Alnus spp esp *A. glutinosa* Alders **AH**, **AI**
Fagus sylvatica Beech **AL**
Populus spp Poplars **POP C**
Prunus spp Cherries & Plums **PRU**
Quercus spp esp *Q. robur* Oaks **AE**
Tilia spp esp *T.* x *europaea* Limes **TIL**
Ulmus spp Elms **ULM**

■Crown pyramidal or fastigiate (narrowly upright) and/or trunk continuous to tree tip (excurrent). Many of the cultivars listed below are not included in the keys but are given here for information. Other tree species can also have fastigiate forms

Acer saccharum Sugar/Black Maple **BH**

Alnus glutinosa Alder **AH**

Betula papyrifera Paper Birch **BET** (occ)

Betula pendula Silver Birch **BET** (ill-defined)

Carpinus betulus 'Fastigiata' Upright Hornbeam **AK** (weakly fastigiate)

Corylus colurna Turkish Hazel **AL**

Fagus sylvatica 'Dawyck' Upright Beech **AL**

Ginkgo biloba esp cv 'Fastigiata' Ginkgo **AO**

Larix spp Larches **AN**

Liquidambar styraciflua American Sweetgum **AP**

Liriodendron spp Tulip-trees **AH**

Malus tschonoskii Chonosuki Crab Apple **MAL**

Metasequoia glyptostroboides Dawn Redwood **BB**

Nyssa spp Tupelos **AI, AP**

Populus 'Balsam Spire' Hybrid Balsam-poplar **POP D**

Populus nigra 'Gigantea' Female Lombardy-poplar **POP C**

Populus nigra 'Italica' Lombardy-poplar **POP C**

Populus nigra 'Plantierensis' Plantier's Poplar **POP C**

Populus tremula Aspen **POP B**

Populus trichocarpa Western Balsam-poplar **POP D**

Prunus avium Wild Cherry **PRU** (ill-defined)

Pseudolarix amabilis Golden Larch **AN**

Pyrus spp Pears **PYR** (occ)

Quercus robur 'Fastigiata Koster' Upright Pedunculate Oak **AE**

Taxodium distichum Swamp Cypress **AN**

Tilia x *europaea* Common Lime **TIL** (ill-defined)

Ulmus minor 'Sarniensis' Jersey Elm **ULM**

■Crown oval, round or spreading (trunk not continuous to tree tip (decurrent))

Acer spp Maples **BH**

Aesculus spp Horse-chestnuts & Buckeyes **BG**

Carpinus betulus Hornbeam **AK**

Fagus sylvatica Beech **AL**

Fraxinus spp Ashes **BB**

Malus spp Apples **MAL**

Pyrus spp Pears **PYR**

Quercus spp Oaks **AE**

Salix spp Willows **SAL**

Sorbus spp Whitebeams & Rowans **AP, AQ**

Tilia spp Limes **TIL**

Ulmus glabra Wych Elm **ULM** (usu)

■Crown vase-shaped

Koelreuteria paniculata Pride-of-India **AI**

Laburnum spp Laburnums **AJ**

Parrotia persica Persian Ironwood **AF**

Prunus cerasifera Cherry Plum **PRU**

Zelkova spp Zelkovas **AL**

199

■Crown weeping (many of the cultivars listed below are not included in the keys but are given here for information. Other tree species can also have weeping forms)

Acer palmatum (various cultivars) Weeping Japanese Maple **BE**
Betula pendula Silver Birch **BET** (strongly so in 'Youngii' Young's Silver Birch)
Fagus sylvatica 'Purpurea Pendula' Weeping Purple Beech **AL**
Fraxinus excelsior 'Pendula' Weeping Ash **BB**
Larix decidua 'Pendula' Weeping European Larch **AN**
Malus spp Weeping Apples **MAL**
Morus alba 'Pendula' Weeping White Mulberry **AL**
Prunus persica Weeping Peach **PRU**
Prunus serrulata 'Kiku-shidare-zakura' Cheal's Weeping Japanese Flowering Cherry **PRU**
Prunus subhirtella 'Pendula' Weeping Winter-flowering Cherry **PRU**
Pyrus salicifolia Willow-leaved Pear **PYR**
Salix babylonica var *pekinensis* 'Tortuosa' Corkscrew Willow **SAL B**
Salix x *pendulina* Weeping Crack-willow **SAL B**
Salix x *sepulcralis* 'Chrysocoma' Golden Weeping Willow **SAL B**
Salix x *sepulcralis* 'Erythroflexuosa' Dragon's-claw Willow **SAL B**
Tilia 'Petiolaris' Pendent Silver-lime **TIL**
Ulmus glabra 'Camperdownii' Camperdown Elm **ULM**

■Catkins present (before lvs)
Alnus spp Alders **AH**, **AI**
Betula spp Birches **BET**
Corylus spp Hazels **AL**
Ostrya carpinifolia Hop-hornbeam **AL**

■Lvs persisting over winter (marcescent)
Acer palmatum Japanese Maple **BE** (some cvs only)
Acer saccharum Sugar/Black Maple **BH** (rarely)
Arctostaphylos alpinus Arctic Bearberry **AN**
Carpinus betulus Hornbeam **AK**
Fagus sylvatica Beech **AL**
Hamamelis spp Witch-hazels **AF** (rarely)
Ostrya carpinifolia Hop-hornbeam **AL** (rarely)
Prunus avium Wild Cherry **PRU** (rarely)
Quercus spp Oaks **AE**

■Frs persisting over winter
Acer spp Maples **BE**, **BH** (helicopters)
Aronia spp Chokeberries **AP** (berries)
Callicarpa bodinieri var *giraldii* Beautyberry **BE** (berries)
Catalpa spp Bean-trees **BB** (bean-like pods)
Colutea arborescens Bladder-senna **AM** (bladder-like pods)
Cotoneaster spp Cotoneasters **COT** (berries)
Crataegus spp Hawthorns **AC** (berries)
Fagus sylvatica Beech **AL** (husks)
Fraxinus spp Ashes **BB** (keys)
Malus spp Apples **MAL** (pomes, often small)
Ostrya carpinifolia Hop-hornbeam **AL** (hop-like)
Platanus spp Planes **AG** (globose burrs)
Quercus spp Oaks **AE** (plant galls resembling frs)
Rosa Roses **AA** (hips)
Symphoricarpos albus Snowberry **BI** (berries)
Symphoricarpos x *chenaultii* Hybrid Coralberry **BI** (berries)

■Early bursting (of leaf buds)

Baccharis halimifolia Tree Groundsel **AJ**
Chaenomeles spp 'Flowering Quinces' **AC**
Fuchsia magellanica Fuchsia **BB**
Genista anglica Petty Whin **AC**
Hippocrepis emerus Scorpion Senna **AJ**
Hypericum androsaemum Tutsan **BI**
Kerria japonica Kerria **AJ**
Leycesteria formosa Himalayan Honeysuckle **BF**
Lonicera fragrantissima Fragrant Honeysuckle **BE**
Lonicera periclymenum Honeysuckle **BC**
Lycium spp Teaplants **AC**
Ribes sanguineum Flowering Currant **RIB**
Rosa Roses **AA**
Rubus fruticosus agg Brambles **RUB**
Sambucus nigra Elder **BI**
Sorbaria sorbifolia Sorbaria **AP**
Spiraea japonica Japanese Spiraea **SPI**
Viburnum x *bodnantense* Bodnant Viburnum **BI**

■Late bursting (of leaf buds)

Acer davidii Père David's Maple **BE**
Acer pseudoplatanus Sycamore **BH** (variable)
Acer rubrum Red Maple **BH**
Acer saccharinum Silver Maple **BH**
Carya ovata Shagbark Hickory **AR**
Castanea sativa Sweet Chestnut **AI**
Catalpa spp Bean-trees **BB**
Fagus sylvatica Beech **AL**
Ficus carica Fig **AG**
Frangula alnus Alder Buckthorn **AG**
Fraxinus excelsior Ash **BB**
Genista aetnensis Mount Etna Broom **AJ**
Ginkgo biloba Ginkgo **AO**
Gleditsia triacanthos Honey-locust **AB**, **AF**
Gymnocladus dioicus Kentucky Coffeetree **AF**
Hibiscus syriacus Hibiscus **AE**
Juglans nigra Black Walnut **AF**
Juglans regia Walnut **AF**
Morus spp Mulberries **AL**
Paulownia tomentosa Foxglove-tree **BB**
Phellodendron amurense Amur Corktree **BB**
Populus 'Serotina' (not included in keys)
Populus tremula Aspen **POP**
Quercus spp Oaks **AE**
Rhamnus cathartica Buckthorn **BB**
Rhododendron luteum Yellow Azalea **AN**
Rhus typhina Stag's-horn Sumach **AG**
Robinia pseudoacacia False-acacia **AB**
Sorbus glabriuscula Chinese Rowan **AQ**
Tilia cordata Small-leaved Lime **TIL**
Toxicodendron vernicifluum Chinese Lacquer-tree **AR**
Ulmus minor Field Elm **ULM**
Vitis vinifera Grape-vine **AD**

APPENDIX OF ADDITIONAL SPECIES

Stop press! Below are additional rarer species that may be encountered by the intrepid (some, arguably, should have been included in the main keys but time and space didn't allow). Brief descriptions are given along with the relevant Group(s) to assist the more experienced user now, rather than wait for a second edition.

Acer circinatum (Vine Maple) - Buds like *A. palmatum* but twigs slightly sticky with resin (and usu stouter, 2-3mm diam) and lf scars lacking 'hula skirt' (but still long-ciliate). **BE**

Acer cissifolium (Vine-leaved Maple) - Terminal bud c5mm, with 2 closely adpressed smaller lateral buds; scales 1 pr, dark purple, often white-hairy (esp at base). Lateral buds adpressed, 3-4mm. Twigs slender (c2mm diam), greenish- to purplish-brown, occ densely hairy at tip. **BE**

Acer heldreichii (Heldreich's Maple) - Terminal bud similar to *A. platanoides* in colour (more shaped like *A. pseudoplatanus*) but twigs without latex and lateral buds usu spreading. **BG**

Acer macrophyllum (Bigleaf Maple) - Superficially like *A. pseudoplatanus* or *A. platanoides* with green to reddish buds but scales not black-edged and twigs green to reddish with white latex. Terminal bud c10mm; scales (1)2(3) prs. **BG**

Acer maximowiczianum (Nikko Maple) - Superficially like *A. griseum*. End bud(s) 7-10mm, conical, acute; scales 7-8 prs, purple-black, buff-hairy esp nr tip. Twigs 2mm diam, densely off-white long-hairy nr tip. Bark not peeling. **BG**

Acer monspessulanum (Montpellier Maple) - Like *A. tataricum* but buds slightly larger (3-5mm) with 5-6 prs dark brown scales. **BG**

Acer shirasawanum (Shirasawa Maple) - Buds like *A. palmatum* but larger (5-7mm) with longer 'hula skirt' to 4mm almost surrounding bud. Dead lvs like *A. japonicum*. **BE**

Actinidia arguta (Hardy Kiwifruit) - Like *A. deliciosa* but twigs always hairless. **AD**

Albizia julibrissin (Silk-tree) - Twigs like *Gymnocladus dioicus* (and v late bud burst) but pith white and only 3 bundle scars. **AF**

Betula ermanii (Gold Birch) - Like *B. utilis* but twigs warty and sparsely long-hairy. Buds hairy, long-ciliate, sticky and v weakly fragrant when crushed. **BET**

Betula medwedewii (Transcaucasian Birch) - Similar to *B. lenta* in inner bark odour but buds larger on stouter twigs and v late bud burst. **BET**

Calycanthus floridus (Carolina Spicebush) - Twigs c3mm diam; inner bark odorous (spicy). Lf scars (±) opp, without interpetiolar ridge, raised, U-shaped, almost surrounding buds; bundle scars 3 (middle largest). Lateral buds naked, blackish-brown, hairy, superposed but sunken in lf scars. Frs capsule-like, persistent, hanging, resembling bats from a distance! **BB**

Carya cordiformis (Bitternut Hickory) - Lf scars like *C. ovata* but twigs thinner (c3mm diam) with brown pith. Terminal buds yellow with sessile glands, 4-angled, 8-12mm, with 1 pr valvate scales. Lateral buds occ superposed. **AI**

Clerodendrum bungei (Gloryflower) - Like *C. trichotomum* var *fargesii* but buds larger (2-5mm) and twigs dark purple-brown. **BB**

Corylopsis spp (Winter-hazels) - Twigs ± warty with v many lenticels, mod slender; pith green. Buds 5-10mm, spindle-shaped to broadly ovate, occ short-stalked; scales 2(3), outermost wrapping most of bud, green to purple, hairless, ciliate, pinnate-veined. Lf scars heart-shaped, small; bundle scars 3. Stipule scars oval, ± equal. **AI**

Decaisnea fargesii (Blue Bean-shrub) - Unmistakable! Twigs stout (c8mm diam), pruinose, with long dead tip; pith v large. Buds lateral, 15-25mm, ovoid-conical, acute; scales 2, ± valvate, green, hairless, not ciliate. Lf scars not raised, shield-shaped, large; bundle scars 5. **AI**

Desmodium elegans (Elegant Tick-clover) - Buds adpressed, 5mm, narrow ovoid; scales 2, striate, resembling those of *Broussonetia papyrifera*, hairy. Twigs 1-2mm diam, zig-zagging, pale brown, long-hairy, ridged; pith green. Lf scars circular; bundle scar 1 or divided. Stipules scars present. **AI**

Dipteronia sinensis (Chinese Money-maple) - Terminal bud naked, similar to *Tetradium daniellii* but yellow-hairy and 5-10mm. Twigs 3-4mm diam, v lightweight; pith ⅔ diam. Lf scars flat; bundle scars 5. **BE**

Enkianthus campanulatus (Redvein Enkianthus) - Resembles a small-budded *Rhododendron luteum*. Twigs ± whorled, 1mm diam, 2-ridged. Terminal bud 7-8mm, broadly ovoid, acute, slightly sticky; scales 6-7, green, reddish nr tip, keeled, apiculate, with sparse obscure adpressed rusty hairs, rusty-ciliate, pinnate-veined. Lf scars triangular, flat; bundle scar 1, nr top. **AN**

Euonymus alatus (Winged Spindle) - Like *E. europaeus* but twigs with wide thin corky wings and buds with 4-6(7) prs of scales. **BA**

Forsythia suspensa (Weeping Forsythia) - Like *F. x intermedia* but twigs ≤2mm diam, hollow (never chambered) and strongly arching or weeping. **BB**

Fraxinus americana (White Ash) - Similar to other *Fraxinus* but lateral buds opp, brown and set in a deep U-shaped notch of the upper edge of lf scars. Terminal bud 2-5mm, usu as wide as long. **BB**

Fraxinus pennsylvanica (Green Ash) - Similar to *F. americana* but lateral buds set in a straight or shallow U-shaped notch of the lf scars. Terminal bud 3-8mm, usu longer than wide. **BB**

Gleditsia caspica (Caspian Locust) - Viciously armed tree like *G. triancanthos*. Lateral buds not sunken, with 1-2 superposed, 4-6mm, conical-ovoid; scales c7, reddish-brown, hairless, occ ciliate. Twigs 2-3mm diam, minutely hairy. **AB**

Halesia monticola (Mountain Silverbell) - Terminal bud a naked folded lf, 8-10mm, with 1 smaller superposed lf below, cream-coloured, densely hairy. Lateral buds spreading, 6-8mm, with minute superposed bud below, ovoid, acute; scales 3-5, purple, the upper hairy. Twigs c3mm diam. Lf scars low, semi-circular, sunken with raised rim; bundle scar 1. Branchlets with chambered pith (30-40 chambers per cm); bark splitting. **AF**

Holodiscus discolor (Oceanspray) - Twigs 5-7-ridged, 2-3mm diam, pale brown, minutely hairy to hairless; pith orange-brown. Buds naked, ± adpressed, ± conical, silky-hairy, 3-5mm. Lf scars shrivelled, raised; bundle scars obscure, 1-3, in a line. Bark shreddy. Dead lvs occ persisting. **AG**

Hydrangea quercifolia (Oak-leaved Hydrangea) - Keys out next to *H. aspera*. Terminal bud naked (young lobed lvs), covered in orange woolly hairs. Twigs mod stout; pith orange-brown. Bundle scars 3. Branchlets with splitting bark. Shrub. **BE**

Indigofera spp (Indigo) - Buds naked, like miniature hands in prayer, 2-3mm, brown, medifixed-hairy. Twig sparsely medifixed-hairy esp nr tip, round, straight, green to dark purple, 2mm diam; inner bark odorous. Lf scar raised, ± semi-circular; bundle scars 3. Stipules persistent, acute. **AM**

Juglans cinerea (Butternut) - Like *J. nigra* but lf scar resembling a sheep's face and separated from bud above by a velvety ridge; pith dark brown. **AF**

Kalopanax septemlobus (Castor-aralia) - Young trunks prickly like *Aralia* but twigs only c5mm diam and lf scars with only (7)9 bundle scars. Terminal bud 4-6mm, dome-shaped; scales 3, dark purple. Twigs green to red; inner bark aromatic. Older trunks with stout woody spurs. **AA**

+*Laburnocytisus adamii* (Adam's Laburnum) - A peculiar (and v variable) chimaera between *Laburnum anagyroides* and *Cytisus purpureus* with characters of both. Twigs green, mod stout, warty, ridged, with larger lf scars than *Cytisus*, with stipule scars and a terminal bud. Woody spurs like *Laburnum* and often with persistent stipules. **AJ**

Magnolia campbellii (Campbell's Magnolia) - Like *M. acuminata* with short adpressed hairs on buds but twigs green, pruinose and lf scars with 15-20 scattered bundle scars. **MAG**

Magnolia obovata (Japanese Bigleaf Magnolia) - Buds 2-4cm, hairless, green to pruinose, minutely dotted with orange-red glands. Twigs usu green. Lf scars with 15-20 scattered bundle scars, with occ orange-red sessile glands. **MAG**

Malus yunnanensis (Yunnan Crab Apple) - Terminal bud like *M. pumila* but larger to 15mm. **MAL**

Neillia affinis (Chinese Ninebark) - Like a large upright (but arching) *Stephanandra incisa* similar in characters of superposed buds, ridged twigs, pith and flaking bark but stipule scars not on pegs. Buds 5-7mm, reddish- to purple-brown. **AF**

Oemleria cerasiformis (Osoberry) - Twigs 3mm diam, reddish-brown, hairless; lenticels orange; inner bark odorous; pith finely chambered (c50 chambers per cm). Branchlets with woody spurs. Terminal bud broadly ovoid, 7-10mm, occ short-stalked; scales c5, greenish, v obtuse, 3-toothed or apiculate, hairless. Leaf scars U-shaped; bundle scars 3. Suckering shrub. **AP**

Oxydendrum arboreum (Sorrel-tree) - Twigs green to red, ± zig-zagging; inner bark odorous. Buds lateral, <2mm, partly sunken, dome-like; scales 3-4(6), reddish. Lf scars shield-shaped; bundle scar 1. Bark deeply blocky. **AJ, AN**

Picrasma quassioides (Quassia) - Terminal bud golden yellow-hairy, naked (young curled lvs), + globose, 5-7mm. Twigs 3-4mm diam, dark reddish-brown with many yellowish flat lenticels. Lf scars ± shield-shaped, white; bundle scars 3, occ divided. Stipule scars present. Small tree. **AG**

Prunus pensylvanica (Pin Cherry) - Similar to *P. serotina* (inc odour) but pith brown. **PRU**

Ptelea trifoliata (Hop-tree) - Twigs 3mm diam, dark brown, brittle, not zig-zagging; pith ⅔ diam; inner bark odorous (spicy). Buds sunken in lf scar, all lateral, superposed, dome-shaped, white silky-hairy. Lf scars U-shaped, almost surrounding bud, low, hairy fringe above bud; bundle scars 3. Shrub or small tree. **AF, AP**

Pterocarya stenoptera (Chinese Wingnut) - Like a slender *P. fraxinifolia* with twigs only 3mm diam and buds 10mm inc stalk. **AF**

Pterostyrax hispidus (Epaulette-tree) - Terminal bud naked (young folded plicate lf), c10mm. Lateral buds smaller, superposed, conical, naked, green but white hairy. Lf scar low, circular to ellipse or shield-shaped, notched at top, large. Bundle scar U-shaped. Twigs 3mm diam, orange-brown, without lenticels. Frs furry with long style (resembling shrews!). **AF**

Pyrus pyrifolia (Asian Pear) - Similar to *P. calleryana*. Terminal buds 7-12mm, acute; scales reddish-brown, buff-hairy esp nr tip and along keel, buff-ciliate. Twigs 3mm diam, olive-brown, v sparsely hairy nr tip. **PYR**

Quercus bicolor (Swamp White Oak) - End buds small and hairless like *Q. palustris* but with only 10-15 scales and bark peeling off small branches in sheets. **AE**

Quercus castaneifolia (Chestnut-leaved Oak) - Like *Q. cerris* but stipules shorter to 15mm and less persistent (esp on lateral buds) and terminal bud usu larger (4-12mm). **AE**

Quercus macrocarpa (Burr Oak) - End buds hairy; small branches develop corky wings like *Ulmus*. **AE**

Quercus phellos (Willow Oak) - End buds like *Q. palustris* but twigs only 1.5-2mm diam (v rarely with occ stellate hairs persisting). **AE**

Rosa sericea ssp *omeiensis* forma *pteracantha* (Winged-thorn Rose) - Unmistakable! Typical *Rosa* but prickles widened into broad wings, usu paired on stem. **AA**

Sorbus decora (Showy Mountain-ash) - Terminal bud purple-black like *S. commixta* 'Ravensbill' but twigs stout (8-10mm diam). **AQ**

Sorbus sargentiana (Sargent's Rowan) - Similar to *S. commixta* but twigs stout (8-10mm diam). Terminal bud to 20mm, bright red, v sticky. Late bursting. **AQ**

Tetracentron sinense (Spur-leaf) - Buds 10-12 x 2mm, narrowly cylindrical, curved, acute; scale 1, overlapping, wrapped around inner scale, orange, hairless, falling leaving line-like scar extending >½ way around twig. Twigs 2-3mm diam, green to purplish; lenticels sparse, raised. Branchlets with woody spurs to 3cm. Lf scars V-shaped, narrowed between bundle scars; bundle scars 3. Small tree. **AG**

Tilia americana (American Lime) - Virtually indistinguishable from the larger buds of *T. x europaea* in winter but often more acute. Lacks epicormic growth (as do some *T. x europaea*). In autumn, leaves glaucous below with long mucronate teeth but twigs not green or hairy like *T. x euchlora*. **TIL**

Ulmus parvifolia (Lacebark Elm) - Twigs v slender (c1mm diam), hairy. Buds 1-2mm, hairless. Similar to a diminutive *U. procera* but trunk with attractive bark flaking in scales revealing orange underbark. **ULM**

Viburnum lentago (Sheepberry) - Fl buds c2cm, long-tapering with a swollen base, reminiscent of a long-beaked bird (e.g. a 'crane's bill'), short-stalked; scales 2, valvate, purple. Lf buds not swollen at base. Twigs with many lenticels. Rotting frs with wet sheep wool odour. Suckering shrub. **BE**

Viburnum plicatum (Japanese Snowball) - Terminal buds naked like a smaller dark brown version of *V. lantana*. **BE**

SYMBOLS & ABBREVIATIONS

♂, ♀ male, female
< less than; << much less than
> greater than; >> much greater than
± more-or-less (qualitative); approximately (quantitative)
° degrees of an angle, e.g. 90° = 90 degrees
x10, x20, x60, etc magnification recommended
agg aggregate
alt alternate
bi biennial
Br Britain
c circa (approximately)
calc calcareous
cf confer; compare with
cv cultivar
diam diameter
Eng England
esp especially
exc except
fl(s) flower(s)
frs fruits
inc including
infl inflorescence
Ire Ireland
irreg irregular
Is Island(s)
lanc lanceolate
lf leaf
lft leaflet
lvs leaves
mod moderate
mtn mountain
N, S, E, W points of compass
nr near
occ occasionally
opp opposite
per perennial
PL plate(s)
pr(s) pair(s)
R rare
Scot Scotland
sect (of a genus) section
sp (plural **spp**) species
ssp subspecies
subgen subgenus
subopp subopposite
usu usually
v very
var variety
vb vascular bundle
VR very rare
yr(s) year(s)

GLOSSARY

Botanists do not always agree on the precise meaning of even some common terms! This glossary should always be referred to in order to check our interpretation of terms used (which may be key-specific). To assist in the use of other literature, a few terms are defined but not used in the keys (typically alternative terms).

ORDER OF VISIBILITY
distinct clearly visible
indistinct visible with careful observation
obscure difficult to see

TERMS
abscission layer a weak zone where a leaf, twig or bud is shed leaving a self-healing scar
acicle a very slender prickle, needle-like
acuminate narrowing gradually to a point
acute sharply pointed
adpressed lying flat; closely pressed against a surface
adventitious arising in an unusual position, e.g. **aerial rootlets** along a twig
aerial rootlets small roots produced along the stems of some climbers as an adaptation to cling to a substrate
aggregate a group of very closely related **species**, usually critical
alternate arranged singly at different lengths along a twig
ambidextrous (of a climber) can be clockwise- or anticlockwise-twining
angled with angles; (of a twig) angles not raised into ridges; cf **ridged**
anti-clockwise twining to the right when the stem is in front of the support, growing from lower left to upper right
apiculate with an **apiculus**
apiculus (of bud scales) a short point, often a protruding midvein (technically a **mucro**) or a vestigial petiole
arc a short curve
armature prickles, spines or thorns (one or more may be present)
armed with prickles, spines or thorns
aromatic pleasantly odorous
ascending growing upwards at an angle
astringent causing a drying sensation in the mouth, usually caused by sharp-tasting tannins
auricle a small ear-shaped lobe or projection
axil the upper side of a junction of two structures
bark the outermost non-living protective layers of twigs, branchlets, branches and trunks; outer bark; cf **inner bark** and **underbark**
biennial (of a stem) where a new stem (**primocane**) grows from a rootstock to its full length in 1st year but does not produce any flowers which in the 2nd yr becomes a **floricane** producing lateral flowering shoots that usually die after fruiting; a stem that lives for two years
bitter almond (odour) a moderately fetid odour associated with the inner bark of some *Prunus* due to the presence of prussic acid (hydrogen cyanide)
blocky (of bark) forming squarish block-like plates or ridges, often deep, reminiscent of crocodile-hide or charcoal briquettes
brachyblast technical term for a **woody spur**
bract a much-reduced leaf or leaf-like structure
branch a thicker older branchlet, 5-many years old
branchlet shoots that are 2-4 years old; cf **twig**
brittle easily snapped, often audibly
bud a compact undeveloped embryonic twig in its resting stage, normally occurring above a leaf scar or at the tip of a twig and protected by either scales or dense hairs
bud burst the emergence of new growth from buds in the spring and may refer to leaves and/or flowers, usually following a period of bud swell; cf **leaf burst**

bud scale a small modified leaf (or stipule) covering the outside of a bud
bud scale scars the scars left on a twig when the scales from a terminal bud drop. The distance from one cluster of scars to the next represents one year's growth. See **girdle scars**
buff pale yellowish-brown
bundle scars small dots or lines on the surface of the leaf scar indicating a point where the veins (vascular bundles) from the leaf were once connected to the twig; also known as **bundle traces** but technically these refer to the fresh marks visible after a leaf is newly removed
burr a large knobbly outgrowth on a tree trunk. Technically, this term refers to an outgrowth with epicormic shoots while a **burl** refers to an outgrowth without epicormic shoots
buttressed (of a trunk) widened at the base for stability, with spur-like root flares extending up the trunk
cartilaginous hard and tough; gristly
catkin a cylindrical cluster of unisex flowers, often dense and drooping
cauliflory flowers (and fruit) occurring directly on branches or trunks
chambered (of pith) with cross-partitions dividing central cavity into numerous hollow chambers; ladder-like; cf **diaphragmed**
cilia hairs along a margin, often eyelash-like
ciliate fringed with **cilia**, usually referring to a bud scale margin
climber a plant growing upwards by leaning, twining or using **tendrils** on another structure for support
clockwise twining to the left when the stem is in front of the support, growing from lower right to upper left
clustered (of buds) with 2-several buds closely arranged, usually at the twig tip
collateral (of buds) lying side-by-side; usually smaller buds either side of a true lateral bud; also known as **accessory buds**
columnar column-shaped
conical cone-shaped
crisped-hairy with curled hairs
crown the collective branches, branchlets and twigs of a tree or shrub, excluding the trunk; the 'head' of the tree or shrub
cultivar a 'cultivated variety' that has been produced or maintained by selective breeding and propagated vegetatively; it may be a true species or a hybrid. Cultivar names are written non-italicised and capitalised in single quotation marks e.g. 'Plantieriensis'
deciduous falling off at a particular season (usually autumn) or stage of growth once no longer required; it may refer to leaves, stipules, branchlets, leaf scars and petiole bases; shedding its leaves in autumn; not **persistent**
declining growing downwards at an angle; cf **ascending**
decumbent lying along the ground with the apex ascending
decurrent (of leaf scars) running down the twig; usually the origin of lines, ridges or angles along a twig; (of a trunk) branched, non-continuous to tree tip
decussate 4-ranked; in opposite pairs with each pair at right angles to the pair above and below
deltoid (of a 3-dimensional body) with the shape of the uppercase Greek letter Δ, i.e. a more-or-less equilateral triangle
dense (of pith) non-porous and firm to the touch; densely packed
diaphragmed (of pith) solid with firm partitions (diaphragms) at intervals (cf **chambered**)
diffuse-porous (of wood) with no significant difference in pore size and the pores evenly distributed (not in bands); the pores are sparse and too small to be easily seen by the naked eye
distal situated away from the point of attachment; not **proximal**
distichous 2-ranked; arranged in two opposite rows
early bursting bud burst typically before the 31st March
eccentric (of pith) off-centre; not centrally placed
ellipsoid (of a 3-dimensional body) elliptical in outline
elliptical shaped like a flattened circle, widest in the middle, tapering equally at both ends (having two axes of symmetry)
end bud a **terminal bud**, or the uppermost **lateral bud** closest to the twig tip (a **false terminal bud**)
entire with margin unbroken by teeth or other indentations; uninterrupted

epicormic growth sprouting from dormant buds on the trunk of a tree
epidermis (of twig or other organ) outermost layer of cells, usually only one cell thick
erose having an irregularly minutely jagged margin; appearing gnawed
excurrent (of a trunk) extending undivided to the tree tip; continuous to tree tip
extra-floral nectary a nectar-producing organ situated away from the flower
false terminal bud the apparent terminal bud of a twig but actually the uppermost lateral bud that
   assumes the function of the terminal bud (always has a dead twig tip or small **twig-tip scar** on the
   opposite side); a **pseudoterminal bud**; cf **end bud**
fascicle a cluster or bundle
fastigiate with branches erect and more-or-less adpressed to the vertical, giving a narrow or
   columnar appearance
felted covered with dense matted hairs giving the appearance or texture of felt or woollen cloth
fetid unpleasantly odorous
fissured (of bark) with shallow longitudinal splits or cracks (usually ≤4mm) on an otherwise smooth
   surface, often irregular on trunks, unlike the deeper more regular patterns of **furrowed** bark
flexible (of a twig) can be tied in a knot without breaking
floricane the second year stem (cane) of some *Rubus* (e.g. *R. idaeus*) that bears flowers and fruit
   then dies; cf **primocane**
fluted (of a trunk) with wide longitudinal grooves near the base
fragmenting (of pith) solid when young but soon disintegrating into a hollow cylinder
furrow (of bark) the valley of the groove; cf **ridge**
furrowed (of bark) 'ridged and furrowed bark'; with deep vertical grooves (usually >4mm), the
   ridges separated by increasingly deeper furrows as the tree ages, often more-or-less regular; cf
   fissured. Ridges may be *uninterrupted, intersecting* or *broken horizontally*
girdle scars a cluster of terminal bud scale scars on a shoot remaining after bud burst
gland an organ (often very small) that produces a secretion
glandular possessing glands
globose spherical or globe-shaped
grafted the artificial union (by man) of plant parts; where two different woody taxa are joined,
   usually one is inserted into the incised trunk of the other leaving a visible scar, swelling or
   difference in bark texture above and below the graft
herb a non-woody plant, or one that is woody only at the base
herbaceous composed of non-woody green tissue; (of bud scales) having the texture, colour or
   appearance of a leaf
herringbone-like of a branchlet with side-shoots regularly spreading in one plane at 45-90°, like
   the stereotypical skeleton of a fish
hexagonal having six sides
hollow (of pith) pith absent
hortal a plant of garden origin
imbricate (of bud scales) overlapping, like roof tiles
incurved curved inwards
inflorescence the arrangement of flowers on the floral axes; a flower cluster
inner bark the inner layers of living bark visible when the outer bark is peeled off; cf **underbark**
internode the part of a twig between two successive leaf scars or pairs of leaf scars (nodes)
interpetiolar between two opposite leaf scars
interpetiolar ridge a narrow horizontal ridge connecting two opposite leaf scars
interpetiolar stipule a stipule located on the twig between a pair of opposite leaf scars, formed
   from the fusion of two stipules - one from each of the pair of opposite leaves
intersecting (of bark) where ridges meet and cross at a point; not parallel; interlacing, like
   shoelaces
involute (of a bundle scar) forming a U-shape with each end turned inwards
keeled (of a bud scale) with a raised ridge or line (vein) running to the apex
laciniate jagged, torn
lanceolate lance-shaped; at least 3 times longer than wide, widest below the middle and tapering
   to apex
lanceoloid (of a 3-dimensional body) lance-shaped
late bursting bud burst typically after the 15th April (all species bursting by the 1st June)

late-deciduous falling late in the winter season e.g. a petiole base raising the leaf scar eventually falling exposing the true leaf scar (e.g. in *Sorbus* subgen *Sorbus*)
lateral at the side
lateral bud any bud that is situated along a twig and not at the true tip
latex white juice (which may dry black) exuding from broken canals or lactifers within the plant tissues, not sap
leaf burst the emergence of new leaves in the spring
leaf scar the mark left on a twig when a leaf falls, usually differing in colour and texture from the rest of the twig
leafing (of leaf burst) the date of first leaf emergence
leaflet a leaf-like segment of a compound leaf
leaf-opposed (at a node) on the opposite side from a leaf or leaf scar
lenticel a distinct mark on the bark, originating as a **stoma**, serving as a breathing pore; typically longitudinally oval or lens-shaped but can be round to linear, raised or flat, often of a different colour to the surrounding bark
lenticellate with many lenticels
limb a main branch that grows from the trunk
linear many times longer than wide, with the margins nearly parallel
lined (of a twig) with two or more weakly raised longitudinal ridges on an otherwise round twig without angles (denoted by a numerical prefix e.g. 2-lined); cf **angled**, **ridged**
long shoot a typical twig (with elongated internodes); cf **short shoot**, **woody spur**
longitudinal running lengthways
marcescent (of leaves) dead but remaining attached to twigs over the winter, usually on lower branches only. Stress from drought or disease can cause marcescence in any deciduous species
medifixed (of a hair) attached at the middle and adpressed, overall having a distinctive appearance due to being pressed down in the middle and all hairs lying more-or-less parallel
microspecies a species differing only in very minor characteristics from other closely related species, typically one of limited geographical range and part of an **aggregate** group of species
midrib the main or central vein of a leaf
monopodial (of growth) with a main stem; growing by apical extension from a terminal bud
mottled (of bark) having a varied colour pattern caused by pieces of outer bark flaking off to reveal different colours or shades of **underbark** beneath
multiplied (of bundle scars) dividing into two or three similar sized scars, usually forming groups
multi-trunked (of a tree) divided at the base into two or more trunks; occasionally incorrectly applied where the trunk divides near the base
naked (of a bud) without bud scales (i.e. young leaves)
node the position on a twig at which buds and leaf scars occur, often slightly swollen
nodule a small woody knob-like outgrowth
oblanceolate inversely lanceolate, widest above the middle and tapering to the base
oblique (of a bud) not positioned directly above the leaf scar, not perpendicular or parallel to the twig; slanting away from the centre line of the twig
oblong longer than broad with nearly parallel sides and rounded at both ends
obovate inversely ovate, widest above the middle and tapering to the base
obovoid (of a 3-dimensional body) inversely ovoid, attached at the narrower end
obtuse blunt; with a more-or-less rounded apex (at an angle >90°)
ochrea (plural **ochreae**) a sheath around the stem formed from two **stipules** fused into a tube, e.g. *Fallopia*
odorous having a noticeable odour which can be pleasant or unpleasant
opposite (of buds and leaf scars) borne in pairs at a node, one on either side of the twig
orbicular circular in outline
orthotropic growing vertically; cf **plagiotropic**
oval elliptical but often only with a <u>single</u> axis of reflection symmetry; cf **elliptical**
ovate egg-shaped in outline, less than 3x as long as wide, widest below the middle and tapering to apex
ovoid (of a 3-dimensional body) egg-shaped
panicle a compound **raceme**; an indeterminate inflorescence in which the flowers are borne on branches of the main axis or on further branches of these

papilla (plural **papillae**) a small elongated or pimple like protuberance on the surface of an organ, usually an extension of one epidermal cell
papillate bearing **papillae**
partite deeply divided from or near to the base e.g. 3-partite spines of *Berberis*
patch-forming forming large stands, often evenly spaced and aged, spreading by **rhizomes**, **stolons** or root-suckers
patent spreading widely and straight; at ± 90° to a surface
peltate shaped like a disc with a stalk attached centrally (stalk rarely visible)
perennial with a life cycle lasting three or more years
persistent not dropping off readily
persistent bud scales papery remnants of bud scales (from previous year's bud burst) persisting at the base of a twig at join with branchlet
petiole a leaf stalk
petiole base the swollen base of a petiole, often persisting after the leaf has been shed and raising the leaf scar, usually eventually falling revealing the true leaf scar; occasionally modified into a **bud scale**
petiolule the stalk of a **leaflet**
phenology the study of the timing of seasonal biological phenomena, e.g. of bud burst or leaf fall
phyllotaxy the arrangement of leaves, leaf scars or buds around the axis of a twig
pith the soft tissue found in the centre of a twig surrounded by the woody cylinder
plagiotropic growing horizontally; cf **orthotropic**
plates typically large flat separated pieces of bark (rarely overlapping), loose or appearing so (i.e. could be prised off), not appearing rigid and fixed like **furrowed** bark; cf **scales**
plicate folded more than once into pleats; fan-like
pneumatophore a vertical aerial root emerging from waterlogged soil or water to carry oxygen to its root systems (e.g. in *Taxodium*)
pollarded (of a trunk) with the branches pruned above head height, promoting new growth, often forming a dense **crown**
porous with many small holes, which water and air can pass through
prehensile capable of grasping or coiling in response to touch
prickle a hard sharp-pointed outgrowth (lacking vascular tissue) along the **internode** of a stem
primocane the first year's vegetative stem (cane) of some *Rubus* (e.g. *R. idaeus*) that will not flower and fruit until its second year
prostrate lying on the ground; trailing
proximal situated near to the point of attachment; not **distal**
pruinose covered with a whitish bloom that is easily rubbed off
pseudoterminal bud alternative term for a **false terminal bud**
raceme an indeterminate inflorescence in which the flowers are borne on short stalks along an unbranched axis flower. The flowers at the base develop first
ranked arranged in rows e.g. 2-ranked, 4-ranked, 5-ranked
recurved curved backwards or downwards
reflexed bent backwards
resin a clear to translucent yellow or brown viscous liquid, often aromatic; gum
resinous having **resin**
retuse shallowly notched at a rounded apex
rhizomatous having **rhizomes**; patch-forming
rhizome a root-like stem usually running horizontally under the ground
rhombic diamond-shaped
rib-bundles much smaller bundle scars in the upper corners of a leaf scar
ridged (of a twig) with angles raised into ridges (occ weak), cf **angled**; (of bark) with prominent ridges or crests between grooves
rigid (of a twig) not flexible; cannot be tied into a knot without snapping
ring-porous (of wood) with the larger pores produced in the spring (early wood) forming distinct rings or bands visible to the naked eye, alternating with bands of smaller pores produced in the summer (late wood); cf **diffuse-porous**
rugose markedly wrinkled
sapling a young tree at least 1m in height (anything under 1m is still considered a seedling)

scales (of bark) typically <u>small</u> flattish overlapping pieces of bark, loose or appearing so (i.e. could be prised off) and often lifting or curling away, not appearing rigid and fixed like **furrowed** bark; cf **plates**. Not to be confused with **bud scales**

scaly (of bark or a bud) with scales

scrambler a plant that grows over other plants or objects for support but lacks any climbing adaptations (e.g. tendrils or twining stems)

sculptured (of a surface) pitted, marked, carved or indented

scurfy covered with small flake-like scales or granules

section a taxonomic rank below the genus and subgenus. Typically used here to split large genera in order to avoid introducing many new binomial names

semi-evergreen with at least some living leaves persisting through the winter but most falling before or with the new spring growth (mild winters may promote this condition)

sepals herbaceous structures that protect the flower in bud and are often persistent on the fruits of many *Malus* species

septate (of a hair) divided into compartments by partitions (septa or cell walls); multi-celled

sessile without a stalk

shaggy (of bark) peeling in longitudinal curved or curling strips free at both ends

sheath a tubular structure surrounding an organ or part of an organ

shoot (scientific use) a single modular portion of twig with one node (including any leaf scar/s and bud/s) and the preceding internode below, thus twigs are actually formed of stacks of shoots; (traditional use) any above ground growth in its first year e.g. terminal shoots (leaders), lateral shoots, water shoots (epicormic growth arising from an arching branch), or basal shoots e.g. suckers or coppice shoots; (colloquial use) a generic term to include twigs

short shoot see **short twig**

short twig intermediate between a **long shoot** and a **woody spur**

shreddy (of bark) strongly peeling horizontally into curly strips

shrub a woody plant smaller than a tree, usually with several stems arising from ground level and with an ultimate height of less than 4m; equivalent to the colloquial word 'bush'

silhouette the two-dimensional outline of a tree

silky having a covering of soft fine straight adpressed (and ± parallel) hairs

smooth (of bark) not peeling, fissured, cracked or furrowed; unbroken

solid (of pith) continuous; not hollow

species a group of organisms that can be readily and consistently recognised by shared characters (and can reproduce); the basic taxonomic rank of classification and denoted by a binomial name

spindle-shaped swollen in the middle and tapering at both ends

spine a stiff sharp-pointed structure originating as a modified leaf, stem or stipule

spiralling (of leaf scars) arranged around the twig in a spiral

spongy (of pith) very porous with large cells; loosely packed and compressible

sprawling spread out over a large area in an untidy or irregular way but <u>not</u> necessarily using other plants or objects as support, lacking any climbing adaptations; cf **scrambler**

sprig an incomplete portion of a **twig** after collection; the terminal portion of a twig

stellate (of a hair) star-shaped; branched with the rays or arms radiating out like a star

stem one of the main 'trunks' of a shrub or the actual trunk of a tree; a generic term for any growth from twig to trunk; one of the three fundamental parts of a higher plant - roots, stem and leaves

stipule scars scars left on the twig when the stipules fall, usually in pairs, small, occasionally unequal or forming a ring around the twig

stipules a pair of bract-like appendages, spines or glands at the base of a petiole, originating from (and attached to) the twig or the petiole. Rarely fused to form an **ochrea**

stolon an above-ground stem usually rooting at least at the tip and capable of giving rise to new plants; any low branch that roots at the nodes

stoloniferous producing stolons

stomata (singular **stoma**) breathing pores occasionally present on a twig (and more rarely on bud scales), visible as little white dots

striae fine longitudinal lines or ridges

striate having **striae**; (of bud scales) fainted ridged by obscure lines (veins) that are more-or-less parallel but converge at tip

strigose with adpressed stiff hairs
subgenus the category of classification intermediate between **genus** and **section**. It has a capital initial letter and is usually used in combination with the generic name e.g. *Sorbus* subgenus *Aria*
subopposite almost opposite; pairs of buds or leaf scars close to but not exactly at the same position on the twig
subshrub a low shrub with herbaceous stems that are woody only at the base, often **prostrate**
subspecies a geographically or ecologically isolated subdivision of a species
sucker a vigorous vegetative shoot produced from a root, often distant from the main stem or trunk
suckering having **suckers**
superposed (of buds) positioned one above the other at one node; one or more buds (usually smaller) inserted above or below the normal lateral bud
suture a seam-like fused junction between two parts of an organ, such as on the bivalve seed pods of *Laburnum* where the suture is opposite to a line of weakness (designed to split to release its seeds)
sympodial (of growth) a lateral growth pattern in which the terminal bud ceases to grow (usually because a terminal flower has formed, or bud aborted) and growth is continued by one of more lateral buds; cf **monopodial**
taxon (plural **taxa**) a taxonomic group of any rank, e.g. species, subgenus, subspecies, hybrid or cultivar
tendril modified stem, leaf or petiole forming a slender twining adaption using for climbing
terminal bud a bud that is at the very end of a twig; a true terminal bud has no **twig-tip scar** below it
thorn a short modified branchlet (or small branch) with a sharp hard point
thorny with **thorns**
translucent very thin, allowing light to pass through but not transparent; semi-transparent
transverse crosswise
tree a tall woody plant with a single main trunk at least 7cm in diameter, a defined crown and a height of at least 4m at maturity; any plant which commonly grows to 3m on a single stem at least 20cm diameter; cf **shrub**
truncate appearing as if transversely cut off
trunk the main vertical stem of a tree; the lower undivided part of a tree (the part below the crown is also known as a bole)
twig a 1st year woody stem to which the buds are attached
twig scar a scar left where a twig has been shed from its branchlet
twig-tip scar a scar left when the tip of the twig has died and self-pruned back to the uppermost lateral bud (visible on the opposite side of the bud to the leaf scar)
twiner a climbing plant that supports itself by winding (twining) around an object
umbel an inflorescence in which all the flower-stalks arise from the same point; umbrella-like
unarmed without prickles, spines or thorns
underbark (of trunks) the younger dead bark (often a different colour) visible where the outer bark has fissured or furrowed, or beneath where it has been shed in plates or scales; where the dead phloem (food-conducting tissue) has become part of the outer bark
upcurved curved upwards or outwards
valvate (of bud scales) two scales meeting at margins without overlapping, like a bivalve
variety botanical subdivision of a species, often differing in a single character from the typical form
vascular bundle a strand of conducting vessels typically with phloem (food-conducting tissue) on the outside and xylem (water-conducting tissue) on the inside
vein an assemblage of strands of vascular tissue in a leaf or similar structure
weeping with branches strongly drooping; vertically hanging down; pendent
whorled (of buds and leaf scars) three or more at the same node
woody spur a slow-growing stubby branch or branchlet with extremely short internodes (usu <5mm) marked by dense ring-like scars left by the crowded **leaf scars** and **bud scale scars**, occasionally resembling a cockerel's spur, often topped by a bud or ending in a sharp point; also known as a **spur shoot** or a **brachyblast**
woolly with long wool-like hairs, often dense and obscuring the surface
xylophyte a tree, shrub or woody climber

Plate 1

Acer campestre
Field Maple **BH**

Acer capillipes
Red Snakebark Maple **BE**

Acer cappadocicum
Cappadocian Maple **BH**

Acer davidii
Père David's Maple **BE**

Acer griseum
Paperbark Maple **BH**

Acer japonicum
Downy Japanese Maple **BH**

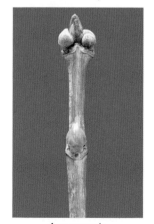

Acer negundo
Ashleaf Maple **BE**

Acer opalus
Italian Maple **BH**

Acer palmatum
Japanese Maple **BE**

Plate 2

214

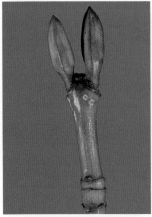

Acer pensylvanicum
'Erythrocladum' Moosewood **BE**

Acer platanoides
Norway Maple **BH**

Acer pseudoplatanus
Sycamore **BH**

Acer rubrum
Red Maple **BH**

Acer rufinerve
Grey-budded Snakebark Maple **BE**

Acer saccharinum
Silver Maple **BH**

Acer saccharum spp *saccharum*
Sugar Maple **BH**

Acer tataricum
Tatarian Maple **BH**

Acer triflorum
Three-flowered Maple **BH**

215

Plate 3

Acer velutinum
Velvet Maple **BH**

Actinidia deliciosa
Kiwifruit **AD**

Aesculus carnea
Red Horse-chestnut **BG**

Aesculus flava
Yellow Buckeye **BG**

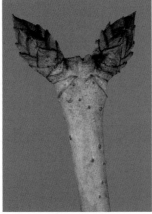

Aesculus glabra
Ohio Buckeye **BG**

Aesculus hippocastanum
Horse-chestnut **BG**

Aesculus indica
Indian Horse-chestnut **BG**

Aesculus parviflora
Bottlebrush Buckeye **BG**

Aesculus pavia
Red Buckeye **BG**

Plate 4

Aesculus turbinata
Japanese Horse-chestnut **BG**

Ailanthus altissima
Tree-of-heaven **AR**

Akebia quinata
Chocolate-vine **AD**

Alnus cordata
Italian Alder **AH**

Alnus glutinosa
Alder **AH**

Alnus incana
Grey Alder **AH**

Alnus rubra
Red Alder **AH**

Alnus viridis
Green Alder **AI**

Amelanchier lamarckii
Juneberry **AP**

217

Plate 5

Aralia elata
Japanese Angelica-tree **AA**

Arctostaphylos alpinus
Arctic Bearberry **AN**

Aronia arbutifolia
Red Chokeberry **AP**

Aronia melanocarpa
Black Chokeberry **AP**

Aronia x *prunifolia*
Purple Chokeberry **AP**

Baccharis halimifolia
Tree Groundsel **AJ**

Berberis thunbergii
Thunberg's Barberry **AB**

Berberis vulgaris
Barberry **AB**

Betula alleghaniensis
Yellow Birch **BET**

Plate 6

Betula lenta
Sweet Birch **BET**

Betula nana
Dwarf Birch **BET**

Betula nigra
River Birch **BET**

Betula papyrifera
Paper Birch **BET**

Betula pendula
Silver Birch **BET**

Betula pubescens ssp *pubescens*
Downy Birch **BET**

Betula pubescens ssp *tortuosa*
Mountain Birch **BET**

Betula utilis
Himalayan Birch **BET**

Broussonetia papyrifera
Paper Mulberry **AI**

Plate 7

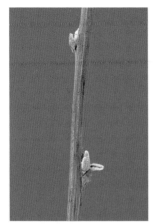

Buddleja alternifolia
Alternate-leaved Butterfly-bush **AN**

Callicarpa bodinieri var *giraldii*
Beautyberry **BE**

Campsis radicans
Trumpet-vine **BC**

Caragana arborescens
Siberian Pea-shrub **AB**

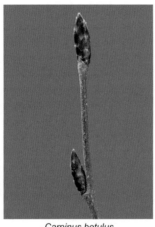

Carpinus betulus
Hornbeam **AK**

Carya ovata
Shagbark Hickory **AR**

Castanea sativa
Sweet Chestnut **AI**

Catalpa bignonioides
Indian Bean-tree **BB**

Catalpa x *erubescens*
Hybrid Catalpa **BB**

Plate 8

Catalpa ovata
Chinese Catalpa **BB**

Catalpa speciosa
Northern Catalpa **BB**

Celastrus orbiculatus
Staff-vine **AD**

Celtis australis
European Nettle-tree **AK**

Cercidiphyllum japonicum
Katsura **BB**

Cercis siliquastrum
Judas Tree **AF**

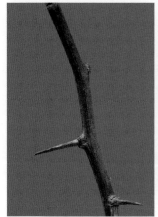

Chaenomeles japonica
Japanese Quince **AC**

Chaenomeles speciosa
Chinese Quince **AC**

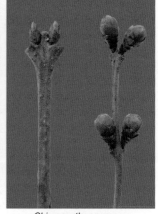

Chimonanthus praecox
Wintersweet **BB**

Plate 9

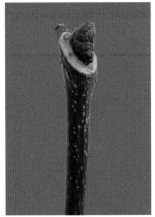

Cladrastis kentukea
Kentucky Yellowwood **AF**

Clematis montana
Himalayan Clematis **BC**

Clematis vitalba
Traveller's-joy **BC**

Clerodendrum trichotomum
var *fargesii* Farges' Harlequin
Glorybower **BB**

Colutea arborescens
Bladder-senna **AM**

Cornus mas
Cornelian-cherry **BE**

Cornus sanguinea
Dogwood **BE**

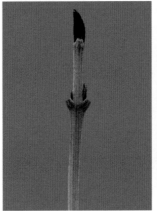

Cornus sanguinea 'Midwinter Fire'
Orange-twig Dogwood **BE**

Cornus sericea
Red-osier Dogwood **BE**

Plate 10

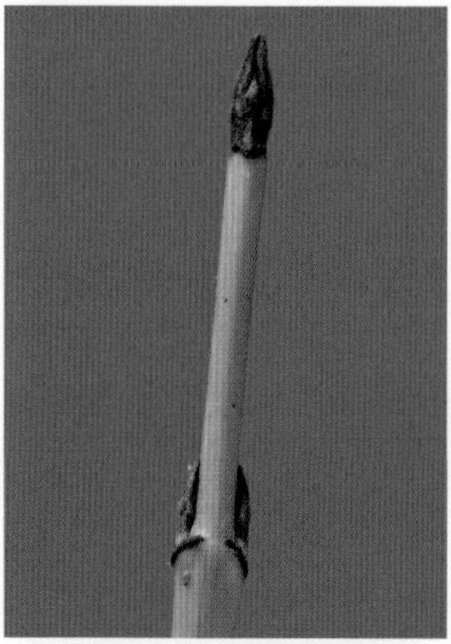

Cornus sericea 'Flaviramea'
Golden-twig Dogwood **BE**

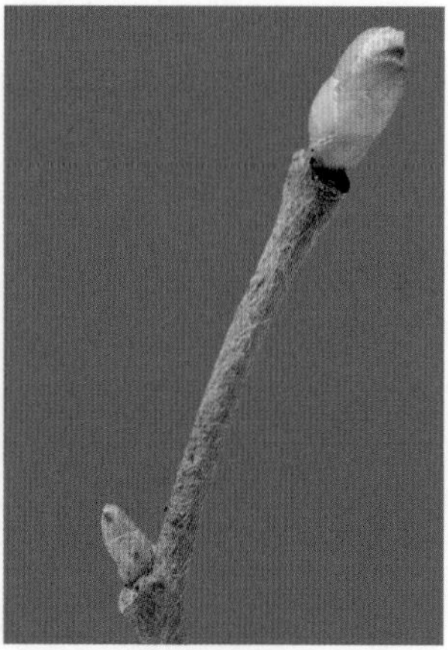

Corylus avellana
Hazel **AL**

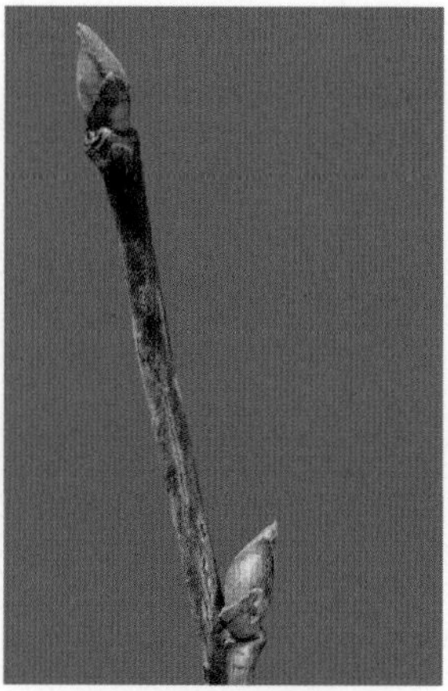

Corylus colurna
Turkish Hazel **AL**

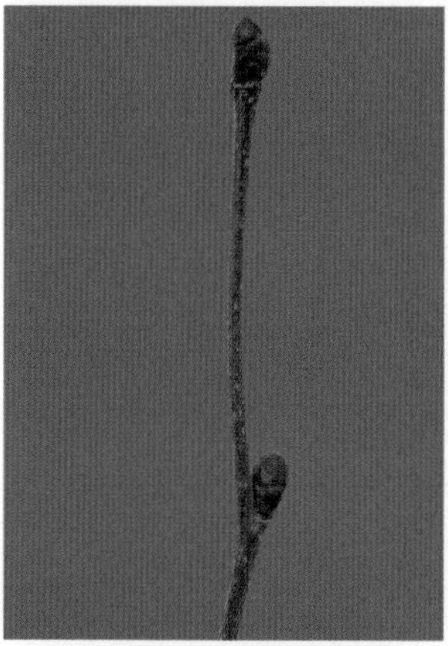

Corylus maxima 'Purpurea'
Purple-leaved Filbert **AL**

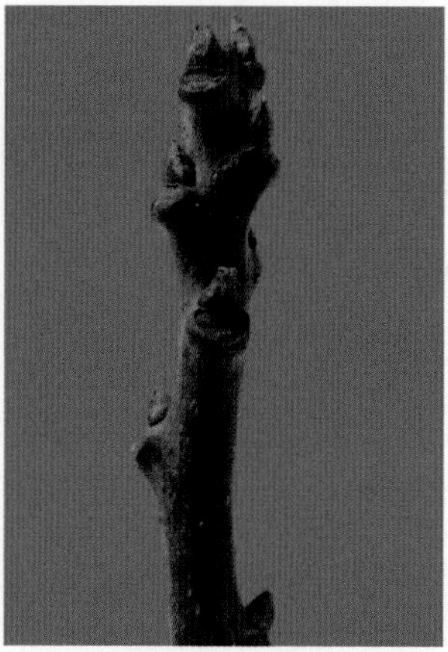

Cotinus coggygria
Smoke-tree **AE**

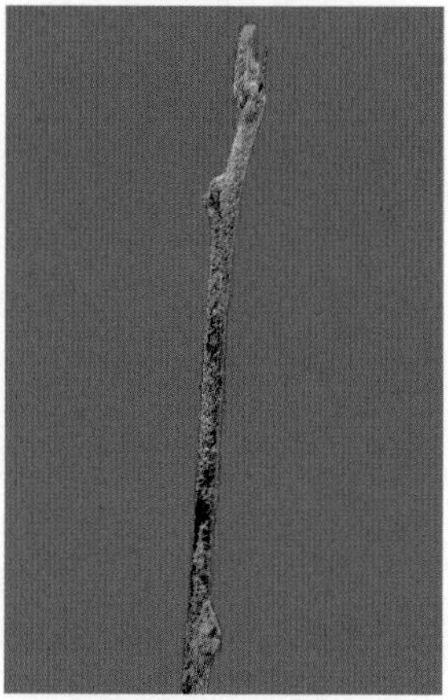

Cotoneaster bullatus
Hollyberry Cotoneaster **COT**

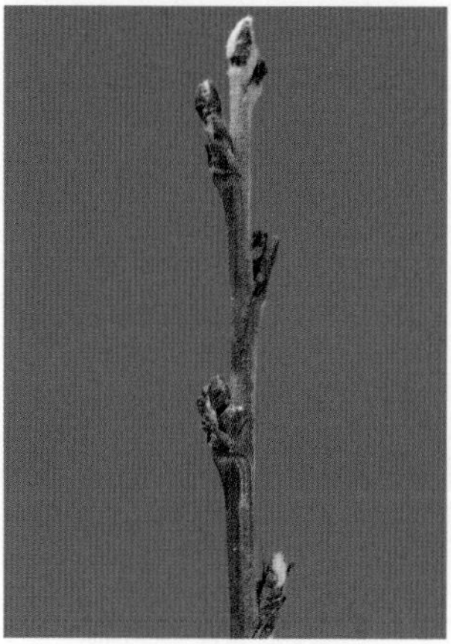

Cotoneaster cambricus
Wild Cotoneaster **COT**

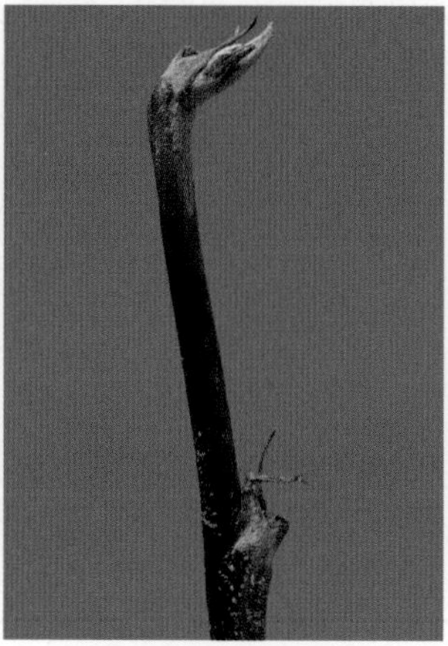

Cotoneaster frigidus
Tree Cotoneaster **COT**

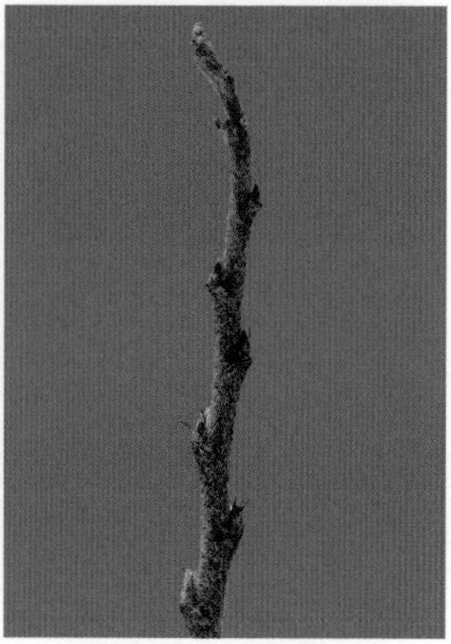

Cotoneaster horizontalis
Wall Cotoneaster **COT**

Plate 11

Crataegus crus-galli
Cockspur Hawthorn **AC**

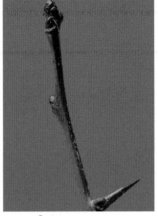

Crataegus monogyna
Hawthorn **AC**

Crataegus persimilis
Broad-leaved Cockspurthorn **AC**

Cydonia oblonga
Quince **AI**

Cytisus nigricans
Black Broom **AJ**

Cytisus scoparius
Broom **AJ**

Cytisus striatus
Hairy-fruited Broom **AJ**

Daphne mezereum
Mezereon **AN**

Davidia involucrata
Dove-tree **AP**

Plate 12

224

Deutzia scabra
Deutzia **BI**

Diospyros lotus
Date-plum **AI**

Elaeagnus angustifolia
Russian-olive **AN**

Elaeagnus commutata
Silverberry **AN**

Euonymus europaeus
Spindle **BA**

Euonymus latifolius
Large-leaved Spindle **BA**

Fagus sylvatica
Beech **AL**

Fallopia baldschuanica
Russian-vine **AD**

Ficus carica
Fig **AG**

225

Plate 13

Forsythia x *intermedia*
Forsythia **BB**

Frangula alnus
Alder Buckthorn **AG**

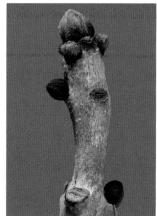
Fraxinus angustifolia ssp *oxycarpa*
Claret Ash **BB**

Fraxinus excelsior
Ash **BB**

Fraxinus ornus
Manna Ash **BB**

Fuchsia magellanica
Fuchsia **BB**

Genista aetnensis
Mount Etna Broom **AJ**

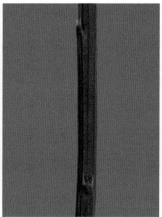
Genista lydia
Lydian Broom **AJ**

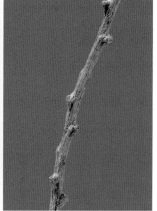
Genista pilosa
Hairy Greenweed **AJ**

Plate 14

226

Ginkgo biloba
Ginkgo **AO**

Gleditsia triacanthos var *inermis*
Thornless Honeylocust **AF**

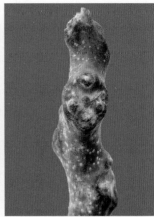

Gymnocladus dioicus
Kentucky Coffeetree **AF**

Hamamelis sp
Witch-hazel **AF**

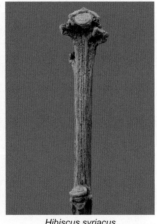

Hibiscus syriacus
Hibiscus **AE**

Hippocrepis emerus
Scorpion Senna **AJ**

Hippophae rhamnoides (♀)
Sea-buckthorn **AC**

Hydrangea aspera
Rough-leaved Hydrangea **BE**

Hydrangea macrophylla
Hydrangea **BE**

Plate 15

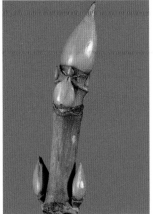

Hydrangea petiolaris
Climbing Hydrangea **BC**

Hypericum androsaemum
Tutsan **BI**

Jasminum humile
Yellow Jasmine **AJ**

Jasminum nudiflorum
Winter Jasmine **BA**

Jasminum officinale
Summer Jasmine **BA**

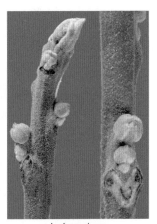

Juglans nigra
Black Walnut **AF**

Juglans regia
Walnut **AF**

Kerria japonica
Kerria **AJ**

Koelreuteria paniculata
Pride-of-India **AI**

Plate 16

Kolkwitzia amabilis
Beautybush **BI**

Laburnum x *watereri*
Hybrid Laburnum **AJ**

Larix decidua
European Larch **AN**

Larix x *marschlinsii*
Hybrid Larch **AN**

Leycesteria formosa
Himalayan Honeysuckle **BF**

Ligustrum ovalifolium
Garden Privet **BB**

Ligustrum vulgare
Wild Privet **BB**

Liquidambar styraciflua
American Sweetgum **AP**

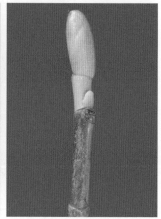

Liriodendron chinense
Chinese Tulip-tree **AH**

Plate 17

Liriodendron tulipifera
Tulip-tree **AH**

Lonicera involucrata
Californian Honeysuckle **BI**

Lonicera periclymenum
Honeysuckle **BC**

Lonicera tatarica
Tartarian Honeysuckle **BI**

Lonicera x *italica*
Garden Honeysuckle **BC**

Lonicera xylosteum
Fly Honeysuckle **BI**

Lycium barbarum
Duke of Argyll's Teaplant **AC**

Lycium chinense
Chinese Teaplant **AC**

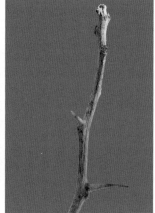

Maclura pomifera
Osage-orange **AC**

Plate 18

Magnolia acuminata
Cucumber-tree **MAG**

Magnolia salicifolia
Willow-leaved Magnolia **MAG**

Magnolia sieboldii ssp *sinensis*
Chinese Magnolia **MAG**

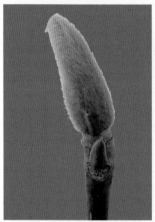

Magnolia x *soulangeana*
Saucer Magnolia **MAG**

Magnolia stellata
Star Magnolia **MAG**

Magnolia tripetala
Umbrella Magnolia **MAG**

Magnolia virginiana
Sweetbay Magnolia **MAG**

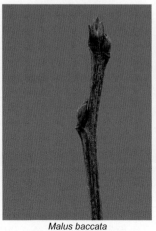

Malus baccata
Siberian Crab Apple **MAL**

Malus pumila
Apple **MAL**

231

Plate 19

Malus sylvestris
Crab Apple **MAL**

Malus tschonoskii
Chonosuki Crab Apple **MAL**

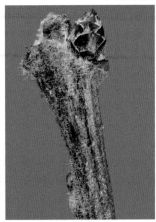

Mespilus germanica
Medlar **AC**

Metasequoia glyptostroboides
Dawn Redwood **BB**

Morus alba
White Mulberry **AL**

Morus nigra
Black Mulberry **AL**

Myrica gale
Bog-myrtle **AP**

Myrica pensylvanica
Bayberry **AP**

Nothofagus alpina
Rauli **AL**

Plate 20

232

Nothofagus antarctica
Antarctic Beech **AL**

Nothofagus obliqua
Roble **AK**

Nyssa aquatica
Water Tupelo **AI**

Nyssa sylvatica
Tupelo **AP**

Ostrya carpinifolia
Hop-hornbeam **AL**

Paeonia sect Moutan
Tree Peony **AP**

Parrotia persica
Persian Ironwood **AF**

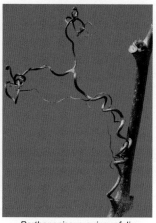

Parthenocissus quinquefolia
Virginia-creeper **AD**

Parthenocissus tricuspidata
Boston-ivy **AD**

Plate 21

Paulownia tomentosa
Foxglove-tree **BB**

Phellodendron amurense
Amur Corktree **BB**

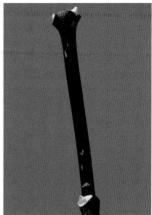

Philadelphus coronarius
Mock-orange **BD**

Philadelphus microphyllus
Littleleaf Mock-orange **BD**

Physocarpus opulifolius
Atlantic Ninebark **AK**

Platanus x *hispanica*
London Plane **AG**

Platanus orientalis
Oriental Plane **AG**

Populus alba
White Poplar **POP A**

Populus 'Balsam Spire'
Hybrid Balsam-poplar **POP D**

Plate 22

Populus x *canadensis*
Hybrid Black-poplar **POP C**

Populus x *canescens*
Grey Poplar **POP A**

Populus x *generosa*
Generous Poplar **POP D**

Populus x *jackii*
Balm-of-Gilead **POP D**

Populus nigra ssp *betulifolia*
Black-poplar **POP C**

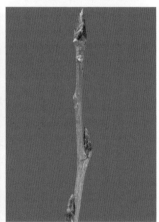

Populus nigra 'Italica'
Lombardy-poplar **POP C**

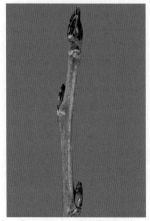

Populus nigra 'Plantierensis'
Plantier's Poplar **POP C**

Populus tremula
Aspen **POP B**

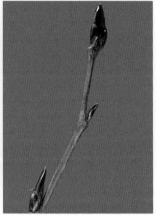

Populus trichocarpa
Western Balsam-poplar **POP D**

Plate 23

Potentilla fruticosa
Shrubby Cinquefoil **AM**

Prunus armeniaca
Apricot **PRU**

Prunus avium
Wild Cherry **PRU**

Prunus cerasifera
Cherry Plum **PRU**

Prunus cerasifera 'Pissardii'
Purple-leaved Cherry Plum **PRU**

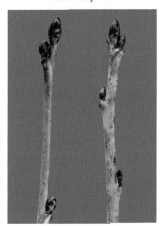

Prunus cerasus
Dwarf Cherry **PRU**

Prunus domestica
Wild Plum **PRU**

Prunus dulcis
Almond **PRU**

Prunus mahaleb
St Lucie Cherry **PRU**

Plate 24

236

Prunus padus
Bird Cherry **PRU**

Prunus persica
Peach **PRU**

Prunus serotina
Rum Cherry **PRU**

Prunus serrula
Tibetan Cherry **PRU**

Prunus serrulata
Japanese Cherry **PRU**

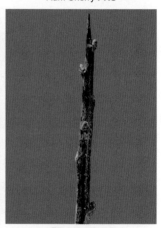

Prunus spinosa
Blackthorn **PRU**

Prunus subhirtella
Winter-flowering Cherry **PRU**

Pseudolarix amabilis
Golden Larch **AN**

Pterocarya fraxinifolia
Caucasian Wingnut **AF**

Plate 25

Pyrus calleryana
Callery Pear **PYR**

Pyrus communis
Pear **PYR**

Pyrus cordata
Plymouth Pear **PYR**

Pyrus elaeagnifolia
Oleaster-leaved Pear **PYR**

Pyrus pyraster
Wild Pear **PYR**

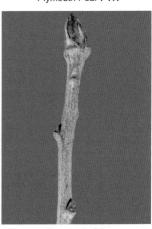

Pyrus salicifolia
Willow-leaved Pear **PYR**

Quercus cerris
Turkey Oak **AE**

Quercus coccinea
Scarlet Oak **AE**

Quercus palustris
Pin Oak **AE**

Plate 26

238

Quercus petraea
Sessile Oak **AE**

Quercus robur
Pedunculate Oak **AE**

Quercus rubra
Red Oak **AE**

Rhamnus cathartica
Buckthorn **BB**

Rhododendron luteum
Yellow Azalea **AN**

Rhus typhina
Stag's-horn Sumach **AG**

Ribes alpinum
Mountain Currant **RIB**

Ribes nigrum
Black Currant **RIB**

Ribes odoratum
Buffalo Currant **RIB**

239

Plate 27

Ribes rubrum
Red Currant **RIB**

Ribes sanguineum
Flowering Currant **RIB**

Ribes spicatum
Downy Currant **RIB**

Ribes uva-crispa
Gooseberry **AB**

Robinia pseudoacacia
False-acacia **AB**

Rosa sp
Rose **AA**

Rosa ferruginea
Red-leaved Rose **AA**

Rosa rugosa
Japanese Rose **AA**

Rosa spinosissima
Burnet Rose **AA**

Plate 28

240

Rubus caesius
Dewberry **RUB B**

Rubus cockburnianus
White-stemmed Bramble **RUB A**

Rubus fruticosus agg
Bramble **RUB B**

Rubus idaeus
Raspberry (floricane) **RUB A**

Rubus idaeus
Raspberry (primocane) **RUB A**

Rubus odoratus
Purple-flowered Raspberry **RUB A**

Rubus parviflorus
Thimbleberry **RUB A**

Rubus phoenicolasius
Japanese Wineberry **RUB A**

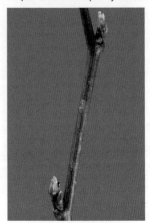

Rubus spectabilis
Salmonberry **RUB A**

Plate 29

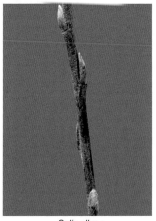

Salix alba
White Willow **SAL A**

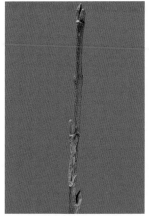

Salix arbuscula
Mountain Willow **SAL C**

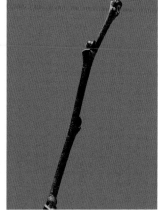

Salix aurita
Eared Willow **SAL A**

Salix caprea
Goat Willow **SAL A**

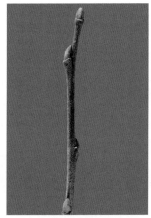

Salix cinerea
Grey Willow **SAL A**

Salix daphnoides
Violet-willow **SAL B**

Salix elaeagnos
Olive Willow **SAL A**

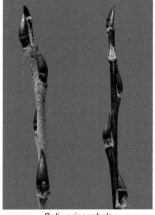

Salix eriocephala
Heart-leaved Willow **SAL A**

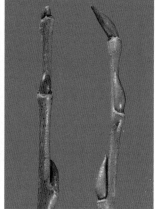

Salix x fragilis (♀, ♂)
Crack-willow **SAL B**

Plate 30

242

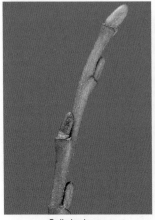

Salix herbacea
Dwarf Willow **SAL C**

Salix lanata
Woolly Willow **SAL C**

Salix lapponum
Downy Willow **SAL C**

Salix myrsinifolia
Dark-leaved Willow **SAL A**

Salix myrsinites
Whortle-leaved Willow **SAL C**

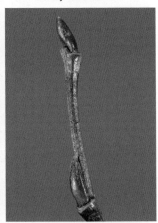

Salix x pendulina
Weeping Crack-willow **SAL B**

Salix pentandra
Bay Willow **SAL B**

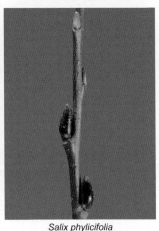

Salix phylicifolia
Tea-leaved Willow **SAL B**

Salix purpurea
Purple Willow **SAL B**

243

Plate 31

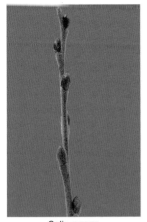

Salix repens
Creeping Willow **SAL C**

Salix reticulata
Net-leaved Willow **SAL C**

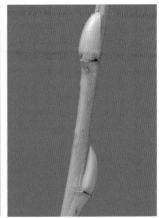

Salix x *sepulcralis* 'Chrysocoma'
Golden Weeping Willow **SAL B**

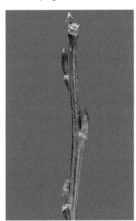

Salix triandra
Almond Willow **SAL B**

Salix viminalis
Osier **SAL A**

Sambucus nigra
Elder **Bl**

Sambucus racemosa
Red-berried Elder **Bl**

Sassafras albidum
Sassafras **AJ**

Solanum dulcamara
Bittersweet **AD**

Plate 32

244

Sorbaria sorbifolia
Sorbaria **AP**

Sorbus subgen *Aria*
Whitebeam **AP**

Sorbus aucuparia
Rowan **AQ**

Sorbus cashmiriana
Kashmir Rowan **AQ**

Sorbus commixta
Japanese Rowan **AQ**

Sorbus domestica
Service-tree **AQ**

Sorbus glabriuscula
Chinese Rowan **AQ**

Sorbus x *hybrida*
Swedish Service-tree **AQ**

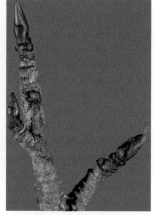

Sorbus 'Joseph Rock'
Yellow-berried Rowan **AQ**

245

Plate 33

Sorbus x *thuringiaca*
Bastard Service-tree **AQ**

Sorbus torminalis
Wild Service-tree **AP**

Spartium junceum
Spanish Broom **AJ**

Spiraea alba
Pale Bridewort **SPI**

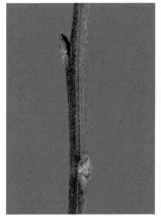

Spiraea x *billardii*
Billard's Bridewort **SPI**

Spiraea douglasii ssp *douglasii*
Douglas' Steeple-bush **SPI**

Spiraea japonica
Japanese Spiraea **SPI**

Spiraea media
Russian Spiraea **SPI**

Spiraea nipponica
Nippon Spiraea **SPI**

Plate 34

246

Spiraea x *pseudosalicifolia*
Confused Bridewort **SPI**

Staphylea pinnata
Bladdernut **BA**

Stephanandra incisa
Stephanandra **AF**

Stewartia pseudocamellia
Deciduous Camellia **AI**

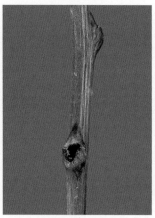

Styphnolobium japonica
Pagoda Tree **AJ**

Styrax japonicus
Japanese Snowbell-tree **AF**

Symphoricarpos albus
Snowberry **BI**

Symphoricarpos x *chenaultii*
Hybrid Coralberry **BI**

Syringa vulgaris
Lilac **BB**

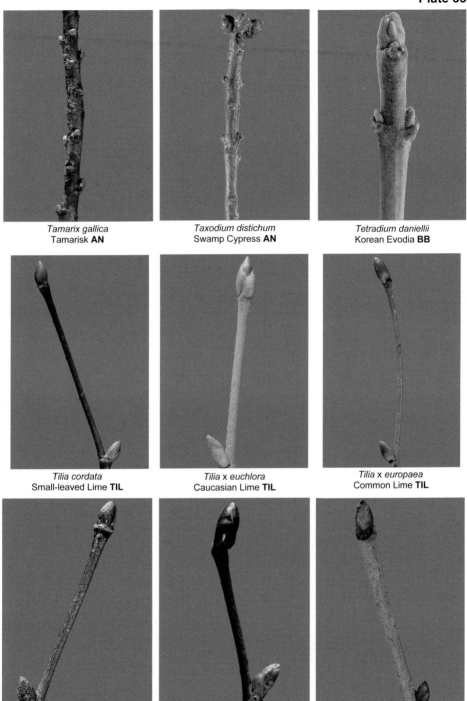

Plate 35

Tamarix gallica
Tamarisk **AN**

Taxodium distichum
Swamp Cypress **AN**

Tetradium daniellii
Korean Evodia **BB**

Tilia cordata
Small-leaved Lime **TIL**

Tilia x *euchlora*
Caucasian Lime **TIL**

Tilia x *europaea*
Common Lime **TIL**

Tilia 'Petiolaris'
Pendent Silver-lime **TIL**

Tilia platyphyllos
Large-leaved Lime **TIL**

Tilia tomentosa
Silver-lime **TIL**

Plate 36

248

Toona sinensis
Chinese Mahogany **AQ**

Toxicodendron vernicifluum
Chinese Lacquer-tree **AR**

Ulmus glabra
Wych Elm **ULM**

Ulmus x *hollandica*
Dutch Elm **ULM**

Ulmus laevis
European White-elm **ULM**

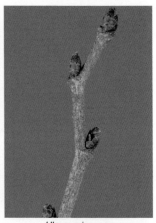

Ulmus minor agg
Field Elm **ULM**

Ulmus procera
English Elm **ULM**

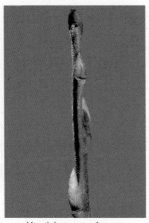

Vaccinium corymbosum
Blueberry **AN**

Vaccinium myrtillus
Bilberry **AI**

249

Plate 37

Vaccinium uliginosum Bog Bilberry **AN**	*Viburnum* x *bodnantense* Bodnant Viburnum **BI**	*Viburnum lantana* Wayfaring-tree **BE**

Viburnum opulus Guelder-rose **BE**	*Vitis coignetiae* Crimson-glory-vine **AD**	*Vitis vinifera* Grape-vine **AD**

Weigela florida Weigela **BI**	*Wisteria floribunda* Japanese Wisteria **AD**	*Xanthorhiza simplicissima* Yellowroot **AR**

Plate 38

250

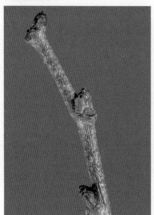

Zelkova carpinifolia
Caucasian Zelkova **AL**

Zelkova serrata
Japanese Zelkova **AL**

INDEX

Groups are primarily referenced instead of conventional page numbers and the main entry (where each species is most likely to key out) is highlighted in **bold**. Plate numbers (PL) are also included.

Notes:

Notes: